SUBMARINES

BRASSEY'S SEA POWER: Naval Vessels,
Weapons Systems and Technology Series:
Volume 7

Brassey's Sea Power:
Naval Vessels, Weapons Systems and Technology Series

General Editor: PROFESSOR G. TILL, Royal Naval College, Greenwich and Department of War Studies, King's College London

This series, consisting of twelve volumes, aims to explore the impact of modern technology on the shape, size and role of contemporary navies. Using case studies from around the world it explains the principles of naval operations and functions of naval vessels, aircraft and weapons systems. Each volume is written by an acknowledged expert in a clear, easy to understand style, and is well illustrated with photographs and diagrams. The series will be invaluable for naval officers under training and also will be of great interest to young professionals and naval enthusiasts.

OTHER SERIES PUBLISHED BY BRASSEY'S

Brassey's Land Warfare: Battlefield Weapons Systems and Technology Series,
12 Volume Set
General Editor: COLONEL R. G. LEE, OBE

Brassey's Air Power: Aircraft, Weapons Systems and Technology Series,
12 Volume Set
General Editor: AIR VICE MARSHAL R. A. MASON, CB, CBE, MA, RAF

SUBMARINES

by

REAR ADMIRAL J B HERVEY CB OBE

BRASSEY'S (UK)

LONDON * NEW YORK

First English edition 1994

UK editorial offices: Brassey's, 165 Great Dover Street, London SE1 4YA
Orders: Marston Book Services, PO Box 87, Oxford OX2 0DT

USA orders: Macmillan Publishing Company, Front and Brown Streets, Riverside, NJ 08075

Distributed in North America to booksellers and wholesalers by the Macmillan Publishing Company, NY 10022

Library of Congress Cataloging in Publication Data
available

British Library Cataloging in Publication Data
A catalogue record for this book is
available from the British Library

ISBN 0 08 040970 9 Hardcover
ISBN 0 08 040971 7 Flexicover

J B Hervey has asserted his moral right
to be identified as author of this work

Cover photo: HMS *Trafalgar* (*Rolls Royce & Associates*)

Typeset by Florencetype Ltd, Kewstoke, Avon
Printed and bound in Great Britain by
Butler & Tanner Ltd, Frome and London

This book is dedicated to all those
who served with me in HM Submarines *Aeneas*,
Ambush, *Oracle* and *Warspite*.

'We are all men of straw
without a good First
Lieutenant.'

Admiral Sir John Woodward
GBE KCB

HMS *Valiant* in the Arctic ice showing:
  – Paris Sonar Intercept array
  – HF Communications Telescopic and Periscopic mast plus conical log
    spiral antenna for VHF/UHF/SHF
  – Search Periscope with backward set ESM Warner
(© *British Crown Copyright 1993/MOD*)

Contents

Foreword

by Admiral of the Fleet The Lord Fieldhouse GCB GBE

This book represents the most capable and comprehensive study of Submarine business available today. It is unique in my experience because it covers in great detail the whole breadth of equipment, technology and use of the modern submarine, both nuclear and conventionally propelled.

I am tempted to describe it as a textbook but that would give the wrong impression, for it is far from a dry treatise, being essentially readable. Written by a distinguished Submarine officer with experience of some 13 years service in sea-going submarines, including command of three conventional and one nuclear submarine, Admiral John Hervey consistently produces an easily understandable text, suitable for the general reader, and very useful to the young naval officer, officers from other services involved with Submarine operations, and employees of companies producing equipment for submarines.

John Hervey's experience as a busy staff officer and in Squadron command is clearly evident in his treatment of the subject, beginning with the description of the job to be done and proceeding through the various aspects of construction, propulsion and weaponry to operational usage and support. For the reader who wishes to be selective, each chapter is concluded with a very well constructed Summary. The whole work is unusually well illustrated with a great number of pictorial descriptions ranging from basic diagrams to attractive operational photographs.

I wholeheartedly recommend this book to the reader as a most capable treatment of a huge subject which manages to combine general interest with specialist knowledge, all based on sound practical experience.

Acknowledgements

Almost all my statistical data on submarines and their weapons systems is taken either from Jane's Fighting Ships or from Jane's Underwater Warfare Systems, two essential works of reference. I would also like to record grateful thanks to the Editor of Janes, Captain Richard Sharpe, for the good humoured way in which he answered my queries whenever I bothered him.

Chapter 3 owes much to a quite excellent visit to Vickers Shipbuilding & Engineering, organised and run by Mrs Joan Hamer.

Mr Andrew Hooper of Rolls Royce & Associates, and his colleagues, made numerous wise suggestions for improving Chapter 5, and illuminated some lapses in memory which had occurred since I did the nuclear course at RNC Greenwich in 1968 – *pace* Professor Edwards!

I am grateful to Pilkington Optronics for permission to draw on their Mast brochure, when describing some of the features of an MTM in Chapter 6. Mr David Lee and his team at Pilkington also prepared the futuristic diagram of the pop-up mast in Chapter 16.

My colleagues at MEL Crawley, (now Thorn EMI), greatly assisted preparation of Chapter 7: by letting me draw on material which originally appeared in MEL Matters, their house magazine, in an article by Commander Peter Evans; and allowing me to quote details of Manta X. Mr Reg Clarke also helpfully vetted my script.

Coverage of modern sonars in Chapter 8 owes much to some excellent advice received from Dr Donald Nairn, of the DRA's Underwater Weapons Establishment at Portland; and to numerous talks with my colleague at Cossor Electronics, Mr David Patterson, once a scientist at AUWE.

I am grateful to Ms Tricia Clark-Jervoise of Marconi Underwater Systems Limited for allowing me access to proprietary published material concerning the Tigerfish and Spearfish torpedoes. And I am indebted to Mr R D Short for permission to draw on his article concerning them, when preparing Chapter 9.

The German Vl diagram in the weapons chapter is based on one in the Illustrated Encyclopaedia of the World's Rockets and Missiles. It is used with permission of the publishers, Salamander Books. Preparation of Chapter 9 was also much assisted by: The School of Maritime Operations, HMS DRYAD, who retaught me the method of drawing Limiting Lines of Submerged Approach; and Ferranti International, who improved my knowledge of modern command displays.

I am particularly grateful to Herr Karl Ruf of Telefunken System Technik of

Ulm, for supplying illustrations of the very impressive modern VLF station at Rhauderfehn—and for obtaining German Armament Procurement Office (BWB) permission to use them in Chapter 10.

The LORAN/DECCA/OMEGA coverage diagram in Chapter 11 is reproduced from The Times Atlas & Encyclopaedia of the Sea by kind permission of Times Books, a division of Harper Collins Publishers Limited.

My understanding of the submarine magnetic signature reduction problem in Chapter 12 owes everything to Mr Sam Bell of Raytheon Submarine Signal Division, Rhode Island, USA; who condensed a month's magnetic course into a six hour presentation on several occasions! He also provided the excellent picture of a BQQ5 Golfball bow array in Chapter 8.

I am especially grateful to Mr Timothy Martin of CJB Developments Limited Portsmouth, who spent much time explaining the very interesting atmosphere control and fuel cell work being done by his impressive company. Preparation of Chapter 13 was further assisted by Mr Derek Bundy of DGME Foxhill Bath, who put me in touch with the right people and found a picture of the Mass Spectrometer.

In Chapter 15, the map of the Tongue of the Ocean area of the Bahamas is reproduced from British Admiralty Chart No. 4401, with permission of HMSO. The illustration of the AUTEC range facility is reproduced from Urick's Principles of Underwater Sound (3rd Ed 1983) with permission of the publishers, McGraw Hill of New York.

I am grateful to Commander Richard Compton-Hall, Director of the Royal Navy Submarine Museum Gosport, for increasing my understanding of the AIP systems discussed in Chapter 16, especially the work being done on GST by Maritalia. And for permission to photograph HMS ALLIANCE on the Museum's premises.

The following figures are all © British Crown Copyright 1993/MOD and are reproduced with the permission of the Controller of Her Britannic Majesty's Stationery Office: figures Frontispiece, 3.12, 3.15, 4.4, 4.7, 5.11, 6.8, 6.10, 8.4, 8.19, 8.23, 9.4, 9.5, 9.19, 9.23, 12.6, 14.6, 14.14, 15.2, 15.3, 15.5, 15. 9, and 16.12.

Whilst preparing the book, I had several conversations with officers on the staff of Flag Officer Submarines, necessarily guarded on their side! – but illuminating nevertheless, and always conducted with great courtesy, which was appreciated. In particular, I would like to thank Lieutenant Mike Walliker, FOSM's Flags, who never failed to rustle up some information, however awkward my query.

I would also like to thank: Ms Judith Blacklaw, of the MOD Whitehall Library; Mrs Margaret Bidmead, the Royal Navy Submarine Museum's archivist; and Mrs Janet Holbourne, at the ASWE Portsdown library; all of whom came to my help at various crisis moments.

Apart from those mentioned above, many other British Defence companies supplied photographs or artwork of their equipment, too many to detail separately, but I owe much to them all for their very ready agreement to help. Their company names are mentioned beneath the relevant pictures.

The Attaché community in London also helped me. And I owe particular thanks to: Contre-Amiral P Garibal, French Defence and Naval Attache; Captain W F L van Leeuwen, Netherlands Defence, Naval and Air Attache; and

Commander M A Dunn, of the Canadian High Commission. Also Le Capitaine de Vaisseau Bied-Charreton of Le SIRPA/Mer in Paris, who allowed me use of the picture of FS RUBIS.

Four other people made major contributions to the work of illustration. Captain Martin MacPherson, DI(NC) in the Defence Intelligence Staff, produced many photographs of Russian submarines. My old friend Norman Polmar provided numerous pictures of US boats from his own archives, and obtained others for me from official US sources. And Vice Admiral Yogi Kaufman USN, provided some very modern US pictures, out of the stock of more than 30,000 which he and his son have taken in recent years. I am most grateful to them. My warmest thanks are due also to John Richards, for some years the Illustrator at the Royal Navy College, Greenwich but now retired, whose skill and experience converted my own drafts into the immaculate diagrams and drawings which play such an important part in the book.

Beyond everyone else, though, I owe an enormous debt of gratitude to my old shipmate, Rear Admiral Richard Heaslip, who battled his way through a fairly tangled first draft; then gave me pages of blunt comments—the only sort you need!—all drawn from his experience of having been Flag Officer Submarines.

I would like to thank: our Editor in Chief, Professor Geoffrey Till, for much support; and that most distinguished of our nuclear submariners, and very good friend, Lord Fieldhouse, for a typically kind foreword, which sadly, he did not live to see in print.

Finally, my thanks to my publishers, Major General Tony Trythall and Jenny Shaw of Brassey's (UK) and my editor, Brigadier Bryan Watkins, an old friend and colleague, for much help and advice in the final preparation of the manuscript.

As for the book, well it must speak for itself. It has been fun to write it, and I hope that it is helpful to those who read it.

J.B.H.
Alverstoke
June 1993

Glossaries

Submarine Types

SS	Torpedo armed diesel powered patrol submarine
SSB	Ballistic missile carrying submarine
SSBN	Nuclear powered ballistic missile submarine
SSG	Guided missile carrying submarine
SSGN	Nuclear powered guided missile submarine
SSK	Submarine used in anti-submarine killer role
SSN	Nuclear powered attack or Fleet submarine

General

ABM	Anti-ballistic missile
ACINT	Acoustic intelligence (recording sonar & sound)
ADCAP	Advanced capability
AEW	Airborne early warning
AGI	Auxiliary general intelligence (spy ship)
AIP	Air independent propulsion
AIV	Automatic inboard venting
AMP	Assisted maintenance period
ASMD	Anti-ship-missile defence
ATP	Air turbine pump
BB	Broad band
CEP	Contact evaluation plot
	Circular error probable (weapon miss distance)
CIGS	Chief of the Imperial General Staff
COB	Carried on board (spares)
COMINT	Communication intelligence (recording W/T)
CTC	Carbon tetra-chloride
DEMON	Demodulator equipment (sonar)
D/F	Direction finding
DOT	Distance off track
DR	Dead reckoning
DSMAC	Digital scene matching area correlator
DSRV	Deep submergence recovery vessel
DWT	Dead weight tonnage

ECCM	Electronic counter countermeasures
ECM	Electronic counter measures
ECE	External combustion engine
EDC	Error detection and correction
EHF	Extremely high frequency
ELF	Extremely low frequency
ELINT	Electronic intelligence (recording radars)
EORSAT	Electronic orbiting satellite
EP	Estimated position
E/S	Echo-sounder
ESM	Electronic support measures
EW	Electronic warfare
EZ	Exclusion zone
FLTSATCOM	Fleet satellite communications
FMOP	Frequency modulation on pulse
FPSE	Free piston Stirling engine
FSH	Full speed hours
GIUK	Greenland-Iceland-United Kingdom
GPS	Global positioning system
GRP	Glass reinforced plastic
GST	Gaseous storage in toroid
HE	Hydrophone effect
HF	High frequency
IFM	Instantaneous frequency measurement
JATO	Jet assisted take off
KT	Kiloton (weapon yield in TNT equivalent)
KW	Kilowatt
LF	Low frequency
LLII	Low light level image intensifiers
LLQSA	Limiting lines of quiet submerged approach
LLSA	Limiting lines of submerged approach
LOP	Local operations plot
LRMP	Long range maritime patrol
MAB	Manual accurate bearing
MAD	Magnetic anomaly detection
MARV	Manoeuvrable re-entry vehicle
MBT	Main ballast tanks
MCM	Mine counter measures
MEA	Mono-ethanol-amine
MEZ	Missile engagement zone
MF/DF	Medium frequency direction finding
MIRV	Multiple independently targetable re-entry vehicle
MPA	Maritime patrol air
MSF	Magnetic silencing facility
MTBF	Mean Time Between Failures
MTM	Main tactical mast
MW	Megawatt

NB	Narrow band
NDB	Nuclear depth bomb
OMC	One man control
OPCON	Operational control
PFV	Programmable firing valve
PMOP	Phase modulation on pulse
PRF	Pulse repetition frequency
PWR	Pressurised water reactor
RAM	Radar absorbent material
RF	Radio frequency
RLG	Ring laser gyro
ROE	Rules of engagement
RORSAT	Radar orbiting satellite
RPV	Reactor pressure vessel
RV	Re-entry vehicle
SAM	Surface to air missile
SAS	Special Air Service
SATCOM	Satellite communications
SATNAV	Satellite navigation
SBD	Submarine bubble decoy
SDI	Strategic Defence Initiative (star wars)
SEC	Submarine element coordinator
SEO	Senior Engineer Officer
SHF	Super high frequency
SG	Steam generator
SINS	Ships inertial navigation system
SLBM	Submarine launched ballistic missile
SLCM	Submarine (or ship) launched cruise missile
SMP	Self maintenance period
SOSUS	Sonar ocean surveillance systems
SSE	Submerged signal ejector
SSIXS	Submarine satellite information exchange system
SUBROC	Submarine launched anti-submarine rocket
SVP	Sound velocity profile
SWAPO	South West Africa People's Organisation
SWATH	Small waterplane area twin hull
TAINS	TERCOM aided inertial navigation system
TASS	Towed array surveillance system
TBP	Time bearing plot
TDHS	Tactical data handling system
TEDS	Turbine electric drive submarines
TERCOM	Terrain contour matching
TG	Turbo-generator
TI/IR	Thermal imaging infra red
TMA	Target motion analysis
TSMA	Temperature swing molecular adsorber
UHF	Ultra high frequency

UQS	Ultra quiet state
UWT	Underwater telephone
VDS	Variable depth sonar
VIMOS	Vibration monitoring system
VLF	Very low frequency
XBT	Expendable bathythermograph

TECHNICAL TERMS

Absorber. Chemical atmosphere cleansing system whose contents temporarily or permanently combine with unwanted gases.

Adsorber. Physical atmosphere cleansing system whose succession of sieves have molecular sized holes to trap specific gases.

Bar. Unit used in expressing pressure, where a millibar is a thousand dynes per sq. cm. and 1 Bar equals 1 atmosphere—or about 15 lbs/sq.inch.

Bottom capture. Seduction by the sea bed of active sonar homing torpedoes.

Cathodic protection. Anti-corrosion protection of an underwater metal fitting achieved by making it the cathode in an electrolytic cell.

Cavitation. Effect caused when a drop in pressure allows vapour bubbles to form in a liquid and then noisily collapse again. The pressure fluctuations can be caused in many ways, but the term cavitation is most commonly used to describe the bubbling effect produced as water passes over the blades of a high speed, or too rapidly accelerating, or badly designed propeller—or over hull projections.

Curfuffle, clunk & clong. Three of the many onomatopoeic words used to describe, and so help identify, transient noises heard by a passive sonar operator.

Data shock. Paralysis of an electronic processing system—or the display operator—due to information overload.

Direct drive. Main machinery system where a submarine diesel engine can be connected—in a straight line—to electrical generating armatures and—abaft them—a propeller shaft. Clutches are positioned between engine and armatures and between armatures and propeller shaft. With both clutches engaged, the diesel directly drives the propeller. With the tail clutch disconnected, the full power of the engine is used to generate current for the battery. With the engine clutch disconnected, but the tail clutch connected, the dual purpose armatures can be used as propulsion motors—drawing electrical power back from the batteries. (See Figure 5.7)

Discrete frequency peaks. Distinctive high spots on a noise frequency spectrum produced by rotating machinery, and hull resonances.

Enabling. Process of sending instructions—down the umbilical wire—to the brain of a homing torpedo—to tell it to arm its warhead and start searching.

First line maintenance. Planned upkeep routines, which can be performed by the submarine ship's company at sea, if necessary using the carried on board spares.

Force multiplier. Sensor or weapon system which not only provides capability itself but enhances the value of other systems. Thus a 'Home-on-jamming' capability in one missile of a salvo is a force multiplier for a radar homer head in another missile of the same salvo. Now, whether the enemy jams or not, one missile will hit.

Girding. An effect by which a towing vessel can be laid on its side, if the towed object starts to exert a lateral pull.

Hotel load. Amount of electrical power needed to provide domestic services (heating, lighting, air-conditioning, cooking etc) and to run other auxiliary machinery—thus reducing power available for propulsion.

Legend range. The range to which manufacturers guarantee that their weapons will run.

Liquid metal coolant. Metal with relatively low melting point, such as lead ($327.5°C$), circulated in reactor primary circuits, to transfer heat energy to secondary plant at a higher temperature than is possible using water coolant.

Mobility kill. Action damage to a war vessel which, whilst not sinking it, renders it incapable of movement.

Moving haven. Imaginary box established around a friendly submarine on passage, inside which own forces may not attack *any* submarine detected. The whole haven moves geographically at the routed speed of the submarine which must stay in its box. (See Figure 10.1)

Octaves. The frequency band which can be covered by a sensor antenna or array. (In sonar systems, the octave top frequency is about double the bottom frequency. In ESM systems, the octave top frequency is about three times the bottom frequency).

Platform correlation. Making the connection between an intercepted transmission and the vehicle from which the transmission, radar or sonar, has been made.

Second line maintenance. Planned upkeep routines carried out in harbour, usually at the Base port with Base Staff assistance, during which the notice for being able to go to sea may be extended to 47 hours.

Steerage. Any information given to a submarine to help it position itself for intelligence collection purposes.

Submove message. Sailing orders sent to the submarine in message form by the authority holding OPCON (Operational Control). It must contain: departure time, details of route to be followed, overall speed to be maintained along the route, dimensions of the moving exercise area (peace) or moving haven (war) established around the submarine, any CHOPS (Changes in OPCON) to be made along the route, and the communications broadcast on which watch is to be maintained.

Support personnel. Shore based members of any submarine force indispensable if proper second and third line support is to be provided (eg periscope workshop artificers).

Teeth personnel. Those fully trained and in a submarine.

Tail personnel. Shore based members of any submarine force who provide important but not necessarily indispensable back up for support personnel (eg transport drivers, catering staff etc).

Third line maintenance. Major planned upkeep routines carried out in a Dockyard, during which the Notice for Sea may be considerably more than 48 hours.

List of Illustrations

List of Tables

1

Introduction

Submarines are 'boats' to those who serve in them but they were classified Major War Vessels by the British Admiralty long before there was a Ministry of Defence and well before the advent of nuclear propulsion or the Polaris missile. It was a logical enough decision. Surface warships are built to float, to move and to fight— in that order. In war, some of them took a lot of damage *above the waterline* and survived to fight again. Very few stayed afloat after two torpedo hits from a submarine, each capable of blowing open a 12 metre wide hole, *below the waterline*. Not surprisingly, the submarine was correctly seen as a threat to anything afloat from the moment it first appeared. In this respect it totally differed from the aircraft, whose potential for sinking ships with bombs and rockets was long underestimated.

All still carry torpedoes, but today there are several types of boat, which have to be differentiated. For this reason, they are given short titles. Used alone, **SS** means diesel powered submarine. Such boats are also known as patrol submarines, or **SSK**s (Submarine Killers) when on anti submarine work. Armed with cruise missiles, an SS becomes an **SSG**. Nuclear powered boats used primarily on offensive operations or escort duties are called **SSN**s, sometimes Attack Boats or Fleet Boats. If also armed with cruise missiles they become **SSGN**s . And those nuclear boats carrying ballistic missiles as part of a national strategic deterrent are known as **SSBN**s.

Modern diesel boats (SS and SSG) are driven by electric propulsion motors, drawing energy from batteries. However, only a very limited amount of energy can be stored, and the batteries have to be recharged, by diesel-generator sets. These diesels need air. When dived, it is drawn through a snorkel tube, which is raised whilst quite close to the surface. Snorkelling slightly increases vulnerability, but is much less risky than surfacing to charge, the method used until the end of the Second World War. By contrast, nuclear boats (SSN and SSBN) have almost unlimited power stored in their reactors, need no access to atmospheric air, and are true submarines.

The modern nuclear powered submarine is Jules Verne's *Twenty Thousand Leagues Under the Sea* come true. Indeed, a 60,000 nautical mile trip would not begin to exhaust the initial fuel loading of even a first generation SSN. Immensely strong in construction and properly shaped for underwater performance, some SSNs can go down well below 500 metres and travel as fast as a Second World War torpedo for weeks on end. Others are almost silent in operation at speeds which would equate to a noisy full speed for a 1960s SS.

Between them, the underwater and above water sensors in a modern submarine may detect, (or receive data link pictures of), surface targets at hundreds of kilometres, a capability now well matched by the weapons they carry. These already include anti-ship, sea skimming missiles and inertially guided cruise missiles; mostly launched from sub surface; and tipped with either a 200 kiloton nuclear device or high explosive warheads which not only do a great deal of destruction but usually start a severe fire as well. Alternatively, attacking a large surface force they may fire torpedoes whose onboard computers select and home on targets from over the horizon range, and whose warheads will break the back of a frigate, or cause huge flooding in the vital areas of an aircraft carrier.

When bombarding the shore, the tactical cruise missiles can engage targets at 2500 kilometres, and the submarine itself can, *with impunity*, be sitting on the enemy's doorstep waiting to launch this devastating attack on Day 1 of a war.

Nor must it ever be forgotten that any submarine can carry two mines for every torpedo, as an alternative load. Indeed, it is the most deadly of all small field mine-layers, because the most clandestine. Results surely speak for themselves. Mines carefully laid by just one French submarine in the Second World War, FS *Rubis*, sank 15 enemy merchantmen and eight warships. In terms of 400,000 ton super-tankers and container ships, sinkings on that scale would be a disaster of almost strategic dimension.

Depending on national priorities, modern submarines may also be excellent anti-submarine weapon systems, arguably the best in terms of probability of initial detection. Moreover, the SSN is the only type effectively able to follow the enemy any distance under the arctic ice cap. For the ASW role, they often carry anti-submarine ballistic rockets, with a nuclear depth bomb or torpedo pay-load; and several different varieties of torpedoes, some capable of passive and active homing, others of running straight to the target area to explode a nuclear warhead.

The ability of an SSN to operate clandestinely in enemy home waters also makes it a good, low profile collector of intelligence in peace and war. However, to carry out this, or any of the other roles discussed in Chapter 2, submarines must be provided with covert means of communication and navigation. They also need minimal 'signatures' in every area, whether it be radiated noise, magnetic, infra red, sound echoing or radar mast cross section. Even then, all can be jeopardised if the submarine is unable to keep control of its enclosed atmosphere, which needs efficient monitoring and continuous treatment.

To equip a navy with a submarine service involves substantial capital outlay, particularly if the submarines are to be nuclear powered. A proper return on this investment can only be obtained if utilisation and upkeep cycles are very thoroughly planned by submarine operating authorities throughout the life of the boats. Running costs are limited by having relatively low numbers embarked but these people must be given specialised training; and extra support facilities are needed to cover items like periscopes and batteries, even to set up a small division of four diesel electric submarines. Much more is needed when contemplating activities such as changing a nuclear reactor core or storing and servicing ballistic missiles. More again will be required if mobile support must also be provided.

Modern diesel electric submarines are impressive war vessels in their own right;

but the questions for any nation of whether to invest in a submarine capability and if so, to what extent, are of course political, and therefore endlessly debatable. Forty three countries currently own some submarines. Six of these nations have SSNs and/or SSGNs: US-83 , Russia-105 , UK-13, France-5, China-5 and India-1 being built. The first five—appropriately, all permanent members of the UN Security Council—also operate SSBNs, some capable of throwing their ballistic missiles to 12,000 kilometres.

Less debatable, because largely a matter of historic record, is the effect which submarines can have on the fortunes of nations at war. For example, in the First World War, when British shipbuilding capacity was about 150,000 tons per month, 12,850,814 tons of merchant shipping was sunk, 7,759,090 tons of it British.

Attrition was made worse by not convoying. However, German submarines also operated at less than full effectiveness, due to rules of engagement, which required them to warn merchant vessels before attacking, and allow crews time to get clear. This policy was abandoned in February 1917. In the first six months of unrestricted warfare, 3,850,000 tons of shipping was sunk, and another 4,677,301 tons by the end of the war, despite the belated introduction of convoying in May 1917. Average monthly sinkings from May 1917 to October 1918 were 361,208 tons. It was fortunate indeed that the Imperial German Navy had started the war with only 28 boats.[1]

In the Second World War, Nazi Germany once again began with only 30 boats, a number which actually fell to 22 by February 1941, before submarine construction seriously started to outstrip losses. Failure to start with enough submarines and, more seriously, failure to give their production proper priority in 1940, wasted the time when Allied anti-submarine forces were weak, and maybe lost Germany the best chance it had of winning the war. Nevertheless, in the North Atlantic alone, the Allies lost 2,233 ships, totalling 11,904,954 tons. In both wars, the attrition of shipping in the Atlantic was so severe that Allied leaders began to doubt whether enough would remain to continue the fight. [2 and 3]

The Allies also used submarines with great effect in the Second World War. For example, in the Mediterranean, between June 1940, when Italy entered the war, and the end of 1944, British submarines and Allied submarines working under British control, sank 286 ships, totalling 1,030,960 tons, mainly carrying vital supplies from Italy to the Axis forces in North Africa. Their contribution to the famous 8th Army's successes is often underestimated.

In the Pacific, American submarines sank 5,320,094 tons of enemy shipping. Much of this was oil tanker traffic but the effect of that submarine offensive is best judged from the figures in Table 1.1, which show the drop in total bulk commodity metric tons imported to Japan over the war years. Unlike the United States, Japanese shipbuilding capacity was never able to replace even as much as half the tonnage being sunk by all Allied forces. By the end, American submarines had virtually made it impossible for Japan to fight anywhere in the Pacific outside her own islands.[4]

Before US SSNs added their Tomahawk missiles to the rest of the Coalition ordnance winging into Iraq in 1991, only one nuclear powered submarine had fired any weapon in anger, but it was a decisive blow. Once in contact, SSNs are difficult to shake off and the ability of the United Kingdom to sink the cruiser

TABLE 1.1
Drop in Japanese Imports 1940–45

Year	Commodity Tons Imported
1940	22,039,600
1941	20,004,430
1942	19,402,090
1943	16,411,880
1944	10,129,610
1945	2,743,200

General Belgrano, seemingly at will, kept the Argentinean Navy close to the coast of South America for the rest of the Falklands War. The strategic gain for Britain was enormous and the action probably saved a great many more lives from being lost on both sides. Had the malign intentions of the Argentinean Junta been recognised early enough to get two SSNs into the Port Stanley area by 2 April 1982, the war might have been still-born on the first day, or never have started. Conversely, had Argentina owned the SSNs and not the British, the risk to the Task Force would have been greatly increased, and that to ships like RMS *Queen Elizabeth II* and *Canberra*, heavily laden with troops, probably unacceptable.

Perhaps the greatest tribute to the effectiveness of the submarine, however, is the enormous amount of money devoted to anti-submarine warfare by all maritime powers. Often, it is well over 30 per cent of everything spent on their navies and a significant amount of that budgeted for air assets as well. A war vessel capable of causing such pain to its enemies deserves the close attention of any serious student of maritime warfare. This, and the fact that it is built with state of the art technology in almost every area, makes it particularly suitable for treatment in a separate volume of the Sea Power series.

In the following chapters, we look first at the roles played by modern submarines, then examine all important aspects of a submarine, from the perspective of its commanding officer, at each stage relating his needs to the capability with which he is, or ought to be, provided. Before turning to the make up of our submarine, however, a few words must be said about those who serve in it.

In common with others in the series, this book is primarily about Technology. But people also are of great importance, particularly in the very special conditions of submarine warfare, where the least act of negligence or incompetence on the part of any single member of the crew can bring absolute, and very swift, disaster. Moreover, a submarine goes, unsupported, deep into enemy controlled waters. Therefore, it needs a most self confident and effective commanding officer, who must have with him exceptionally well trained, and able, officers and men.

Preferably, these submariners should be volunteers, as they all have to perform their duties, in conditions of some discomfort, and at close quarters to one another. Even an SSN does not seem particularly spacious, when the 105 man crew is frequently augmented by another 20, there for training or carrying out trials. And the six or seven officers of an OBERON class SS, throughout an eight week patrol, will be living, sleeping and eating in a wardroom quite a bit smaller than an old style railway compartment. The other 60 men onboard live in equally cramped quarters. All this makes a submarine a pleasantly egalitarian work-place. But it is not for the faint of heart, the claustrophobic or those who suffer from a prima donna temperament.

2
Roles

Technological invention sometimes leads to sudden increases in capability and dramatic new roles. Nuclear power and nuclear weapons are classic submarine examples. More often, equipment changes occur gradually, as nations try to give boats greater effectiveness, or make them less vulnerable, whilst operating in existing roles. Either way, impact of the new technology only becomes clear when viewed in an operational context. Therefore, tactical scenarios are used in some later chapters. To make these understandable, it is necessary first to consider why so many nations do have submarines, what their use might be in various kinds and scales of conflict, and how they fit into the spectrum of naval operations.

MARITIME STRATEGY

In strategic terms, maritime forces are used either to achieve sea control, or to deny use of the sea to others. Sea control does not require removal of *all* enemy forces, but they must be suppressed enough in a contested area to allow own surface units sufficient use of it. Similarly, sea denial does not mean preventing movement of *all* enemy surface ships. To win, one has only to throttle enemy activity to the point where it becomes insufficient to reinforce their amphibious landing, sustain their army of occupation or to re-supply their island nation with food or other essential imports.

Submarines have important anti-ship and anti-submarine roles to play in support of either type of strategy, and in both these roles may act offensively, defensively—or both.

OFFENSIVE SEA CONTROL

Offensively, submarines can patrol near an enemy base. It is one of their great advantages. Here, they act alone, or as part of a ring fence, to kill threats to sea control, at source. For instance, before Kuwait could be recaptured in 1991, much war material had to be moved by ship to Saudi Arabia, through the Mediterranean, past several nations rather sympathetic to Iraq. Imagine the political embarrassment if half the British Main Battle Tanks had wound up on the sea bed, in a non-British ship, sunk by an unidentified submarine. Who knows what was done, but covertly putting our boats outside relevant naval bases, ready to prevent interference with such shipping, would have been a sensible, unobtrusive, precaution. (Figure 2.1)

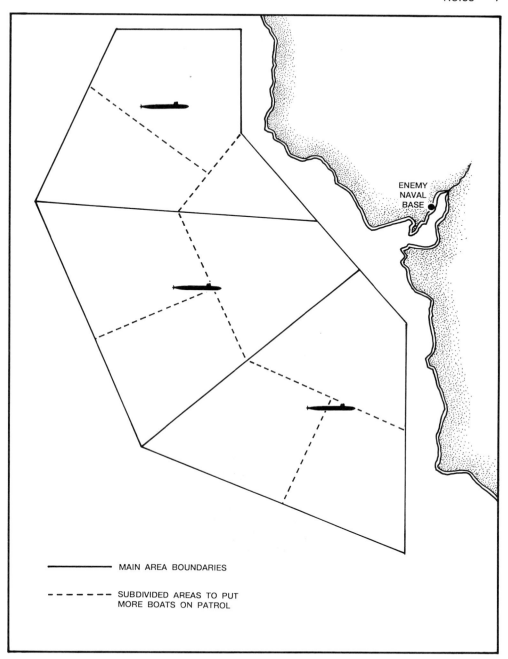

ENEMY
NAVAL
BASE

MAIN AREA BOUNDARIES

SUBDIVIDED AREAS TO PUT
MORE BOATS ON PATROL

Fig. 2.1 Offensive sea control—ring fence

Another option is to establish offensive submarine patrols in a choke-point, through which enemy forces must pass to carry out their sea denial task. With nearby land in friendly hands, this submarine trap can be made more deadly by putting ASW (*Anti-Submarine Warfare*) ships, MPA (*Maritime Patrol Air*) aircraft, and minefields in nearby areas. Also, by monitoring the approaches with seabed planted listening devices. Thus, in any East-West confrontation, the GIUK (*Greenland-Iceland-UK*) gaps became a likely place for NATO to conduct submarine and other barrier operations, for sea control of the Atlantic. They also provided a possible choke point for Russian offensive submarine operations, aimed at keeping enough sea control of the Norwegian Sea to conduct amphibious landings in Norway and maybe Iceland. (Figure 2.2)

Before any war starts, submarines on offensive patrols collect intelligence and provide early news that a major deployment of enemy maritime forces has begun. Nations with no access to satellite reconnaissance information often regard the warning provided by such surveillance activity as a prime reason for having submarines. And one must remember that even satellite reconnaissance cannot spot submarines deploying from cavernous bases carved out of a mountainside.

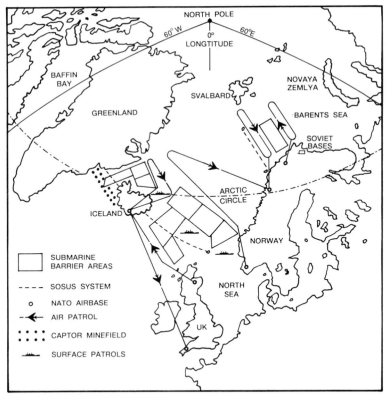

Fig. 2.2   Soviet appreciation of NATO dispositions for offensive sea control-barrier operations.

At low levels of conflict, one can use SSs or SSNs for either type of offensive sea control. At high levels, it is best to use SSNs close to the enemy bases. They are less worried by modern enemy ASW aircraft; and being more mobile, once deployment starts, can slip out of their areas, to trail significant enemy surface groups, ready to engage them. Very high quality SSNs may also be able to take up the trail of submarines passing through a barrier, to discover where the enemy is concentrating—but then the barrier will need adjusting. Of course, once war begins, any boat attacks any enemy unit coming through its area, and needs sensors and weapons good enough to enable it to do so.

DEFENSIVE SEA CONTROL

Friendly surface ships usually move in groups for mutual protection. These may be naval battle groups, military sea lift convoys or resupply trade convoys. Defensive operations in support of such groups must start before they sail and continue until they reach their destination. The support may be direct, in the form of a loose but fairly close escort; or indirect, where the intention is to start attrition of incoming threats earlier and further away, thus providing defence in depth, on which all modern naval tactics are based.

Depending on the enemy order of battle, friendly surface groups may be attacked by surface, submarine or air forces. All three can launch missiles, and all carry shorter range weapons as well. Defence against aircraft and their missiles is multi-layered: first interception by own aircraft, (if available), followed by engagement with ship launched missiles, then gunfire. Submarines are no help here. However, they have a very useful role to play against the other two threats. And if they can take out a submarine or immobilise a surface ship before it launches missiles, they kill part of the potential air-borne threat too. Since sub-surface launched missiles are some of the hardest to engage, this help is doubly welcome.

We have seen already that our own submarines like to lie in wait outside a departure port, and so may enemy boats. If our surface group is sailing straight into deep water, flushing out these lurking enemies is a job tailor made for escorting submarines with long range active underwater sensors. Once the group is at sea, submarines stationed out in the deep field in indirect support, and using passive underwater sensors, have a good chance of detecting and engaging enemy boats, which are still using speed to close the force and before they have enough information on the surface units to launch attacks. Meanwhile, already in the deep field, our submarines are well placed if they have to be detached to intercept and engage surface units threatening the group. (Figure 2.3)

However unsophisticated the enemy, escorts are always needed. Strengthened by SSNs, they give more confidence to those deploying our surface groups, that they will arrive intact. So, the United States Battle Groups taking part in Operation Desert Storm would have had SSN escorts with them, whether or not their Tomahawk missiles were required for bombarding Iraq. Also, these boats are useful at the far end. Once surface forces remain relatively stationary for a prolonged spell, they need protection against enemy boats creeping into their operating area. This can be given by drawing a defensive cordon around it, or by

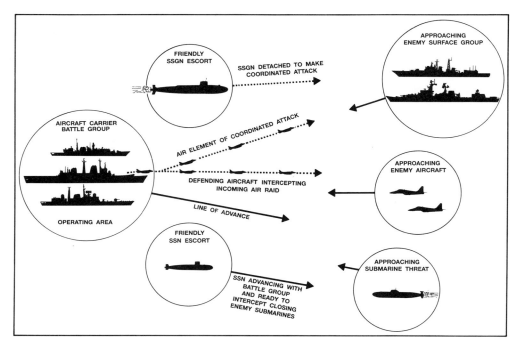

Fɪɢ. 2.3   Defensive sea control around a Battle Group

using a restricted geographical area, such as the Red Sea, and putting submarine escorts at its entrance.

Only an SSN can handle the submarine escort role, for which there are three essential requirements: enough speed to keep up with the surface group, underwater sensors which can work effectively at this speed, and good two way communications with the surface group Force Commander. The weapon load should include cruise missiles, because they shorten the time it takes to carry out an attack on an incoming surface threat.

OFFENSIVE SEA DENIAL

The great anti-commerce, offensive submarine campaigns of the two world wars were all waged in pursuit of sea denial strategies. In such titanic struggles, lasting years, an occasional good month is not enough. The number of ship cargoes arriving safely has to be kept permanently below the dangerously insufficient level. To sustain such a high sinking rate, one must bring about enough encounters and make full use of them. Keys to success are large numbers of boats, early news of enemy movements, good commanding officers, and coordination of attacks to overwhelm defences with a local concentration of force.

Submarines do not move about in fleets, but many of these requirements are met when one has enough boats to organise them in packs, as both Germany and the United States did in the Second World War. Based on satellite or other intelligence, the pack is disposed in a loose line, strung across the expected enemy route. Modern sensors ought then to ensure that someone makes contact. That boat gives everyone else an updated enemy position. With the long range weapons and good satellite communications of the 1990s, it is then, relatively, much easier than it was in 1943, to arrange a simultaneous pack attack on the surface group. A well organised shore command may be able to coordinate the submarine attacks with others by air and surface forces.

Only three nations currently have enough submarines to mount a major sea denial campaign: the United States, Russia and China. The first two have predominantly modern boats and enough shipbuilding capacity to replace submarine losses quickly. China does not. Moreover, such campaigns become long wars of attrition. Bearing in mind Russian politico-economic difficulties in 1993, the USA may now be the only one of the three able to sustain a really long campaign. And since their SSNs are needed much more to defend their many Battle Groups, prolonged sea denial warfare may not be seen again.

This does not mean that NATO can happily forget that the combined Russian Northern and Baltic Fleets field 48 SSNs, 21 SSGNs, 10 SSGs, and about 62 SSs. Although some Russian SSNs may have to escort SSBNs; and some SSGNs/SSGs are probably earmarked for sea control of the Norwegian Sea; an impressive margin of strength is left to mount a short, sharp Atlantic sea denial campaign. Moreover, large scale removal of NATO army equipment from Europe to the USA, as part of the peace dividend, actually increases the significance of the threat, since NATO sea lift shipping then has more material to bring back across the Atlantic in any future East/West crisis.

The Atlantic Russian threat has dropped by about 21 submarines in the last three years, but a much greater reduction than this is needed to remove legitimate Western concern.

DEFENSIVE SEA DENIAL

Whether major submarine campaigns are a thing of the past or not, more defensive sea denial operations are almost bound to be required at intervals, and submarines will play an increasingly important part in them. The world is peppered with small island nations whose large continental neighbours regard them acquisitively. Without exception, these islanders supported Britain at the UN in April 1982, for good reasons. Some variation of the Falklands scenario could face many of them. Since that was also a good example of the need to mount sea control and sea denial operations together, it is worth examining again.

Having struck the first blow by invading the islands, Argentina was faced with the need to re-supply her troops, eventually ten thousand of them. To stop her doing it by sea, Britain declared an EZ (***Exclusion Zone***) around the islands, and defended its perimeter with submarine and other forces, a very typical low level defensive sea denial scenario. Meanwhile Admiral Woodward and his Task Force were approaching from the north-east, ready to retake the islands, if diplomacy failed.[1]

Arguably, this operation required sea control all the way from the United Kingdom to the Falklands, clearly an area much larger than the EZ established

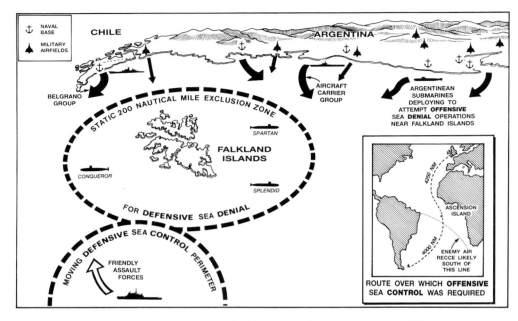

FIG. 2.4   Sea control and sea denial during the Falklands operations 1982

purely for sea denial purposes, which Assault Forces would not enter until just before the landings. So, to the British, it was always irrelevant whether *Belgrano* was inside or outside the EZ. It was also irrelevant to them whether she was steering east or west when torpedoed. She and her escorts were a strong group, well within range to interfere before the landings, and were believed, correctly, to be manoeuvring to coordinate their attack with other hostile forces. Moreover, with a worst case appreciation that the Argentinean Air Force might sink 25 per cent of the ships, no margin of strength existed for accepting surface ship inflicted casualties as well.

Conqueror attacked, therefore, to keep offensive sea control of the area. She required governmental approval to engage, which was given, via satellite communications, because the appreciation in the United Kingdom was that the action could not safely be delayed. However, in other circumstances, she might have been told to attack by the Force Commander, to increase his defensive sea control. The net result was to persuade the Argentinean Navy to inflict sea denial on itself, throughout the region, not just the EZ. One could not have a better example of the usefulness of SSNs.

LESSER ROLES

Submarines can helpfully carry out a number of other tasks, either in support of a Falklands type operation, or as stand alone activities, during some contretemps at a lower level, between any two powers. For example, prior to an invasion, final reconnaissance is needed, beach gradients have to be measured, and Special Forces like the SAS must be landed. Always, submarines are the best way to get agents in and out of an island. They can also carry small quantities of supplies to beleaguered island garrisons, when the enemy has sea control. The Argentinean boat *Santa Fe* was sunk off South Georgia in 1982, whilst on this sort of mission.

At another level, nations with submarines can threaten a virtual blockade of a key enemy port, without having to risk surface ships in the process. If needs be, approaches to the port can then be mined or any ship trying to use it can be sunk. For example, had South Africa owned British OBERON class submarines, instead of the shorter ranged French DAPHNE class, they could have shut Luanda, 3400 kilometres to the north, to cut Cuban resupply of Angola during the long confrontation with SWAPO.

However, South Africa acquired its small division of SSs, like many a submarine-owning nation, because it was unsure of the intentions of another nation in its area, and this nation was building up a surface navy. The South Africans certainly did not want the expense of matching the Indian Navy ship for ship, but they did wish to show that they were capable of mounting defensive sea denial operations in their Indian Ocean home waters.

Many nations also use their submarines, in peace and war, to provide opposition for other maritime forces being exercised in their war role. This is an entirely correct use of submarines, but often involves playing an offensive sea denial role. If their own wartime role is offensive or defensive sea control, time must be set aside, within these exercises, or separately, for submarines to acquire the necessary skills.

THE DETERRENT ROLE OF SSBN

A strategic nuclear weapon system must be credible and affordable. Since it is designed to deter, credibility depends entirely on how it is viewed by potential enemies. They must believe that if they use their strategic nuclear weapons, in a first strike, ours will be used in a second strike retaliation. And no matter what they do before or after launching their first strike, enough of our weapons are going to penetrate their defensive systems, as to cause an unacceptable level of damage in their country.

Nuclear warheads can be delivered by land-launched or air-launched systems, and the superpowers back up their SSBNs with large numbers of both. But making either system credible is expensive. Land systems can be taken out as part of the enemy first strike, so a vast panoply of early warning equipment is needed, to ensure that our missiles take off before enemy ones arrive. Or sometimes, missiles are shuffled underground, between a large number of sites, in a vast peanut-under-the-shells game, to ensure that some survive. Keeping aircraft permanently airborne, to protect air launched systems, is also very costly.

By comparison, SSBNs represent an almost ideal deterrent system. The launching vehicle is mobile and may be hidden anywhere within a vast area of sea, which gets bigger and bigger as ever longer range SLBMs (**Submarine Launched Ballistic Missiles**) are fitted. These long ranges also enable Russian SSBNs, with missiles targeted on North America, to patrol well under the Arctic ice cap.

To meet the threat of Russian SSBNs using the ice for cover; and of Tomahawk armed Western SSGNs, with cruise missile targets in North Russia doing the same; the SSNs of both sides in the Cold War had to spend much time preparing themselves for under ice warfare. However, unless the SSBN commanding officer is incredibly careless, an SSN has great difficulty in trailing a quiet SSBN out to any operating area, let alone one under the ice. And finding even one SSBN, when one does not know where to start looking is nigh impossible. Even so, enormous care is taken to decrease the risk of detection still further. No nation could bank on being able to pre-empt such a system. Understandably, nations like Britain, France and China, have invested in SSBNs because they provide the only deterrent which can be made credible on its own, at a price they can afford. (Figure 2.5)

SUMMARY

Maritime forces are employed to ensure that our own surface forces can continue to use an area, or to deny its use to enemy surface forces. Submarines can have offensive and defensive roles in support of both strategies. They may work

FIG. 2.5   Area covered by a TRIDENT II D-5 missile-armed submarine placed in the Irish Sea

in coordination with other friendly forces, but can also be sent into areas where no one else could go—or where it would be embarrassing for them to be seen. In all roles, they may be pitted against either ships or other submarines. And for both, they remain one of the most dangerous opponents.

The multi-role nature of modern submarine operations, and the fact that they are conducted at so many different levels, make nonsense the old saying that submarines are the weapon of the weaker power. Many small navies do use them, because they give such good warning of hostile intent, introduce an element of uncertainty to the calculations of their enemies, and provide a means of raising the political ante. However, all large navies also have submarines, because they add great strength to any deploying group, and can be very flexibly employed. And those nations which have a nuclear deterrent all know that the SSBN mounted part of it is the most credible. For Britain, France and China, it is also the only deterrent system they could have afforded.

3

Construction

A submarine presents a difficult constructional challenge with almost no room for error over weights and volumes. It has to be a safe and stable ship when on the surface, with a centre of gravity that is not too high and an adequate reserve of buoyancy, as explained in Volume 2 of this series.[1] Yet it must be possible to neutralise this reserve buoyancy quickly when diving and restore it promptly on surfacing. Once underwater, the submarine has to achieve exact neutral buoyancy in a wide range of sea water salinity conditions. For Russian submarines, these may include the high specific gravity, very salty—so seemingly buoyant—Mediterranean, to the near fresh water Baltic. It must also be possible to remove enough water from within the submarine to compensate for loss of internal volume, hence real loss of buoyancy, which will occur when the submarine is taken deep and its hull contracts.

Hulls have to be very strong. Water pressure increases by another atmosphere every nine metres, and at 300 metres, a 533 mm torpedo tube bow cap will be holding back about 86 tons. It must also survive the sudden shocks produced by exploding enemy ordnance. Once built, the boat needs to achieve high underwater speeds, quietly. This requires an external shape quite different to that best suited to high surface speed. Moreover, it cannot be replenished at sea and has to carry everything it needs, particularly fuel, for maybe an eight to twelve week deployment. Above all, like any warship, it must be designed around the number, size and complexity of the weapons intended for it.

STRENGTH

To withstand sea pressure, the submarine is given a thick inner shell. For maximum strength, this pressure hull should be a sphere, or number of small spheres, without openings. In practice, it is usually a cylinder with a thick dome at each end, but the requirement to minimise the number and size of hull penetrations is always an important design objective.

Pressure hulls are made of high grade, high tensile steel, (or a titanium alloy in some Russian boats), and may be many centimetres thick, depending on chosen operating depth. Sheets of this hull plating are first cold rolled, then welded together, to form circular half sections of pressure hull cylinder. Further strength is added by fitting 'T' cross section ribs, called frames, and four to six complete bulkheads. (Figures 3.1–3.3)

Fig. 3.1   Welding a new hull section (*Photo: VSEL*)

Once two half sections have been welded together, the whole section is brought upright and taken to a preliminary assembly area. Here, as far as possible, it is fitted out by bolting on complete modules, which have been carefully assembled in quieter areas, and already carry all necessary, planned pipe runs, as well as machinery. As each section completes, a new empty one is welded on and the fitting out continues. Later, units of three or four sections joined together are taken to a main assembly hall by a giant trans– porter, to be united to form the submarine. Then, final outfitting takes place, including installation of many kilometres of electrical wiring.

The key to the whole process is end-to-end quality control. It starts with test-ing, treating and documenting every plate of steel. It continues with rigorous examination by radiography and ultra-sonics, after any bending or welding, to ensure that all joins are sound; and that no sources of weakness have been caused in the plating. Hull linearity must also be proved after each new section has been added, to avoid building a banana.

Titanium hulls are much more difficult to construct because the metal on either side of a weld oxidises, creating weakness, unless all such work is carried out in an inert gas (usually nitrogen) atmosphere. This is not easy to achieve when sections are 10 metres wide. On the plus side, weight for weight, titanium is much stronger than steel, a fact which has allowed Russia to build the ALFA class SSN with a stated ability to go down to 700 metres. This compares favourably with the 450

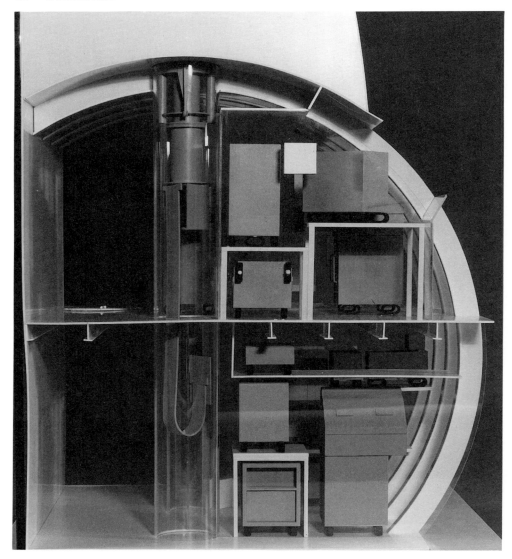

FIG. 3.2 Model of cross-section of 'O' Class hull showing internal frames
(*Photo: Thorn EMI*)

metres diving depth usually quoted for the 6910 ton LOS ANGELES class United States SSNs currently building.

However, depth figures can be misleading. ALFA is barely half the displacement of LOS ANGELES, and small is strong. A better comparison would be with the Russian SIERRA class, whose 8000 ton titanium hulls are probably not taken much beyond 550 metres, albeit still an impressive figure.

Of course, the true significance of Russian diving depths cannot be appreciated without also knowing the exact depth floor, at which NATO torpedoes would be

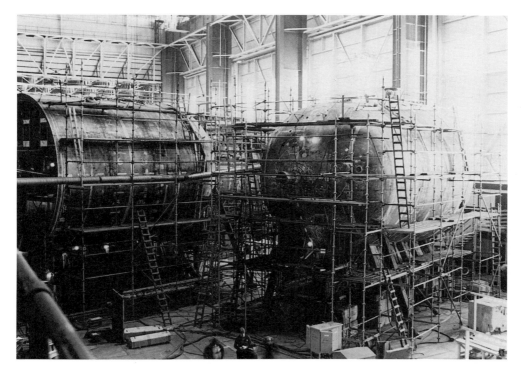

Fig. 3.3   Domed end of a pressure hull (*Photo: VSEL*)

crushed by external water pressure. But it has been suggested that ALFA class submarines can outdive the weapons chasing them.

Whatever the published data, the commanding officer needs to know three figures for his own submarine: *collapse depth*, *safe depth* and *working depth*. Collapse depth is worked out first and forms the basis for calculating the other figures. In the British 1945 *A* class it was 850 feet. A safe depth, sometimes called *test depth*, was then set at 500 feet, representing a generous safety factor of 1.7.[2] It is not dangerous, but it is bad practice to make frequent dives to safe depth, because heavy working of the hull ages it prematurely and undesirably adds to permanent magnetism (see Chapter 12). A good working depth for the A class was 350 feet.

Force majeure, submarines in action have been near to their collapse depth, and have survived. It is also some comfort to know that when an A class hull was deliberately lowered as an experiment, it collapsed at 876 feet. A look at the wreck showed that the first thing to give way was the surround of the forward torpedo embarkation hatch, the largest break in the continuity of the hull, because it had to be elliptical to accommodate the passage of a torpedo. In PERMIT class United States SSNs, whose torpedo tubes are amidships, hull diameter allows weapons to be embarked vertically through a small circular hatchway, removing this source of hull weakness. (Figure 3.4a and b)

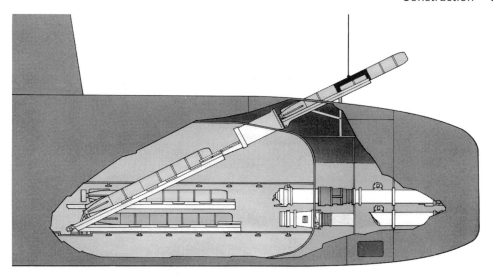

FIG. 3.4 a. (*left*) Torpedo embarkation in US PERMIT Class SSN (*Photo Norman Polmar*) b. (*above*) Torpedo embarkation in UK SSNs (*Diagram: Strahan & Henshaw*)

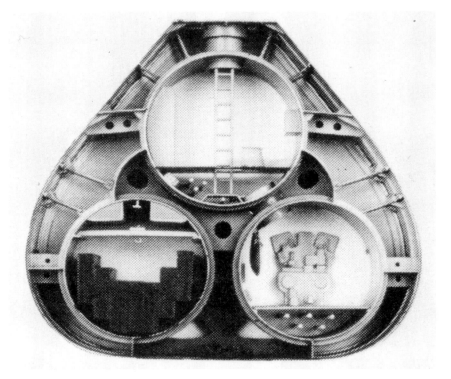

FIG. 3.5 Triple Hull layout in Netherlands POTVIS Class (*Photo: Royal Netherlands Navy*)

Fɪɢ. 3.6   Russian TYPHOON Class SSBN at Severomorsk Northern Fleet Base.
Note: 20 missile hatches for SS-N-20 SLBM: ice damage to the front of the fin and
the huge size of the boat (man just visible at the jackstaff) (*Photo: YOGI INC 1991*)

MULTIPLE HULLS

One method of retaining strength, whilst increasing the volume carried is to build with more than one pressure hull. The Netherlands POTVIS class submarines have a triple-hull, three cylinders arranged in a triangle. The top cylinder takes the crew, navigation equipment and armament. The lower two house the propulsion and power generation gear. (Figure 3.5)

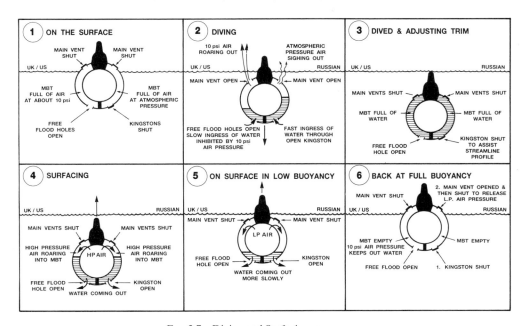

FIG. 3.7   Diving and Surfacing sequence

US submarines have often had a separate upper cylinder for the combat team, and the latest Soviet SSBNs of the TYPHOON class are so large that they seem to be built with four pressure hulls: two side by side for propulsion and strategic missile launch tubes, one forward for a tactical weapon centre and a fourth above all the others for the combat team. The advantage to be gained can be judged from POTVIS's diving depth of 300 metres, about 100 metres more than that of similar sized, monohull submarines built of the same sort of steel in the late 1950s. (Figure 3.6)

BALLAST TANKS AND BUOYANCY

An adequate reserve of buoyancy on the surface is created by fitting MBT (*Main Ballast Tanks*). These have vents in the top and a means of opening them to the sea at the bottom. Some have just free flood holes, others quick operating valves, called 'kingstons'. Both high and low pressure air pipes feed into the top of the MBT. To dive, vents and kingstons are opened and sea water entering the bottom of the tanks expels the air through the top. Once the MBT are full of water

FIG. 3.8   USS *Georgia* (SSBN 729) diving for sea trials in Dabob Bay,Washington.
The main vents are open and the main ballast tanks (MBTs) venting (*Photo: YOGI
INC 1992*)

the submarine is more or less neutrally buoyant and can dive. To surface again,
Main Vents are shut and bottled high pressure air is released into the top of the
tanks, driving water out into the sea through the bottom. Once firmly on the surface, remaining water is blown out slowly with low pressure air. (Figure 3.7)[3]

Many different options have been tried for siting the MBT, inside and outside
the pressure hull. Submarines now being built all have external MBT, usually a
large number contained in a complete, second, outer hull, the Russian system;
or in two, smaller groups, which are virtually extensions of the pressure hull forward and aft, the US and UK system. The Russian method gives great reserve
buoyancy, (as much as 40 per cent instead of say 15 per cent), some attenuation
of radiated machinery noise, and better protection against an impacting
enemy torpedo. The US/UK method gives a smaller overall outer hull area,
reducing drag, and the reflecting surface available to enemy active sonars.
(Figure 3.8)

In addition to MBT, several auxiliary ballast or trimming tanks will be fitted
inside the pressure hull to allow the submarine to achieve exact neutral buoyancy
and compensate for movement of weights from end to end. The precise number,
capacity and positioning of tanks varies widely but there must be enough scope
to ensure that they need never all be full or empty, no matter how light the
submarine is after eating all the food and firing all the weapons during a

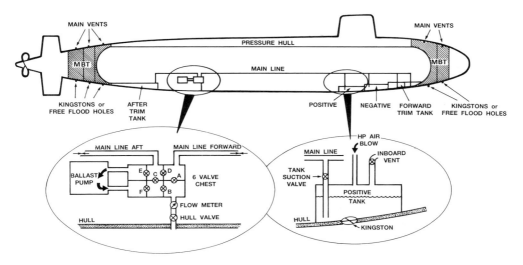

1. TO FLOOD WATER INTO POSITIVE SLOWLY: OPEN POSITIVE SUCTION & INBOARD VENT
                                          & VVE "A" ON 6 VVE CHEST

2. TO GET WATER OUT OF POSITIVE SLOWLY: OPEN POSITIVE SUCTION & INBOARD VENT
                                          & VVEs "D" "E" & "F" ON 6 VVE CHEST -
                                          START PUMP THEN OPEN VVE "B"

3. TO GET WATER OUT OF POSITIVE QUICKLY: OPEN POSITIVE KINGSTON & USE HP AIR BLOW

FIG. 3.9   MBTs and basic Main Line layout

Mediterranean patrol; or heavy, when full loaded and deep in the near fresh waters off the entrance to a Norwegian fjord.

The trimming tanks are all connected in parallel, via their own suction pipes, to a common salt water line, called Main Line in British submarines. It has a single hull valve to allow flooding in and a multi-stage pump to get water out. When deep, pumping is slow but the alternative of blowing water out is unacceptably noisy, under normal patrol conditions. However, a need can arise to become lighter or heavier quickly and some of the trimming tanks forward of the centre of gravity, as well as having main line suctions are fitted with hull valves and blows. In diesel and battery driven submarines, who lack rapid acceleration, one tank is most usefully kept empty, ready to flood with temporary *Negative* buoyancy, when needing to go deep quickly from periscope depth. In SSNs making long passages at high speeds, which can conceal a gradually growing imbalance in the trim, the special tanks are best kept full, ready to use as a *Positive*, to be blown should the boat be very heavy when suddenly forced to slow down. (Figure 3.9)

HULL SHAPES

The pressure hull cylinder(s) and MBT must be encased in a free-flooding, well streamlined, outer shell, which has a shape optimised for high underwater speed: ideally, low length to beam ratio (less than 8:1), bulbous bow, maximum width at about a quarter length from the bow and then tapering almost to a point at the

Fig. 3.10   USS *Billfish* (SSN 676) in floating dock for sand blasting and repainting of the hull. Note her bulbous bow (*Photo: YOGI INC 1989*)

stern. Such tear-drop shapes promote smooth water flow and are a feature of several large, fast-moving sea mammals. (Figure 3.10)

Although the USA pioneered the tear-drop hull in the experimental diesel submarine USS *Albacore* in the 1950s, successive classes of US SSNs have shown a gradual rise in length to beam ratios: SKIPJACK 8:1, PERMIT 8.8:1, STURGEON 9.5:1, LOS ANGELES 10.9:1; as the basic design has been stretched to fit in more equipment. Significantly, plans for the next generation of US SSNs, the innovative SSN 21 SEA WOLF class, include restoring the ratio to 7.7:1, the lowest it will ever have been in an SSN anywhere and near to the ALBACORE figure of 7.46:1.

REDUCING DRAG

The restrictive processes which can dissipate propulsion energy in surface ships were fully described in Vol 3 of this series. In short they are: wave generation; dragging along water in the boundary layer close to the hull; and energy used to pull along even more water when laminar flow is upset by turbulence, due to projections and breaks in the streamlining. Tear-drop hull submarines consume a huge amount of propulsion energy, producing waves, when they are surfaced and partially out of their element. Doing 25 knots, an SSN will still be producing a discernible, humped wave pattern on the surface of a calm sea when at a keel depth

FIG. 3.11 USS *Houston* (SSN 713) using up energy wave making (*Photo: US Navy*)

of 46 metres. At 60 metres and deeper, wave-making stops and the problem becomes purely one of minimising drag, mainly by removing discontinuities in the outer hull. (Figure 3.11)

Mammals like dolphins secrete a substance through their skins which maintains laminar flow and gives them very small boundary layers. One contribution to the 42+ knot speed of Russian *Alfa* class SSNs may be ejection from their hulls of substances called polymers, known to have a similar effect. It is certainly possible to smooth over hulls with synthetic coatings, though these tend to be incompatible with meeting an important signature reduction requirement, the fitting of anechoic tiles outside the hull to reduce effectiveness of enemy active sonars.

SIZE

The nature of the weapons and sensors to be carried is the main determinant of size. A large hull has many disadvantages but the vital statistics of successive classes of Russian SSBNs show a remorseless increase in submarine tonnage as larger numbers of newer, longer range, more sophisticated SLBMs are introduced. (Table 3.1) Longer ranges meant bigger rocket motors and longer missile lengths. Meanwhile, the basic hull diameter of the YANKEE and DELTA SSBNs was not altered with increasing tonnage, that is their beam width stayed the same.

Fig. 3.12   DELTA IV Class Soviet SSBN (1987). Showing hump behind the fin
(© *British Crown Copyright 1993/MOD*)

TABLE 3.1

Russian SSBN Sizes

Vessel	YANKEE	DELTA 1	DELTA 2	DELTA 3	DELTA 4	TYPHOON
Tons	9,450	10,200[1]	11,300[2]	11,700[3]	12,150	26,500
Beam	11.6 m	12.0 m	12.0 m	12.0 m	12.0 m	24.6 m
Missiles	16	12	16	16	16	20
Types	SS-N-6	SS-N-8	SS-N-8	SS-N-18	SS-N-23	SS-N-20
Range	2400 –	7800 –	7800 –	8000[4]	8300	8300
(km)	3000	9100	9100		(Mirvd)	(Mirvd)
Rocket	1 stage	2 stage	2 stage	2 stage	3 stage	3 stage
Motor	Liquid	Liquid	Liquid	Liquid	Liquid	Solid

Notes: 1. SS-N-8 missile was longer than SS-N-6 and casing had to be humped to
accommodate it.
2. Submarine 18.0 m longer than DELTA 1 to fit extra 4 launch tubes.
3. SS-N-18 missile was longer than SS-N-8, causing further growth in DELTA hump.
4. 6500 km for MIRVd variant.

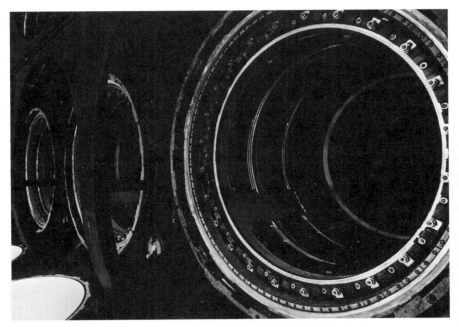

Fig. 3.13   a. USS *Nevada* (SSBN 733) in the Explosive Handling Wharf at Submarine Base Bangor, Washington, with all 24 missile hatches open (*Photo: YOGI INC 1987*)   b. Close-up view of the missile hatches prior to C4 (TRIDENT I) loadout (*Photo: YOGI INC 1987*)

FIG. 3.14   *XE5* (X-craft midget submarine) with Lieutenant Westmacott on deck
(*Photo: RN Submarine Museum*)

Therefore, as missile lengths grew, the upper part of the vertical launch tubes had to project more and more through the top of the pressure hull, and be faired into a box-shaped casing hump in rear of the fin. (Figure 3.12)

The DELTA hump was good for neither fast nor quiet performance. Restoring good underwater profile and survivability, whilst adding four more launch tubes, and switching to solid fuel rockets, has led the Russians to build the TYPHOON class, at 26,500 tons, currently the world's largest submarines. Similar considerations have dictated the size of the 18,700 ton US OHIO and 15,000 ton British VANGUARD classes, with their 12,000 kilometre D5 SLBMs; though the Americans have always produced a new submarine before the missile designed for it was ready, avoiding the need to distort existing hull shapes. If necessary, they fit liners inside the new, wider launch tubes, to take the old narrower missiles, whilst waiting for the new ones to appear. (Figure 3.13a and b)

Size has always been a hotly debated issue for SSN and SS builders too. Small ought to be good. It means strong, fast and deep. But it also means noisy, inadequate weapon carrying capacity and cramped inside—which in turn often means no hope of retrofitting new systems and therefore a foreshortened life. SSN design difficulty is also increased by having to carry so many different weapons for the various roles.

One can build very small submarines. The British X-craft which immobilised the German battleship *Tirpitz* in 1943 were only 35 tons. They could lay two delayed-action explosive charges, of about two tons each, underneath ships at anchor, having been towed to within 60 miles of their target by a larger submarine. They were

FIG. 3.15   Russian OSCAR Class SSGN. Note: Six shutters, each covering two
launchers, on the starboard side (© *British Crown Copyright 1993/MOD*)

easier to design than a modern SSN, because they were purpose built for only one
job, just as TYPHOON has been purpose built to threaten destruction of US
ICBM launch sites, or several cities, from under the Arctic ice. (Figure 3.14)

The X-craft had to be small for operational reasons, to penetrate enemy
defences round their targets. They could be small because they only carried a tiny
crew, for a short time, to make a very limited distance trip. These then are the
other size-drivers: the number of men on board, the length of patrol planned and,
in diesel boats, the distance the fuel has to carry the submarine.

USE OF CASING SPACE

The space between the pressure hull and outer shell, particularly large in multi-hull submarines, can be used to site onboard sonar equipment well away from interfering self-noise sources. It may also house weapon launchers for externally carried torpedoes, anti-ship tactical missiles, land-bombarding cruise missiles and certain sorts of mine. For example, the principal passive and active bow sonar array in the LOS ANGELES class SSN is more than 40 feet from the forward dome bulkhead of the pressure hull. In between, room has been found for 12 vertical Tomahawk cruise missile launchers. The Russian OSCAR class SSGNs carry their main armament of 24 SS-N-19 missile launchers in the casing space, each one angled up at 40 degrees. (Figure 3.15)

High pressure air bottle groups have been placed in the casing space but this increases the number of hull penetrations without bringing much benefit. Indeed, as a design principle, the casing should be kept as empty as possible and not treated as a convenient place to stow awkward portable fittings, such as the torpedo embarkation rails. SSBNs and SSNs roll quite heavily at periscope depth on a rough day and anything working loose in the casing will increase the noise signature very undesirably. No commanding officer wants to have to surface to sort out such problems. At best it risks compromising the submarine's presence in the patrol area. At worst, a fatal air attack.

THE FIN

The fin, alias sail, provides underwater handling stability, a bridge platform for those conning the submarine when it is on the surface and a supporting structure for seven or eight masts. The masts in turn strengthen the fin, which would have to be much more substantial without them. It needs to be very strong for pushing up through Arctic ice and to withstand the water flow pressure at high speed. It should also be well rounded into the hull to shrug off ice, maintain laminar flow and reduce sonar reflection. The TYPHOON fin seems well calculated to meet all these needs.

The location of the fin tends to be dictated by the position of those masts, like optical periscopes, which must be hull-penetrating. To keep the submarine as deep as possible, whilst using periscopes, helps ship handling in bad weather and increases the amount of water already overhead when going deep in emergency. It is a good design aim but means sinking the periscope wells almost to the keel plating, to allow use of maximum possible periscope length. To accommodate other things in the internal layout, some not easily altered, such deep wells can be sited in only a few places, though greater use of non-hull-penetrating masts may ease this problem in future.

Choosing the correct fin height is also important. Overshort and there will be too much unsupported mast. Submarine speed will, therefore, have to be unduly limited when masts are up, which can restrict critically the ability to carry out certain tasks, such as a close look at a surface ship during surveillance operations. If too tall, it raises the centre of gravity and the fin produces an undesirably abrupt movement, known as a snap roll, when deep and altering course at speed. Careful modelling in a water tank is needed to get it right.

SUMMARY

A submarine has an outer hull, tear-drop shaped for high underwater speed, inside which are one or more pressure hulls for strength and depth range, external MBT to change role from surface ship to submarine and internal tanks to maintain neutral buoyancy underwater. The hull size depends primarily on the weapons to be carried but also on: the number of men to be embarked, the length of patrol intended and, for an SS, the distance the fuel has to carry the submarine before refuelling. At the design stage, there is very little room for error over weights, volumes or dimensions, one of the most difficult calculations being the positioning and size of the fin. At the building stage, everything depends on quality control.

4

Control Surfaces and Ship Handling

In addition to the rudder which any ship has for steering, a submarine needs hydroplanes to allow depth to be altered and then maintained in a controlled manner. They act like the elevators of an aircraft and can be moved between 30 degrees of rise and 30 degrees of dive.

Early boats had a single set of hydroplanes, fitted aft near the rudder, an arrangement still seen in many small submarines of the swimmer-delivery and DSRV (*Deep Submergence Recovery Vessel*) types. Larger boats have a second set of hydroplanes, either on the sides of the fin or about one eighth of a length from the bow. (Figure 4.1)

FIG. 4.1   Britain's first submarine—*Holland I*. She had after hydroplanes only and, in other ways, was very like modern submarines, with uppper and lower rudders and a low length/beam ratio (*Photo: RN Submarine Museum*)

AFTER HYDROPLANES

The after planes are much bigger and have much more effect than the fore planes. Indeed, when deep and in good trim, or when above 12 knots, only the after planes are needed. They form a hinged rear section of an after horizontal stabilizing surface, substantially wider than the hull. Typically, with a maximum hull beam of 10 metres, the width at the after planes is likely to be 13 to 14 metres. It is always the limiting dimension for getting into a dry dock. (Figure 4.2)

FORE HYDROPLANES

Fore planes are needed for accurate depth keeping when slow and shallow at periscope depth. British submarines invariably have them in the bow position. Large boats with tear-drop hulls have a tendency to be sucked up towards the surface when shallow and foreplanes fitted well forward are better able to overcome such movement. They are also more helpful when wanting to go deep in a hurry.

The main reason for fitting foreplanes on the fin is to remove the water flow and hydraulics noise associated with their operation well away from the submarine's bow mounted main passive sonar. However, fin mounted foreplanes are too close to the surface turbulence and too far aft to give really good control over the bow when shallow. Their operating gear takes up space in the fin badly needed for extra masts; and they are an embarrassment when breaking up through ice, although this can be reduced by making them able to go vertical. (Figure 4.3)

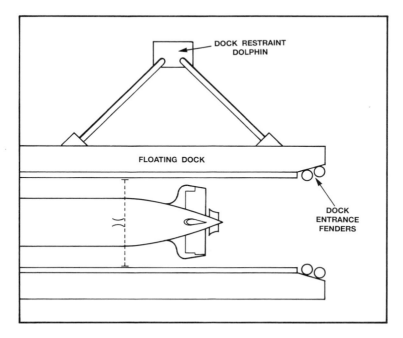

FIG. 4.2   Stern section of a large submarine in dry dock, showing after hydroplanes arrangement (See also Fig 5.11)

Fig. 4.3   USS *Billfish* (SSN 676) after surfacing through Polar ice. Her foreplanes
are vertical. Note the crew are in thick cold weather clothlng. (*Photo. USN courtesy
of YOGI INC*)

Bow mounted foreplanes can usually be retracted flush with the hull, as in the
British TRAFALGAR class and most Russian boats, or be folded up-and-inward,
to protect them from damage whilst berthing and by rough weather on the surface. When running deep and fast, they should be put at their no-effect balanced
angle, usually a slight amount of dive, and kept available to assist recovery
from after planes failure. Alternatively, to reduce water flow self-noise, they can
be retracted, but then the submarine must have more room to take emergency
recovery actions. (Figure 4.4 a and b)

SAFE OPERATING ENVELOPE

To prevent disaster occurring, after a jamming of the after planes, a submarine
is normally handled within an established safe operating envelope. As submarine
speed increases, more and more of the usable envelope is given up, creating wider
margins above and below, which can absorb excursions: towards the surface,
maybe ice, above; or the submarine crushing depth below. There is also an increasing minimum speed requirement when nearing safe depth, to maintain enough
residual momentum to bring the submarine shallow, following a flooding accident.
The shallower depth reduces the pressure outside and lessens the rate of water
ingress. (Figure 4.5)

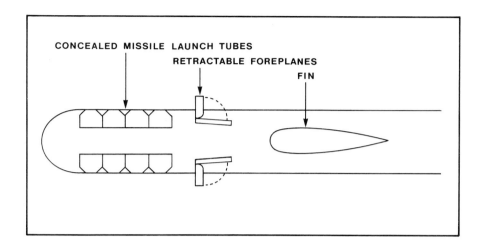

Fig. 4.4   a. Russian CHARLIE Class SSN showing shutter open on retractable
foreplanes (© *British Crown Copyright 1993/MOD*)
b. CHARLIE I bow configuration

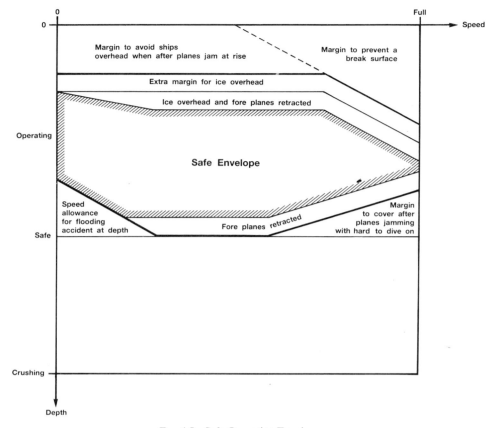

FIG. 4.5   Safe Operating Envelopes

RUDDER

The rudder in twin screw diesel submarines is very similar to that in surface ships, with a lower section only. In almost all nuclear powered submarines and in modern, fast, tear-drop hulled diesel-powered submarines, such as the British UPHOLDER and Netherlands ZWAARDVIS classes, the rudder has an upper and lower section. With the after planes, the rudder forms a cruciform of roughly matched size, left and right, top and bottom, to give all round good manoeuvrability. (Figure 4.6 a and b)

The huge rudder is so effective that a VALIANT class SSN doing over 20 knots could comfortably and speedily reverse course at either end of the underway noise range, within the confined space of Raasay Sound, (north of the island of Skye), using just two or three degrees of wheel, thus maintaining speed during the turns. Using the full 30 degrees of rudder movement, those on the controls need to be strapped in, because the rate of turn is dramatic. But the boat also loses speed rapidly. Tactically, it can be better to use less wheel and keep up the speed. (Figure 4.7)

FIG. 4.6   Two Netherlands submarines: The triple-hulled POTVIS with lower rudder only; and (above) ZWÄARDVIS with cruciform control surfaces (*Artwork: Royal Netherlands Navy*)

ONE MAN CONTROL

Manning the hydraulically operated controls of the hydroplanes and steering in 1940s era submarines was a three man job. The after planesman concentrated on the angle on the submarine, watching the bubble on a spirit level, the fore planes-man on the depth, shown on a gauge. A third man manned the wheel. Today, instruments are digital and all three functions can be handled by one man, though two joystick controls are often provided. If so, a junior operator controls the steering with one, and a senior watch-keeper both sets of planes with the other. Correct angles for each set of planes are calculated and applied by the OMC (*One-Man-Control*) computer each time the joystick is moved. The OMC can also make alterations of course and depth automatically, in response to orders set on the digital instruments, but it improves operator skills to do without this facility. (Figure 4.8)

Fɪɢ. 4.7   Russian TYPHOON Class showing part of the huge upper rudder. For comparison, note the size of the men on the bridge (© *British Crown Copyright 1993/MOD*)

HANDLING CHARACTERISTICS

At less than ten knots, a submarine is little different to a surface ship when altering course, but from twelve knots or more, it starts to handle underwater like an aircraft in air. Thus, it heels into the turn and, as it heels, so the rudder starts to act partly as an after hydroplane, adding a dive component to the turn. When at high speed, therefore, it is important to pull back the joystick and put rise on the planes immediately a large wheel order is given, just as the nose of an aircraft must be held up during a tight turn, if it is not to go into a descending spiral. In short, planesman and helmsman always have to work closely together.

CONTROL SURFACE FAILURE

A sudden upwards depth excursion towards the surface, caused by a jammed hydroplane, when at speed, is serious—especially if under ice. It is best handled initially by putting the wheel hard over, to take advantage of the dive effect of the rudder and because this helps to take way off. A sudden downwards excursion is best handled by keeping the wheel amidships and going astern as soon as possible. This will tend to drag down the stern and once headway is killed, if the submarine is roughly in trim, there is no serious problem left.

FIG. 4.8   Single operator using the Ferranti Naval Systems One Man Control in
HMS *Upholder* (*Photo: VSEL*)

RESIDUAL MOMENTUM

If the ahead throttles are shut and the propeller allowed to trail in an averagely
slippery 4500 ton tear-drop hulled submarine, making 20 knots straight and level,
it will still be logging about 5 knots 20 minutes later. It is this immense residual
momentum, always carried by a nuclear submarine, which makes it so important
to go astern early in an emergency. It is wise also, if forced to berth an SSN without tugs, to take off the bulk of the headway well short of the jetty and coast in
slowly. Meanwhile, the surfaced submarine will be virtually unaffected by the
wind, since, like an iceberg, more than 85 per cent of it is unexposed.

5

Propulsion and Power Generation

Most submarines currently in service use one of two methods for power generation and propulsion. In the first, heat is drawn continuously from a nuclear reactor and used, indirectly, to raise steam. This is then applied to TGs (*turbo driven power generators*) and two propulsion turbines, clutched to a common gear train and a single propeller. Submarines with two propellers have the whole system duplicated. Alternatively, all the steam is used to generate current, and electric motors turn the shaft(s). In the other method, called diesel-electric, diesel generators are run intermittently to produce the electrical energy which powers the propulsion motors.

THE NUCLEAR SYSTEM

The large size of civilian nuclear power stations tends to make one forget that a reactor is a very compact source of energy, ideal for submarines. For example, even the French boat *Rubis*, (at 2670 tons dived displacement, currently the world's smallest SSN), has a single PWR (*Pressurised Water Reactor*) capable of generating 48 megawatts within a 7.5 metre wide hull. The Soviet TYPHOON class SSBN, in a 24.7 metre beam hull, has two PWRs, capable of generating about 350 megawatts. 80,000 shaft horsepower is delivered, enough to drive her 26,500 ton hull through the water at 27 knots.

The good energy/volume ratio of a submarine PWR is achieved by enriching the uranium fuel. Natural uranium is mostly U 238, with a very small amount of the radioactive isotope U 235. A large amount of it is needed to make a reactor. By contrast, submarine PWR fuels, whether metal or oxide, are given a very heavy loading of U 235. This enrichment serves two purposes. It keeps the reactor quite small; yet puts enough reactivity in it to give the submarine an unrefuelled endurance equivalent to the time span between major dockyard refits, maybe even enough to equate to half the life of the submarine itself.

Essentials

The essential parts of the PWR are:

▶   Fuel elements

▶   Control rods

► Moderator

► Coolant

► Pressuriser

► Reactor Pressure Vessel (RPV)

► Shielding

Fuel—Control Rods—Moderator   A reactor is a generator of neutron flux. However, most neutrons emitted by radioactive elements are moving too fast to interact easily with fuel atoms, and so are likely to escape from a small reactor. Slowed to thermal speeds, by passing them through a moderator, such as pure water, they have a good chance of splitting other U 235 nuclei. Heat energy, radiation and several more neutrons are emitted after each collision. These neutrons split more U 235 nuclei on a statistically predictable basis, as an expanding chain reaction develops. However, the chain reaction is controllable only because some neutrons are delayed, that is they come from further decay of the fission products. Without these, the neutron life cycle would be too short to produce the stable flux needed for core power management.

The fast and slow neutron concept can be likened to taking a stealth Fast Patrol Boat through a busy shipping lane at night and forgetting that no one can see you. Go through at 40 knots and you are in the bad area for a very short time. The probability of collision is low. At infinite speed it is zero, provided the line of sight is clear. This is the fast neutron. Go through at 8 knots and sooner or later some idiot will run into you! This is the slow neutron.

Once the neutron activity is self sustaining, the reactor is said to be critical. The engineering challenges are to:

► Keep control of the approach to criticality

► Draw off power in the most efficient and safe way.

When the reactor core is first placed in the submarine RPV everything is inert. The U 235 fuel elements are fixed and spaced evenly in a pattern which will promote neutron flux within the core, minimise neutron loss to the sides and use up the fuel evenly. Between fuel elements are the moveable control rods. The U 235 has to be sheathed in protective metal cladding and the control rods made of a highly neutron absorbent material, such as boron.

Once the pure water moderator is added to the RPV the reactor is subcritical and can be taken critical by careful and partial use of the control rods. The approach to criticality is made very delicately and neutron flux meters monitor its progress throughout, as activity increases towards intermediate and power range flux levels. Reactor protection systems will 'scram' the reactor, that is use the control rods to shut down neutron activity, should there be any indication of an uncontrolled upward movement towards supercritical reactivity levels, or some loss of ability in the power removal systems mentioned below.

Coolant—Pressuriser   Connected to the RPV are one or more primary loops, in which are placed primary coolant pumps and a pressuriser. As the system heats up, a steam bubble is formed and held in the top of the pressuriser and used to raise pressure in the whole primary system, including the RPV. This enables a high temperature to be achieved in the primary coolant, without any boiling in the RPV, which would be undesirable as it might disturb the even distribution of coolant flow between the fuel elements. Hence the name pressurised water reactor. (Figure 5.1)

The action of circulating water in the primary loop allows the water moderator to act also as the coolant but the heat energy taken from the core cannot be used directly to do work because some radioactive impurities may be in the water, even when it is regularly bypassed through an ion-exchange fitted treatment loop to remove them. Instead, heat is extracted from the primary loop via a heat exchanger, which generates steam in a secondary, low pressure loop. It is this non-radioactive steam which drives the propulsion turbines and the TGs.

The secondary system is a simple saturated steam plant, with condensers under the turbines and TGs, feed pumps and a feed tank, fed by an evaporator. However, it is a mistake to engineer the secondary any less well than the primary system. The two are closely tied together by their joint activity within the heat exchanger SGs (*Steam Generators*), and problems for one quickly become problems for the other.

Normally, the responsiveness of the primary system to demands for power from the steam system is very helpful for the commanding officer and the acceleration of an SSN is impressive.[1] It occurs because any sudden but reasonable demand for steam draws heat off the heat exchanger. The temperature of the primary loop coolant then falls, making it denser. When this water enters the RPV, it acts as a more efficient moderator, because it is more dense; and more neutron/nucleus collisions occur, immediately raising the heat in the primary loop. The system then quickly stabilises at the new power level required to meet the throttle watchkeeper's needs. When slowing down, less steam is taken off, the coolant (moderator) entering the RPV is hotter, so less dense, and fewer collisions occur.

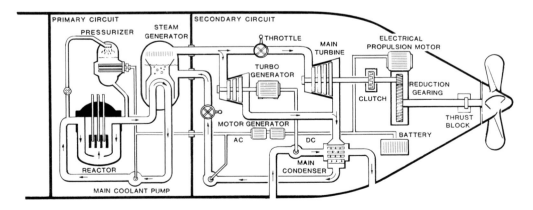

Fig. 5.1   Layout of a PWR system (*Rolls Royce & Associates*)

The output from the RPV becomes cooler and once again the power automatically adjusts to the lower level needed.

Protection circuits   Reactors are well guarded against a wide range of events, including: unreasonable demands for power, many different sorts of possible, though some highly unlikely, material failure, and human error. Protection circuits take quite a large slice of total installation cost. Partly, their high expense is due to having to make them both reliable and responsible. Thus, they must, and do, give a 100 per cent reliable guarantee that their reactor will be scrammed automatically, when it is necessary. But they must also, and do, act responsibly, in not shutting down their reactor unnecessarily, since this could be operationally embarrassing. Therefore, very high quality software writing and multi-path logic systems are needed. It is important too that those manning propulsion throttles, those putting load onto TGs and those moving reactor control rods, all work closely together, to avoid operators themselves causing an automatic shut-down of a perfectly safe reactor. (Figure 5.2)

FIG. 5.2   Watchkeeping in the Manoeuvring Room Simulator (*Photo: Rolls Royce & Associates*)

RPV—Shielding—Safety   As the first containment boundary, the RPV is very strongly built and needs to be shielded locally with polythene blocks and lead to absorb neutrons and Gamma radiation. It also makes sense to put tanks holding diesel for the emergency generators, and any others likely to remain full, up against the reactor compartment bulkheads as additional *gratuitous* shielding.

From the moment a reactor is first taken critical and always after that, there must be coolant passing through the RPV, even when plant is shut down in harbour, since fission products remain in the core and continue to break down further, giving off decay heat. Without cooling, temperatures could rise to the point where parts of the core melt. Fortunately, most modern nuclear boats can rely on natural, convection circulation through the RPV to carry away such heat. This also allows some boats to run at their most economical and best listening speeds without using their primary coolant pumps, which tend to be the noisiest part of the plant.

Endurance and Range

In his biography of Admiral Rickover, Norman Polmar mentions that the first ever nuclear submarine, USS *Nautilus*, steamed 150,000 nautical miles on her third reactor core, and had a top speed of over 20 knots. If these statistics are true, one might say that her third core was capable of delivering 7,500 FSH (***Full Speed Hours***). Or, to put it another way, she could, non-stop, make nine full speed, 16,000 nautical mile round trips from Britain to the Falkland Islands—in 300 days—and still have some fuel left.[2]

Writing in *The Nuclear Engineer* in January 1984, C C Horton, managing director of Rolls Royce & Associates, pointed out that one year of full speed operation of a typical submarine will consume a litre or so of uranium fuel. However, operationally, it is more useful to know that one is starting with 7,500, or how ever much, FSH than a litre or so of fuel; because fuel consumption will be too slow to track it day by day. But one can monitor and computer-log use of speed over time, and deduct the result from a starting figure of 7,500. Indeed, a system similar to this is used.[3]

As will be discussed in Chapter 15, the precise number of FSH left in the boat at any one moment is quite hard to determine, and of course SSNs do not blaze around at full speed just for fun. The example above is given only to emphasise the SSN's immense potential for rapid deployment a long way from base.

NUCLEAR PERFORMANCE IMPROVEMENTS

When the USA put USS *Nautilus* to sea in 1955 with a PWR, thanks to the brilliant work of Admiral Rickover, it was the first submarine propulsion system able to operate indefinitely without an air supply from the atmosphere, itself a huge achievement. Since then, designers of all later SSNs have been striving to provide longer reactor core life for ever faster, quieter, better armed but still small submarines. All this, to be created without losing the essential safeness of the PWR and still within the budget.

Reconciling such design objectives is not easy. To justify the large capital outlay, and to perform its many roles, an SSN must carry a variety of weapons and plenty of them, which means a big hull to contain them. Big hulls require large power plants, and are expensive. High speeds require small hulls but often mean noisy boats. Quiet operation can equate to uneconomical use of reactor power. Nevertheless, in some areas much has been achieved, and with complete safety.

Nuclear Electric

All early SSNs were very noisy because propulsion turbine and gear-train vibration was transmitted directly to the hull. This was not too significant with SSNs operating in an anti surface ship role but it was a serious handicap when up against other, quieter submarines. One answer was to dispense with the gear train, harness all the steam power to turbo-alternators and use current so generated to turn a propulsion electric motor. Two such TEDS (*Turbine Electric Drive Submarines*) were built by the US: USS *Tullibee* in 1960 and USS *Glenard P Lipscomb* in 1974. They were both very quiet submarines, *Lipscomb* having many other special new noise reduction features.

Unfortunately, TEDS plant was heavier, took up more space and was less efficient than turbine and gearing. *Lipscomb* became a 6480 ton SSN only capable of about 24 knots. As the US wanted their next generation of SSNs to operate in support of fast carrier task groups, and felt they could not afford two different classes, they decided to build no more *Lipscomb*s but to incorporate everything else learnt about noise reduction into the new submarines. Meanwhile, a different solution was sought for reducing gearing noise, the machinery raft. (See Chapter 12.) SSNs of the 6927 ton USS LOS ANGELES and 5208 ton UK TRAFALGAR classes represent the result of this compromise reasoning. They are quiet at impressive speeds and can do 32 knots to keep up with the carriers; but they are not as fast as the fastest Soviet SSNs nor as quiet as *Lipscomb*. (Figure 5.3)

The small French SSNs of the RUBIS class also use a nuclear electric combination and are capable of more than 25 knots. The first came into service in 1983. They are good boats but not as quiet as TEDS should be, and are now undergoing extensive noise reduction refits, which shows that propulsion noise is not everything. A submarine is only as quiet as the noisiest thing on board. (Figure 5.4)

Water Cooled Reactor Developments

France is said to have developed an integral system for RUBIS. This usually means that the steam generators have been adapted to allow their incorporation within the RPV. But it can also be used to describe systems where an RPV is adapted to double as a pressuriser. Both aim to deliver higher power output from a smaller volume, and generally lighter system. Either would be helpful for a small hull. However, in a marine environment, it is not easy to make integral systems meet all design aims.

British plant in VALIANT and RESOLUTION class boats all owed much to generous provision of a US S5W-based reactor for HMS *Dreadnought*. However, work at the Naval Reactors Establishment Dounreay, has been continuous since those mid-1960 days. True, it has resulted mainly in more efficient engineering, rather than startling new design. But all improvements are important. Once at sea,

FIG. 5.3   USS *Portsmouth* (SSN 707) Fast and quiet (*Photo: Norman Polmar*)

FIG. 5.4   FS *Rubis* in Toulon Roads (*Photo: Marine Nationale Photothetique—SIRPA MER*)

after validation on Dounreay prototype rigs, they have led to increased power, and longer life, from improved cores of essentially unchanged dimensions. Plant noise levels have also been reduced. (See Chapter 12) (Figure 5.5)

Probably, the most important PWR advance, in the USA, has been the development of the natural circulation reactor plant mentioned above. The prototype was taken to sea in USS *Narwhal* in 1969, where it proved to be both quiet and reliable. Like Britain, the US has also made substantial advances over core life and power take off. But the engineering challenge for all PWR designers has been formidable. With an unchanged hull, one has to double power to raise speed 25 per cent. Given that PWRs must be operated at relatively low temperatures, they have done well to get significantly increased top speeds.

Fig. 5.5 Prototype submarine reactor at Dounreay (*Photo: Rolls Royce &
Associates*)

Liquid Metal Coolant

To achieve still greater power take-off, and to push SSN speeds much above 35 knots, one has to abandon water and use a ***liquid metal coolant***. This gives much higher average temperatures throughout the primary loop, which can be smaller and lighter, since it does not have to contain liquids under pressure. Metal coolant gives up heat very effectively in the SG and much hotter, more efficient steam is delivered to the secondary plant.

USS *Sea Wolf* commissioned with a metal cooled reactor in 1957. It worked quite well but potentially was a very dangerous system because the coolant chosen, liquid sodium, not only becomes radioactive but oxidises rapidly in air and reacts violently with water. Any primary loop leak, in addition to spilling coolant—bad enough—would also create a serious fire. The plant was removed in 1960 and all future US SSNs were fitted with PWRs.[4]

Meanwhile, Russia is thought to have continued an active liquid metal research programme. Certainly, in 1970, after a long period in development, they produced the prototype of the ALFA class SSNs, a boat with a very smooth, tear-drop shaped hull, known to do at least 42 knots, albeit very noisily. Such performance is just possible with the sort of PWR fitted in the Russian ice-breaker *Arktika*, (which would fit into an ALFA hull). But it has generally been attributed to two lead/bismuth liquid metal cooled reactors, generating steam for TGs, the output of which is used to turn a pair of motors on a single shaft. A lead/bismuth primary coolant would not produce gamma emitters when irradiated, and the steam generators could be outside a smaller reactor compartment, with both primary and secondary machinery being run in unmanned spaces. This would allow a considerable weight saving on lead shielding, always a bit thin in Soviet boats anyway. (Figure 5.6)

Such a power plant would not be comfortable to have onboard, because when shut down in harbour, it would need constant steam heating to prevent the lead coolant solidifying. However, whatever was in the ALFA appears to have been thought safe enough to justify installing it in at least one new class of slower but quieter, more heavily armed SSNs, the MIKEs, and possibly the SIERRAs also, both of about 8000 tons dived displacement. Sadly, the first of the MIKEs, submarine *Komsomolets* is lying in 5000 feet of water south-west of Bear Island, following a disastrous fire in its after two compartments on 7 April 1989.

This disaster was not directly attributed to use of liquid metal coolant. However, operating with unmanned machinery spaces, unless they are very well monitored with remote sensing equipment, can lead to fires remaining undetected longer and becoming harder to combat. Officers there at the time have certainly spoken of: 'an electrical short circuit sparked fire and losing control of high pressure air and hydraulics in the affected compartments'—a very bad combination.

In short, there is no denying that the overall Russian reactor and building programme has been a considerable success, measured in terms of producing a 42 knot boat, which still has room in its hull for twenty torpedoes. However, the quietness of the United States and British SSNs and SSBNs and their reactor safety record is also impressive. Great speed is not a great help if accompanied by great noise—and leaving a heat streak in the sea. Moreover, public opinion in the

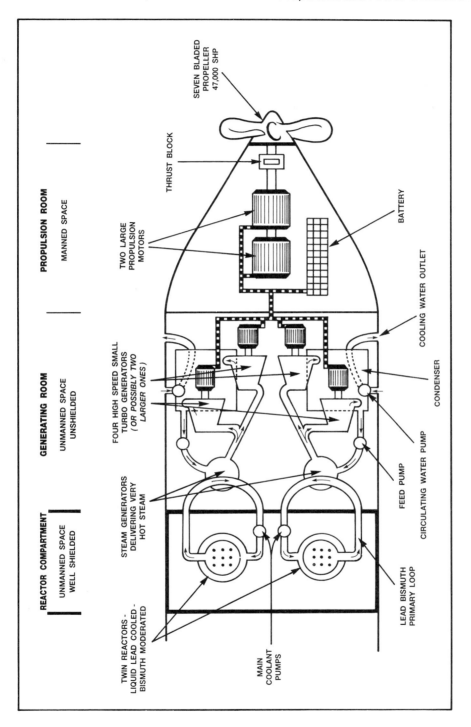

REACTOR COMPARTMENT | GENERATING ROOM | PROPULSION ROOM

UNMANNED SPACE WELL SHIELDED | UNMANNED SPACE UNSHIELDED | MANNED SPACE

SEVEN BLADED PROPELLER 47,000 SHP

THRUST BLOCK

TWO LARGE PROPULSION MOTORS

BATTERY

COOLING WATER OUTLET

FOUR HIGH SPEED SMALL TURBO GENERATORS (OR POSSIBLY TWO LARGER ONES)

STEAM GENERATORS DELIVERING VERY HOT STEAM

CONDENSER

FEED PUMP

CIRCULATING WATER PUMP

TWIN REACTORS - LIQUID LEAD COOLED - BISMUTH MODERATED

MAIN COOLANT PUMPS

LEAD BISMUTH PRIMARY LOOP

FIG. 5.6   Possible layout of Russian ALPHA class boat—a modified TEDS with much higher power and hotter steam

West would not have accepted with such equanimity the succession of fires and other fatal accidents which have bedevilled Soviet nuclear submarines. It is all a matter of priorities.

THE DIESEL ELECTRIC SYSTEM

Two submarines can be seen in the United Kingdom Submarine Museum at Gosport, a HOLLAND class and an A class. HOLLAND 1 commissioned in 1901. The last of the A class, HMS *Andrew*, did not finally pay off until 1974, yet there is an astonishing similarity between their propulsion arrangements. Substitute HOLLAND's single, dangerous petrol engine for a safe, reliable diesel, duplicate everything and there would be the A class, twin shaft, **direct drive** propulsion system. Direct drive is still an option on the two shafts of Russian JULIETT class SSGs, but they have a third diesel for extra power generation.

Direct drive was a neat, economical system, very well suited to submarines with large, heavy, slow (up to about 440 rpm) diesels, and easily accommodated in long thin hulls, designed more for making surface transits than running submerged. However, the death knell of the heavy diesels, as Dr Gates mentioned in Volume 3 of this series, was that their low frequency noise travelled very long distances, making the submarines easy prey for modern ASW systems. The huge size of all the components also made an A class engine repair job on patrol particularly awkward.

Modern Diesel Systems

The modern diesel-electric system has higher capacity batteries, which are charged by smaller component, faster running, over 1000 rpm diesels, coupled to their own dedicated generators. Power from the battery is used to turn quite separate propulsion motors, regardless of whether the engines are running or not. The diesels produce much higher charging rates and can restore power to the battery very quickly. A significant amount can be put back in a 15 to 20 minute charge. Keeping diesel running periods this short makes it difficult for enemy long range sonar systems to classify contacts correctly, and vector aircraft into position to relocate them, before they have gone quiet again. (Figures 5.7 a and b)

The modern system has other advantages over direct drive. Fast revving diesels produce much higher frequency noise, which travels only a short distance in water and interferes markedly less with the performance of the submarine's own sonar. Not being connected to the shafts and propellers, the diesels can also be sound insulated from the hull more effectively. Moreover, as the shafts are short, they no longer have to be parallel to the fore and aft line of the submarine. Angling them outwards increases clearance between the top of the propeller and the stern. This prevents passage of the top blades producing a fluctuating pressure field and sympathetic vibration in the hull, known as 'blade rate', which can be very apparent on a good sonar display.

The end result is a much quieter submarine properly tailored for underwater work. The comparative performance figures speak for themselves. The direct drive British A class submarine could manage 16.5 knots on the surface, for which it was

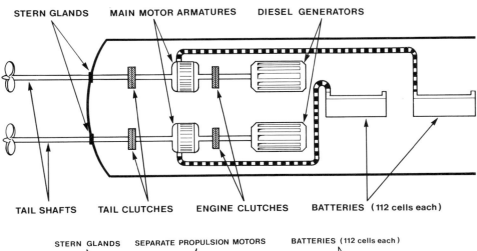

STERN GLANDS   MAIN MOTOR ARMATURES   DIESEL GENERATORS

TAIL SHAFTS   TAIL CLUTCHES   ENGINE CLUTCHES   BATTERIES (112 cells each)

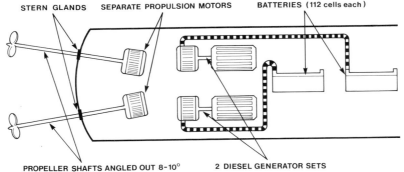

STERN GLANDS   SEPARATE PROPULSION MOTORS   BATTERIES (112 cells each)

PROPELLER SHAFTS ANGLED OUT 8-10°   2 DIESEL GENERATOR SETS

Fig. 5.7   a. Direct drive diesel layout   b. Diesel-electric layout

built, but only 8 knots dived, when discharging the battery at the maximum rate. It was normally routed from one area to another at 4 knots, to recognise that, when running diesels at periscope depth, it would receive constant attention from anti-submarine forces following up long range sonar detections.

The British OBERON class diesels can only give the submarine 12.5 knots on the surface but it can achieve 17 knots dived at the maximum battery discharge rate, for a short run into an attacking position. An OBERON can also make an 8 knot dived transit and float the electrical load, whilst only running diesels for about one third of the time. Even in 1993, coming to the end of its life, it is still a very quiet and elusive submarine, capable of surviving in areas of quite heavy enemy ASW air coverage.

The difference is even more marked when the A class is compared with diesel powered submarines currently being built. The British UPHOLDER class also is only capable of 12 knots on the surface but, with a teardrop hull shape, can manage a 20 knot dash on the battery and 12 knots using diesels at periscope depth. The Japanese YUUSHIO, Swedish VÄSTERGÖTLAND and Russian KILO classes also can all produce this sort of performance.

Endurance

Fuelling at sea, though practised by German submarines in both world wars, is impracticable in any area where the enemy has a strong air presence. Therefore, modern diesel-electric submarines are given a large unrefuelled range, far greater than any surface warship, except those few who are nuclear powered. The 3800 ton Russian TANGO class SSs, built between 1973 and 1982, have made deployments from a base in the Murmansk area to the Mediterranean and West Africa. They are larger, therefore probably longer range boats than the 2500 ton Russian FOXTROTs, who have a surface range of 29,000 kilometres at eight knots.[5]

By contrast, when forced to stay on battery power, a 1960's SS could do a 16 knot dash for something under two hours, go twelve hours at 8 knots, or creep away at 4 knots for say 48 hours. Even these figures are illusory because they assume starting with the battery fully charged. Operationally, it seldom is.

Modern batteries, with higher capacities and using more efficient, certainly more expensive, cells than the traditional lead acid type, are capable of giving a 1990s era diesel submarine an unrecharged performance much better than the above figures.

In addition to greatly improving its survival chance, such ability to delay charging for a much longer period may make all the difference between success and failure for a submarine on offensive operations, lying in wait for a surface force, whose arrival is to be preceded by heavy enemy ASW air activity. However, it is inescapable that the diesels will have to be run sooner or later. If the enemy can prevent that, the patrol area is not tenable for the SS or SSG.

This need to increase time between charges for SSs has led to development of several novel, closed cycle systems, such as fuel cells and Liquid Oxygen/Diesel External Combustion Engines, which are examined as future trends in the last chapter.

SNORTING

Appearance of the snorkel, or snort, system in second world war German U-boats was the most significant event in the history of submarines prior to the invention of nuclear power. Without a snort, diesel submarines had to surface to charge their batteries and would have gone out of business years ago, overwhelmed by MPA (*Maritime Patrol Aircraft*), equipped with increasingly effective anti-submarine radars. With a snort, diesel submarines are alive and well nearly 50 years later. Even nuclear submarines need a snort, to use with their emergency diesels, and to ventilate the boat, should there be a problem with their atmosphere control equipment.

A snort system provides a pipe for drawing air into the submarine whilst it is at periscope depth, both for the people and the engines. Simultaneously, another pipe provides a conduit to the surface for the combustion gases. Early systems had a combined induction and exhaust mast of a fixed length, which lay horizontally alongside the boat's external casing until needed. Then it was brought upright hydraulically, rotating round its heel, and held against the back of the bridge with a locking pin. The top of the induction had a float mechanism like that in a

Fɪɢ. 5.8   HMS *Ambush* with early, hinged snort induction (*Photo: Author*)

lavatory cistern, which stayed shut when the mast was under water but dropped open in air to uncover the top of the induction tube. Water was drained out of the induction into an auxiliary ballast tank and the engines could then be run. Once started, their own exhaust pressure blew the water out of the exhaust mast system. (Figure 5.8)

The major shortcomings of the early equipment all concerned the induction. The mast had to be exposed for a long time, draining down, before anything was achieved, increasing detection risk unnecessarily. It could only be removed from sight quickly by taking the whole submarine deep, often resulting in long delays before the engines could be restarted. It was so narrow that engine speeds had to be limited to avoid sucking the air out of the submarine, and creating vacuum levels which represented a dangerous lack of oxygen for the people. It was always the limiting factor on performance.

In modern snort systems, the induction and exhaust masts are both periscopic, allowing their height to be adjusted. They are fully designed into the mast nest within the streamlined fin. An air supply is led to the top of the induction, allowing it to be drained down whilst still below the surface, so delaying the moment of exposure to airborne radar of another mast. Indeed, with good drill, the engines can be started and already charging the battery, when the induction is first raised to break the vacuum which they will be drawing. (Figure 5.9)

Fig. 5.9   Modern snort induction—USS *City of Corpus Christi* (SSN 705) (*Photo: Norman Polmar*)

The masts can be lowered very quickly should interception of approaching enemy radars indicate that it would be wise, temporarily to suspend charging. The tactical situation can then be monitored from periscope depth and a calculated decision made whether or not to take the submarine deep as well.

Having one mast dedicated to it, the induction gives a much better air flow and ceases to be the limiting factor. In the British *Oberon* class submarines, the induction is so efficient that it is possible to run the diesels unsupercharged with the top exposed only about 50 per cent of the time. The raising and lowering of the induction is known as 'gulping'. It creates a more intermittent radar signature and can be a useful ploy when trying to make distance in the face of heavy air cover which persistently stays at the near dangerous enemy radar level.

Snorting Precautions

When snorting, the submarine is operating underwater with two large holes open in the hull and subjecting the people to conditions which border on the start of anoxia. The care taken must reflect these facts. For example, sighting ports are needed in the pipe leading to the auxiliary ballast tank. When opening up the induction, they must be watched carefully to ensure that the submarine is not draining down the whole Atlantic past a jammed head valve.

Once snorting, one of the engine room staff must stay close to an instant, mechanical means of shutting the induction at the hull, which they will operate the moment a full bore of water comes down, perhaps because the top of the mast has been knocked off.

Barometers, marked with green, amber and red sectors, representing degrees of human tolerance for vacuum must be fitted in both combat centre and engine room. One reason to stop snorting is an excursion into the red. Finally, on a calm day a course must be chosen which does not put the wind right astern, where it can blow carbon monoxide laden exhaust gases back down the induction.

Snort precautions have been mentioned in detail simply to make the point that although submarine commanding officers have to be aggressive minded people to do their job, they must also show exactly the same respect for vehicle safety which is found in the best, and longest lived, racing drivers.

REDUNDANCY AND SECONDARY SYSTEMS

Most diesel submarines have ample redundancy. They have two or three engines and two shafts, and are backed up by at least an 8000 ampere-hour battery. Only the latest diesel-electric submarines are not so well placed, (eg British UPHOLDER and Japanese YUUSHIO classes have two diesel generators but only one propulsion motor and one propeller shaft). This is the penalty paid when combining higher speeds with quieter running.

All nuclear submarines have auxiliary diesels and usually one 112 cell section of battery, which is kept fully charged. It is needed to carry the high *hotel load* produced by the steam plant auxiliaries whilst recovering from a partial reactor scram or, at worst, until the diesels are running following a full scram. It can only cope for about two hours, which emphasises the need for good scram recovery drill.

All Russian nuclear submarines except CHARLIE class have two reactors. Many have two shafts, though not the quieter, more modern SSNs. British, US and French nuclears all have a single reactor and a single shaft, but there is substantial redundancy in those reactors which can be operated with one primary coolant loop shut down. To offset the single shaft risk, it is normal to be able to declutch individual turbines, for single turbine operation, and some SSNs have a secondary, electric propulsion motor on the shaft, between propeller and turbine gear-train, from which it can be declutched. It only gives very slow speed.

PROPELLERS AND PROPULSORS

Despite the redundancy factor against it, the argument for fitting a single propeller is overwhelming. The 1990s submarine has to be moved through the water

at 20 knots, with no cavitation from either hull or propellers, with negligible radiated noise and only minimal self-noise interference on the submarine's own hull
mounted sonars.

As already mentioned, angling the shafts outwards in a diesel-electric submarine helps prevent blade-rate noise but once high submarine speeds are
required, two small propellers, however well designed, cannot produce the
required thrust without starting to cause a lot of noise. They are in the wrong
place, their shafts may have to be supported with turbulence producing 'A'
brackets and, when angled outwards or downwards, they have a poor water
flow into them. Above all, they have to be rotated too fast. With well
designed propellers, a twin shafted submarine can patrol quietly at slow
speeds; but once it starts to transit at high speeds, it immediately forfeits the
sonar advantage to a single screw submarine proceeding at the same speed.
(Figures 5.10 and 5.11)[6]

The single screw is normally fitted at the tip of the stern, abaft rudder and after
hydroplanes. The gradual tapering of the tear-drop hull towards the stern, the
absence of any external shafting and the fitting of the propeller at right-angles to
the fore and aft line of the submarine, all promote a good water flow, with minimal

FIG. 5.10 Stern of HMS *Alliance* showing clutter produced by 'A' brackets and
shafts (*Photo: Author*)

FIG. 5.11 Model of single screw hull used by the Defence Research Agency, Haslar
(*Photo: DRA Haslar*) (© *British Crown Copyright 1993/MOD*)

eddying. The large diameter propeller, maybe 4.7 metres in an SSN, can exert the required thrust with comparatively low revolutions per knot and need never cavitate.

Viewed from astern, a rotating propeller appears to produce a disc. Maximum propulsion efficiency is achieved when all water passing through the disc area is positively thrust astern, and none just waterfalls through it. Such efficiency also reduces vibration, the prime source of noise after cavitation. It is achieved by fitting seven or eight thin, overlapping blades, each one shaped like a cashew nut. Even when stationary, such screws look almost solid. The trailing edges of the blades are further treated to discourage *cavitation* inception. (Figure 5.12)

Casting such a propeller is a difficult foundry job and even the very best, whilst not cavitating, will produce some undesirable vibration at high speeds. To overcome these twin problems, a new engineering concept was developed, the pump-jet propulsor.

Details of pump-jet are still classified information, but clearly it is a cased system—(see Figure 9.11)—and potentially could achieve a very high degree of control over water passing through the disc area. The only seeming disadvantage of it could be the awkwardness of the task when changing a propulsor. Divers and cranes can remove and replace quite large propellers with submarines afloat. Working on a pump-jet unit is likely to involve docking.

Following prototype trials in HMS *Churchill* in the early 1970s, Britain has put pump-jet into a number of SSNs of later classes.

Fɪɢ. 5.12   Seven-bladed propeller on Italian submarine *Leonardo da Vinci* (*Photo: By kind permission of Cdr CJ Eliot RN*)

SUMMARY

Submarines use nuclear or diesel-electric systems. Both are viable, both are still being built and both are capable of further improvement. Both also give the submarine very long range but only the nuclear system can exploit it at high speed and without exposure to airborne radar detection.

The challenge with the nuclear reactor is to make a safe approach to criticality and operate efficiently in the power range. The PWR described in this chapter has proved a very safe system, capable of propelling British and American SSNs at well over 30 knots, and quietly at impressive speeds. Higher performance can be achieved with liquid metal coolant in the primary loop but some increased operating risk would have to be accepted.

The continuing effectiveness of the diesel-electric submarine is due very largely to the introduction of high speed engines, high capacity batteries, the improved snort system and the abandoning of direct drive.

Both systems have adequate redundancy. It is reduced slightly when a single multi-blade propeller is fitted, but the operational advantages of single screw are enormous. Pump-jet has the potential to increase them still further and is the way ahead for quiet operation.

6
Masts

Every nuclear submarine commanding officer would like to be able to claim total independence of the surface. In reality, operating authorities are constantly supplying new above water devices to improve submarine navigation, communications, coordination with friendly forces and battle management ability. All these devices have to go on a limited number of masts in the fin, which cannot be made larger without slowing the submarine. Hence the importance of not cluttering the fin area with fore-planes operating gear.

CURRENT MASTS

In addition to the snort induction and exhaust, already discussed in the last chapter, submarines currently at sea have a basic outfit of five other masts:

- ▶ Attack periscope
- ▶ Search periscope
- ▶ ESM (passive radar intercept) mast
- ▶ HF communications mast
- ▶ Radar (active surface warning) mast

Periscopes

The attack is used when closer than 9 kilometres to an enemy ship and as a 'first sniffer', when coming up from deep. The top metre of it is not much bigger than an arm and fist. The search is about 21 centimetres in diameter at the top. It is used for watchkeeping, that is to give warning of the approach of aircraft and ships, and for identification. It must always be up if any other mast is in use. Both periscopes provide bearings and ranges of surface targets. Their information is sent electronically to the submarine TDHS (*Tactical Data Handling System*).

All periscopes have two magnification levels: usually x 1.5, low power, which gives a wide 32 degree field of view, useful for quick all round looks; and x 6, high power, whose 8 degree field is more suited for slow, careful search. Modern periscopes made by Barr and Stroud (UK), Kollmorgen (US) and SAGEM in France also have a x 12 magnification, essential for good periscope photography.

Gradually, first search and later attack have acquired extra capabilities. Apart from still cameras, these include: artificial horizon sextant for astral navigation; T/V cameras; top window heating to shed ice; and LLII (***Low Light Level Image Intensifiers***). All these extras add to the weight and complexity of the masts, which now require torque drives to help turn them, and substantial umbilical cords to power their services and download information. (Figures 6.1 and 6.2)

Other Basic Masts

In older submarines of all nations, especially SS, the ESM mast is often the only one carrying any radar intercept facility, even though airborne anti-submarine radars are now quite capable of detecting either periscope, which means a minimum of two masts always being up: the periscope and the ESM.

FIG. 6.1   USS *Olympia* (SSN 717) showing attack periscope and search periscope with warner-cum-communications aerial on top. Note also the bulge for the sonar towed array on the starboard side. (*Photo: US Navy*)

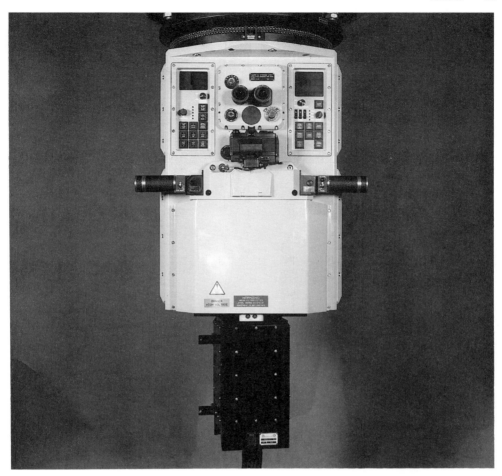

FIG. 6.2   The bottom end of the search periscope . Note the umbilical cable. (*Photo: Barr & Stroud*)

ESM and radar aerials in the earlier boats were both placed on hull penetrating masts. In British submarines, HF communications masts also were hull penetrating and made taller by being telescopic. They provided the only means of talking long distance to shore until the advent of satellites. (Figure 6.3 and 6.4)

Least useful of the five basic masts is the radar. Originally fitted to carry out night attacks, it compromises the submarine's position the moment it is operated and is virtually unusable, even for navigation, once in the patrol area. However, it does represent a spare mast when fitting something new. If necessary, a portable yacht-type radar can be carried for safe passage close to base.

NEEDS WHEN COOPERATING

Mast requirements remain reasonably modest, as long as submarines are patrolling alone, primarily in the anti-submarine role, and relying on their own,

F<small>IG</small>. 6.3   HMS *Warspite* (SSN) showing:
– Radar mast
– Telescopic/periscopic HF communications mast with plate to fair it to the top of
  the fin
– Snort induction
– Snort exhaust
  (*Photo: Author*)

FIG. 6.4 US SSN showing communications and ESM masts. Sail planes vertical for ice penetration (*Photo: Norman Polmar*)

mainly under water sensors to find the enemy. They increase sharply, however, when cooperating with friendly forces, as is common today.

SSNs and SSGNs acting in the escort role, need to talk to the Force being protected, whose commander may be at an over-the-horizon distance. And when detached to intercept a well armed surface threat, they will be trying to ensure that their missiles arrive at the target simultaneously, and coincidentally with those from other friendly forces—to saturate enemy SAM (**Surface to Air Missile**) defences.

Submarines on offensive, barrier sea control patrols, also may be trying to co-ordinate their weapon launch on approaching enemy surface units. In some instances, they could be firing at a fast moving target from 540 kilometres. Alternatively, they may be using a friendly aircraft as their long range weapon system, to engage an approaching enemy submarine.

Many of these engagements rely heavily on information from satellite reconnaissance, shore headquarters and other vehicles, who may: provide targeting information, signal the moment to fire, and assist mid-course missile guidance. All cooperation requires good, often satellite, sometimes data stream, communications—and very accurate knowledge of one's own position—and that of everyone else. This all means more masts, but their number must be kept as small as possible.

TWO MAST BASIC OUTFIT

Experiments have shown that a great deal can be put on one mast before it returns a radar echo larger than that produced by two separate masts, no matter how little is on them. Therefore, leaving aside the snort masts, future need is for a two mast basic outfit: a periscope and a tactical mast.

Optical Sensor

A low profile optical sensor (attack periscope) is still needed for use inside 9 kilometres with some degree of safety, but it should have its own ESM warning antenna, enabling frequency and amplitude of enemy radars to be established, especially those from airborne ASW radars, (mainly in the I/J band of 8.0–18.0 GHz). It could also helpfully carry a small communications antenna.

Electro-optics are not yet good enough to substitute for the optical sensor on this mast and even when they become so, it would be wise to keep one visual path to the surface totally independent of electrical supplies.

Main Tactical Mast

Everything else should be on the search, which needs to be expanded until it becomes an MTM (*Main Tactical Mast*), carrying all battle management mast requirements for use with the enemy outside 9 km. An MTM would only be raised when the environment had first been sniffed by the optical mast warner.

MTM DESIGN

MTMs developed by companies like Pilkington Optronics are already coming into service. National preferences will vary but they should embody as many as possible of the features listed in the following paragraphs. (Figure 6.5)

Electro-optical Sensor

A T/V camera is needed capable of carrying out a pre-programmed, methodical periscope search and displaying the resulting video picture, plus action re-play, to several displays. The camera must be gyro stabilised, to hold it on the line of sight, and also steady, which means minimal mast vibration.

Thermal Imaging Infra-Red (TI/IR)

Facilities are needed either for LLII; or better, to display the target image hot/cold contrasts, with a TI/IR (*Thermal Imager/Infra Red*), working in the 8–12 microm band. TI/IR gives a clearer image when the scene is moving fast across the picture frame and is better able to adjust to ambient light conditions. (Figure 6.6)

The T/V and TI/IR can be made alternate pictures on a single display, provided they both work on a common, say 525 line 60 Hz, field rate basis.

Survey to Zenith

Since the ASW helicopter is one of the most serious threats to any submarine, the MTM must be able to see directly overhead. This may mean fitting a

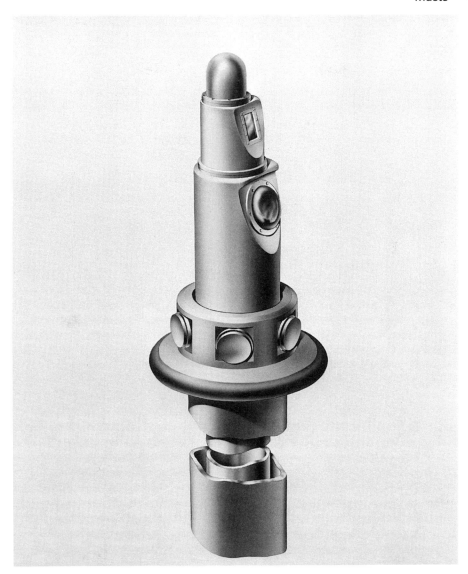

FIG. 6.5   Pilkington optronics mast, showing (*top to bottom*):
– OMNI ESM and communications facility
– Visual band camera window
– Thermal imaging window
– ESM DF ports
– Hydrodynamic fairing
– Inner drive tube
(*Artist's impression—Barr & Stroud*)

FIG. 6.6   Photograph taken with thermal image camera, as fitted to the search periscope. The black areas are the main sources of heat. (*Photo: Barr & Stroud*)

supplementary, fisheye lens, coupled to an automatic detection system. Such devices act like burglar alarms, reacting to changes in the existing overhead pattern, a method less prone to false alarm from passing sea birds than a visual search conducted with no horizon as a point of reference.

Radar ESM

The MTM also needs its own ESM facility, capable of safeguarding the submarine when no other mast is up. It too should give signal amplitude, but needs to cover a wider frequency band, preferably 2.0 to 18.0 GHz—and eventually up to 40.0 GHz, ready for the likely spread of airborne radars into the K-band. (Figure 6.7)

For battle management purposes, it needs to give a target bearing sufficiently accurately to correlate the information with that from other sensors such as sonar, a process known as data fusion. This can probably be achieved with a six-port array, such as Pilkington envisage, especially since rotation of the MTM mast could give several readings of bearings, taken at different azimuth positions, which would promote bearing accuracy.

Intercept Enemy Communications

Tactical masts need a stub aerial on which enemy HF communications can be intercepted. The associated processing equipment should be able to sweep to find the communications in use and to follow them, even when they have frequency-hopping capability. Intercepted information can be valuable both for short term tactical and long term intelligence purposes. Amount of enemy traffic can also indicate degree of alertness of individual commands, even when their messages are indecipherable.

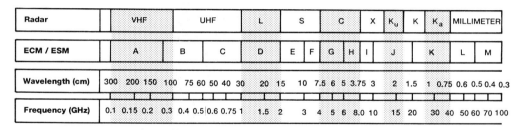

Fig. 6.7 Chart to show electromagnetic bands, frequencies and wavelengths

Receive Friendly Communications

The submarine may also need to receive friendly HF and UHF tactical communications on the MTM, either from allied ASW aircraft when carrying out SUBAIR coordinated operations, or from the OTC (*Officer in Tactical Command*) when acting in support of surface forces, as mentioned above.

Transmit Communications

There is a need to be able to transmit to a satellite, using the MTM, especially if it can be done covertly, for the same reasons one wishes to be able to receive friendly tactical communications. However, there are other ways of getting a message out of the submarine. (See Chapter 10)

Navigation and Other Requirements

Lastly, it must be possible to receive satellite navigation information on the MTM; and cabling space inside the mast needs to be set aside, as at present, for top window heating to stop ice formation.

OTHER FUTURE MAST NEEDS

It would be splendid if all the capabilities mentioned in the next five paragraphs could also be on the MTM but, almost certainly, adding any of them would increase the mast echoing effect beyond the minimum two mast figure. They will, therefore, probably have to remain on separate masts, except where combinations can be achieved.

Extra Capability Radar ESM

A higher capability ESM mast is needed to refine intercept bearings to an accuracy suitable for discriminating between radars close together in bearing, for targeting long range weapons, and to mount more comprehensive antenna arrays. (see Chapter 7)

Active Radar

If an active radar must be carried, it is possible to combine it with the extra capability ESM. The Russian *Snoop Pair/Rim Hat* surface surveillance radar cum ESM in the *Oscar II* class SSGNs is just such a dual purpose mast head. In the longer term, it would probably make more sense to abandon radar and fit a laser range finder, which could be used with slightly less certainty of counter detection. (Figure 6.8)

Extra Capability Communications ESM

In addition to reading enemy communications, one needs a good D/F bearing of the transmitter, because, with the higher speeds of an SSN, it is tactically practicable to consider running down an intercepted bearing, particularly when the nature of the enemy traffic suggests that it might be coming from a fairly stationary SSG on patrol.

It would be possible to combine D/F loops and extra capability radar ESM on one mast but probably not if it was already combined with the radar.

FIG. 6.8   Russian OSCAR II Class SSGN showing SNOOP PAIR/RIM HAT radar/ESM mast (the biggest one). Also showing, from aft, are: PERT SPRING (satellite navigator); HF communications mast; PARK LAMP (VLF reception) and SHOT GUN (VHF/UHF) antennae and the attack periscope. (*British Crown Copyright 1993/MOD*)

Fig. 6.9   Two US 688 Class submarines: a. Periscope sleeves lowered   b. Sleeves raised (*Photos: Norman Polmar*)

HF Communications Transmitter

The HF Ship-shore communications transmitter will still be needed, by all submarines, if only as a back-up against the day when an enemy blots out all the satellites. It is an inescapable extra mast but does not have to be a hull penetrator.

EHF Communications

To speed up liaison with other forces, it is necessary to be able to send and receive data stream. Such Extremely High Frequency communications will probably always need another separate, mast-mounted dish aerial, like *Punchbowl* in the Russian OSCAR class submarines.

MAST CONSTRUCTION

Optical sensors and other hull-penetrating masts are made of stainless steel to minimise vibration, which ruined the view whilst snorting when periscopes were made of brass; and to give enough strength to use the mast at speeds of about 12 knots and under. Maximum mast-up operating speeds can be raised substantially, and vibration further reduced, by fitting a tear-drop cross-section hydrodynamic sleeve round the part which remains submerged, a normal American practice. This increases the target speed at which a look can be taken at a surface ship's external fittings, and is essential if relying on a T/V camera. (Figure 6.9)

The mast is supported in three bearings: one at the hull penetration, one at mid-fin and one at the top. Periscope fin bearings have adjustable metal shims to keep the long optical tube absolutely straight. Final adjustment, called collimation, should always be carried out with the submarine afloat, as the fin flexes differently in dock.

Fig. 6.10   Russian ECHO II Class SSGN with hinged HF mast. Note that there are no shutters over the other masts in this generation of SSGN (©*British Crown Copyright 1993/MOD*)

FIG. 6.11   USS *Boston* (SSN 703) showing how mast tops are faired into the top of the sail, either by shutters or shaped plates (*Photo: US Navy*)

Non hull-penetrating masts can be made of other materials, such as GRP (***Glass Reinforced Plastic***) and shaped for good water flow from the start. They are usually telescopic, though Russian HF communications masts are sometimes hinged, like the early British snort inductions. Hinged whip aerials are also common. The great advantage of non hull penetrators is that they reduce the weakening of the hull which comes from cutting seven or more large holes all close together. They also allow some flexibility over the siting of the fin. Less favourably, they can produce serious cable wrap-up problems, especially if the mast is carrying a sensor, such as a radar ESM, with several cables to be dispensed from, and recovered to, a common cable drum outside the hull. (Figure 6.10)

If enough ESM electronics is sited at the masthead to convert the raw, received RF signal to digits, these can then be sent down to the processing and analysing equipment by a single digital coaxial cable. This solves the wrap-up problem but increases the complexity of the masthead electronics, and so the risk of failure. Unlike a surface ship, a submarine cannot carry out masthead repair work whilst on patrol, particularly in an SSBN. So, for ESM purposes, many submariners prefer hull-penetrating masts, which allow RF coaxial cables and even waveguides to be led down the mast to receivers inside the hull, and keep the masthead simple. It is not an easy choice. The trend is towards more non hull penetrators, but everything depends on the confidence placed in the mast and ESM equipment manufacturers to build a watertight, trouble free system.

PRACTICAL CONSIDERATIONS

When masts are fully lowered, the hole through which they emerge is covered by a sliding shutter, (or, sometimes in Russian boats, a hinged half clam-shell), which maintains streamlining of the fin. When fitting anything new to a mast, it is important to ensure that nothing is sticking up far enough to obstruct the operation of the shutter. Otherwise, it will have to be left permanently open, slightly increasing radiated noise signature. (Figure 6.11)

Similarly, when fitting anything new at the top of an optical sensor mast, it is equally important to ensure that it does not increase the amount of water draining down over the top window when the mast is first raised. Such drainage can slow the speed of taking a first all round look and spoil snapshot photography. The answer, often, is to fit omnidirectional warners and UHF stub aerials slightly to the rear. (see frontispiece)

SUMMARY

Mast needs have increased, particularly in SSNs and SSGNs, because both offensive and defensive operations in support of sea control strategies may require submarines to work with other forces. But, it is important that the number of masts be kept low to avoid increasing fin sizes. Much can be achieved by adopting a two mast basic outfit and a Main Tactical Mast concept. This puts enough capability on one of the two basic masts, the search periscope, to ensure that the three or four others still needed, are used much less often, and then only when the tactical advantage to be gained fully justifies exposing an extra mast. One up at a time becomes the normal mast rule, and proper ESM coverage is given at every stage, a subject explored more fully in our next chapter.

7
Electronic Support Measures

Electronic Warfare (EW) is as old as the use of the electromagnetic spectrum itself and has always had to increase in capability to match the increasing complexity and ingenuity of new radars and communication systems introduced by other navies and air forces. In the Second World War, as German U-boats used HF radio to talk to Admiral Doenitz's headquarters ashore, so British convoy escorts gradually received HF/DF communications ESM equipment, to warn of their presence, and fix their position for pre-emptive attack. As RAF Coastal Command aircraft used ASV II anti-submarine search radars, so German U-boats were fitted with METOX, the first crude hand-held radar ESM, to allow them to dive before the aircraft obtained contact.

THE EW SCENE

In Volume 5 of this series, the whole of which was devoted to EW, Dr Kiely neatly defined the three elements of the subject:

> ▶ *ESM* – Electronic Support Measures—making use of enemy transmissions for own ship's benefit—ie *Passive EW*.

> ▶ *ECM* – Electronic Countermeasures—spoiling enemy transmissions for his ship's use—ie *Active EW*.

> ▶ *ECCM* – Electronic Counter-Countermeasures—preventing the enemy spoiling our own ship's transmissions—ie *Preventive EW*.

In surface ships, ECM and ECCM are now both very complicated activities. ECM requires orchestrated use of jammers, towed decoys and the sowing of chaff, both to confuse the enemy radar picture and to lure his missiles away from one's own ship onto false echoes. ECCM involves the expensive building into radars of the ability to see through jamming, and hours of patient training of operators, to ensure that they can still function in the presence of enemy ECM.

In submarines the scene is simpler. ECCM is restricted to giving missiles a choice of terminal homing methods to defeat enemy ECM; and radars the ability to transmit over a very narrow arc, hopefully reducing to one, the number of counter detection bearings given to the enemy. However, intercept by the target on that one bearing is still so certain that radar is seldom used.

ECM does not really exist because countermeasures are mechanical rather than electronic, that is, masts are all lowered and the submarine disappears before an enemy gains contact. It is an effective response provided that timely warning is received. In short, submarine EW is mainly a passive, radar-ESM business, and warning is the top priority requirement, whenever operating against strong ASW air opposition.

FOUR ESM TASKS

Although very important, warning is not the only function of a submarine's ESM. Altogether, there are four tasks, some of which also use communications ESM. They are:

▶ Warning

▶ Tactical target identification and tracking

▶ Passive targeting

▶ Intelligence gathering

WARNING

Effective warning depends on the strong transmitted pulse of a radar always being detectable, after a one way journey distance R, some time before the aircraft has reached a position distant R minus x, where that bit of the scattered pulse which echoes back to the aircraft is strong enough to be detected, having covered the distance R – x twice. (Figure 7.1)

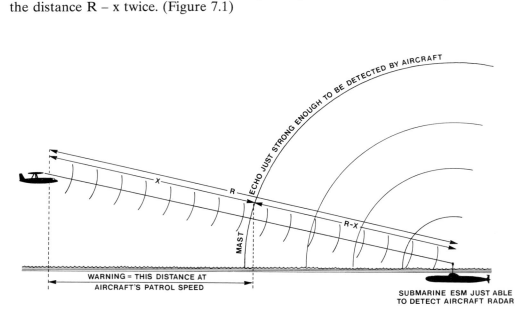

FIG. 7.1   Principle of reciprocal intercept

The time advantage is called the principle of reciprocal intercept. For example, METOX regularly detected an approaching ASV II at 30 miles but ASV II was only capable of detecting the surfaced submarine at 15 miles. Thus, with x equal to 1/2 R, U-boats had ample time to dive. The figure x can be increased by applying RAM (**Radar Absorbent Material**) to the submarine masts.

High sensitivity is needed in the ESM antennae for long interception range; and a high system dynamic range to produce rapid response to radars already at a dangerous level when suddenly activated, or detected when first raising the warner, whilst still absorbing details on a mass of other fainter radars. Above all, the system must be able to survive the **data shock** of returning to periscope depth in a busy area.

To give 100 per cent probability of detection, 360 degrees azimuth coverage is needed continuously and, ideally, 0–90 degrees vertical coverage; but on the optical sensor warner, the first sniffer, a read out of bearing is not required so much as an indication of the closeness and identity of the emitter.

Even when theoretically within range, detection of dived submarines by airborne radars is much less certain than the warner's earlier interception of the radar, fortunately for submariners! It depends on:

▶ Number of masts exposed

▶ Echoing characteristics of masts

▶ Effectiveness of RAM

▶ Inherent nature of radar—(ie power output and whether wave length is well matched to one mast size)

▶ Meteorological propagation conditions

▶ Prevailing sea state—an all important factor.

By calculation, by knowing the performance of enemy radars and by trials with friendly ships and aircraft, it is possible to establish the amplitude of a received signal likely to cause detection, in a range of sea states and with different mast combinations. Using this data, warning thresholds can be established for different types of radars, not just airborne. Crossing these thresholds should visually and audibly alarm the operator, and the command, through a link to the TDHS (**Tactical Data Handling System**).

Different warner channels are required for different frequency brackets, to allow for the laws of physics and the capabilities of the various radars to be detected. Channel widths should be adjustable to allow narrow bracketing of particularly significant frequencies, but with just enough scope to cover possible enemy use of a nearby alternative RF (**Radar Frequency**). This cuts down the number of channels needing very low amplitude thresholds, and therefore the unnecessary alarm rate.

The following sorts of warning ought to be given:

▶ *Threshold crossing.* Automatically, on detection of a single pulse above the permitted amplitude in the relevant warning channel. This should be before and independently of any attempt made to process and identify the pulse, and indeed must still function even when all processing has failed.

▶ *Probable hostile* On appearance of any such emitter, regardless of amplitude. This will be after initial automatic processing and before final command classification.

▶ *Specific emitter.* Immediately, on appearance of certain emitters in the system mission library, such as particularly dangerous ASW airborne radars, regardless of amplitude on detection.

▶ *Captain's choice.* Any other event the CO chooses. He must be very closely involved with the tasking of the ESM.

When aircraft are carrying out long, unalerted ocean patrols, reciprocal intercept advantage is likely to remain fairly reliable but it should always be remembered that aircraft patrolling a choke point, or approaching a datum position established by some other means, maybe SOSUS (**Sonar Ocean Surveillance Systems**), may well try to trap the submarine by:

▶ Delaying activation of radar until near datum—or

▶ Transmitting only to one side, to make first illumination of the target at a strength which will guarantee detection

▶ Detuning radar frequency and altering other parameters, so that warners are slow to classify correctly.

Warning is not an exact science. Signal amplitude can never be equated directly to range because it depends on many other unknowns, including angle of bank and course of the aircraft. However, the modern warner does at least give the basis for starting to make risk calculations. Depending on the tactical situation, the commanding officer may decide that he can, or must, accept a percentage increase in risk. The relevant warning threshold must be adjustable, to reflect this decision exactly. Then, although the warning will never be perfect, the risk will be logically taken and accurately applied.

TACTICAL TARGET IDENTIFICATION AND TRACKING

Whether delegated or not, tactical target identification always remains a command responsibility, because the consequences of a mistaken classification: opening fire on an innocent neutral, or being successfully attacked by an assailant before firing a shot oneself, are very serious. Both occurred during the Iran/Iraq war, even though the surface ships involved had quite sophisticated modern equipment.

To help the commander of a submarine with target identification, it is normal practice to maintain an overall CEP (**Contact Evaluation Plot**) of sonar and other detections, the coordinates of which are gyro bearing and time. The CEP, originally produced by laborious hand plotting on continuous rolls of squared graph paper, is today generated electronically, via a link to the TDHS, and can have its data stored in computer memory. One day, it will be replaced by a large, flat data-fusion T/V screen, which provides information in response to voice commands. Clever fusing algorithms will be needed but the purpose of the CEP will be the same: to correlate, store and display all the information so far collected and deduced about particular contacts.

Evaluation of targets held on sonar alone can be a slow process, especially when operators are maintaining only tenuous contact and having to rely on unaided human interpretation of patterns on video graphics, which take time to become clear. An ESM contact on roughly the same bearing can bring great illumination and speed up the process of identification. One pulse may be enough to determine everything, if it clearly comes from a radar fitted in only a few enemy ships, one of them the target being sought. It is seldom that sonar alone provides anything so positive.

If the submarine has already been manoeuvred relative to the sonar contact, to produce an approximate target range, (see Chapter 8 for method), the ESM detection may provide the last piece of data needed to justify a long range weapon launch. Without the ESM data, or some other corroborative evidence, it might be necessary to take the submarine much closer to achieve the same degree of certainty of identification, maybe even in to visual sighting distance, before opening out again to fire. This would be a riskier weapon launch sequence. It would also involve a long delay, sometimes a more important consideration when trying to meet a coordinated weapon launch deadline.

Of course, the enemy may not be so obliging as to radiate on radars, but if they do whilst the submarine is at periscope depth, it must be a certainty that ESM will detect and correctly classify their transmissions, no matter how short they are, and today they are measured in small numbers of nanoseconds, (thousandths of a millionth of a second, or $10^{-9)}$.

The six-port ESM component of the MTM facility, which is probably capable, at best, of about +/– 5 degrees bearing accuracy, should be able to relate most radars intercepted to their associated sonar contacts. When the tactical situation allows a higher capability ESM mast to be raised, a dish aerial on it would measure bearings to an accuracy of better than +/– 2 degrees. This could sort out radars close together in bearing and would be good enough for tracking purposes.

An accurate ESM bearing is important for two other reasons. It is the one measurable parameter of the enemy radar which cannot be made agile and it remains unaffected by water conditions.

With some oceanographic anomalies, the sound path in water is not only refracted downwards and upwards, (see Chapter 8), but also significantly bent sideways when listening over long distances across ocean current boundaries. The target, therefore, may be genuinely held by sonar on a bearing of 010 degrees but if one could see for sixty miles would really be at 015 degrees. In these conditions, the ESM dish will hold it on 015 degrees—or at worst somewhere between 013 and 017 degrees. The overall tracking accuracy will benefit from the cross-check provided.

PASSIVE TARGETING

The ESM is even more important when relying on onboard sensor data for passive targeting weapons such as anti-ship Tomahawk, or very long range, straight running, nuclear tipped torpedoes. To defeat enemy countermeasures and prevent missiles selecting some unimportant escort instead of the main target, missile radars usually scan a relatively small sector, perhaps 20 degrees either side of their nose, and are not switched on until late in their flight path, about ten miles short of the target. If target range is 60 nautical miles and a missile is fired down a 5 degree bent sonar bearing, its sector-scan radar will not see the target when it switches on. (Figure 7.2)

Switched on at 50 nautical miles down a 2 degree inaccurate ESM bearing, the radar will have the target in view, albeit with little to spare. Similarly, a big bang torpedo fired with a 5 degree course error is likely to detonate with the target outside its kill radius. A three degree improvement in firing course accuracy will here convert a nasty shake up into permanent damage and perhaps a *mobility kill*.

ESM can also give a pre-firing final range check, by comparing intelligence of the enemy radar parameters with the measured signal strength. Once again, as when acting as a warner, it will not produce an absolute range but it may be accurate enough to spot a gross error.

Intelligence Gathering

Although listed last, collecting *Electronic Intelligence (ELINT)* is not the least important function of a submarine ESM system. Indeed, until someone in a nation collects enough ELINT about their potential enemies to produce a substantial EW data-base, there can be no tactical use of ESM, and no properly focused ECM and ECCM.

The submarine is a good collector of ELINT and COMINT (*Communications Intelligence*), because a potential enemy tends to forget that it might be present. Against all overt intelligence collectors some precautions are always taken. Radars are strangled during significant satellite passes and whilst snooping reconnaissance aircraft drone by. ELINT ships are marked and the equipment trials they might have witnessed get diverted to different areas; but it is not feasible to stop all activity, everywhere, continuously, because submarines might be around somewhere. Consequently, if it takes care to avoid counter detection, a submarine

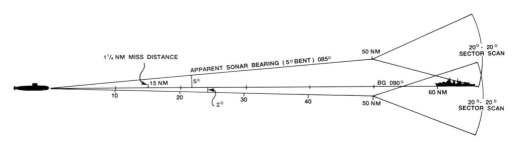

FIG. 7.2   Passive targeting—bearing accuracy

should always have good opportunities for adding to the national data base. To profit from these, however, it must be able to record every parameter of every electronic system which the potential enemy is likely to have developed.

SYSTEM CONFIGURATION

All four of the ESM tasks require the same essential components shown in Figure 7.3 (page 84), namely:

▶ Antenna

▶ Receiver and Processor

▶ Display

▶ Recorder

Antenna

Submarines use three sorts of ESM antennae. Two were shown on the Pilkington Optronics mast in Figure 6.5. At the top was an omni-directional (Omni), under a cover which also houses a communications ESM aerial. Omnis are ideal for warners. They are small, and emerge from the water into the hostile environment before anything else. They give frequency and amplitude, thus identity and rough proximity, but not threat direction. Lower down, was the six-port multiple fixed array, giving D/F bearings of radars to 5 degrees accuracy. On a separate mast would be the rotating dish antenna, which refines bearings to 2 degrees, but cannot be used as a first detection antenna—because it might be looking in the wrong direction when a very short burst of pulses arrives, perhaps from an attacking aircraft.

A D/F array needs as many layers of horns or spiral antennae as there are frequency bands to be monitored. Individual band widths are governed by practicalities such as space, cost and technology available. Currently, this normally produces a three times rule. By the rule, if frequency coverage needed is 2.0–18.0 GHz, a common submarine requirement, there will be a minimum of two tiers of antennae, covering the *octaves* 2.0–6.0 and 6.0–18.0 GHz. If only one layer is fitted, it will be covering the higher octave, where airborne radars are found.

Receiver and Processor

In the early days, there were two main types of ESM receiver. One used broad band amplifiers covering the full range of the radar frequency spectrum. The other used the superheterodyne principle (superhet), in which a narrow band receiver is preceded by a mixing stage, fed by a local oscillator. The local oscillator is swept, or stepped, through the frequency band and incoming signals are mixed down to the narrow band of the receiver amplifier.

The broad band receiver will detect all signals within its dynamic range, typically 60 decibels, but its sensitivity will be considerably less than a superhet receiver. Whereas the superhet, for all its high sensitivity, may yet miss short duration signals, if the receiver is not tuned to that particular signal frequency when radar pulses arrive.[1]

Most modern submarine ESM systems use broad band amplifiers, to ensure 100 per cent probability of detection, coupled to a device which carries out accurate IFM (*Instantaneous Frequency Measurement*) over the complete frequency spectrum, without tuning a local oscillator. Invented in the late 1960s, IFMs greatly sped up the first stage of processing and restored some of the sensitivity forfeited by not using a superhet.

Working on a digitised version of the received RF signal, the processor has to perform three tasks: sort incoming pulses, segregate connected groups of pulses into pulse trains, and match known radars to these groups. Each stage is carried out in parallel for all emitters present, resulting in a very high data rate, which could not be handled until micro-processing was invented. Frequency agility puts still greater demands on processing, as does the need to recognise features like FMOP (*Frequency Modulation On Pulse*) and PMOP (*Phase Modulation on Pulse*), which may help pinpoint individual ships in an enemy group—not just identify a type of radar. (Figures 7.4 and 7.5)[2]

Measured and deduced parameters, such as: bearing, frequency, pulse width, pulse amplitude, pulse repetition frequency and scan nature (and rates); are all averaged, then used to identify emitters against a library of at least 2000 radar modes. This is not a large number when an ESM system has to cover all NATO and Russian emitters which might be met during a major deployment of forces by both sides—and many of them have several modes.

Specifications for ESM systems include a commensurate pulse density, which the processor must be able to handle, many thousands per second, and the shortest and longest pulse, say 50 nano-seconds to 100 microseconds. The short end is limited by the processor's recovery time, the time between stopping recording one pulse and starting on the next. When pulse density exceeds the specified figure, it is inevitable that some pulses will be missed, but it is important that the processor continues to analyse all the others correctly, and does not suffer a nervous breakdown. Such robustness is known as graceful degradation.

Displays and Operators

Displays have to be considered in conjunction with the role of the ESM operator. In the 1960s submarine four channel, broad band ESM systems, notably the MEL UA4, the display was a cathode ray tube on which radial lines indicated true bearings of intercepted radars, and length of line gave signal strength. Warning was the operator announcing 'dangerous racket' when a line reached the edge of the screen, or some agreed lesser distance.

In UA4, one display could be switched between four channels or a separate display used for each channel. There was no automatic analysis but experienced operators, listening to the audible note of the radar PRF, and timing the radar's aerial rotation rate, could spot many of the simpler radars in service 20 years ago. Others would have to be sought in books of reference. For operations where better analysis was needed, the broad band system would be supplemented by a superhet receiver. This showed frequency as an angular quantity.

The commanding officer had to rely entirely on the UA4 operator's skill, when assured that Contact 'A', although a dangerous racket on signal strength, was just a harmless Banana Split radar in a high performance aircraft, likely to be up at 50,000 feet.

Automatic analysis adds so much more weight and credibility to this sort of report, that it is tempting to think that operators might soon become superfluous. This is unlikely for three reasons:

▶ *Unknowns*. Radars may be met that are not yet in the library, particularly on the first day of war, when the enemy might well switch to all their alternate frequencies. Human judgment will then be vital.

▶ *Work load*. When at periscope depth, monitoring the ESM data is a full time job. No one else can fit it in as a spare time task—certainly not the commanding officer, nor those already doing other jobs in the combat centre.

▶ *Filtering*. To avoid overloading the combat team, some filtering and rearrangement of data must be done before it is passed to them. This applies to information from all sensor systems. Only warnings should be given to the command and operator simultaneously, and that is not to cut the operator out but to bring in the CO early.

Moreover, **Platform correlation**, as opposed to radar identification, often requires injection of knowledge not easy to pre-programme; maybe some item from a general intelligence report on movement of enemy ships only recently received. A sensor operator will line up choices for the command, who then make a final classification, incorporating such wider knowledge. It does not mean that the command team should take over the sensor operator task. Rather, the command should have good dialogue with the ESM, calling forth as much information, or as little, as is needed by the tactical situation.

The MANTA System

It is unarguable that automatic analysis allows the operator to be a slightly less experienced person, provided the display is properly designed. One of the best examples of a good modern display is that in the MEL MANTA system, which has the extra merit of being a modular ESM, able to handle the changing needs of many nations.

MANTA has two display screens, side by side and an easy-to-use keyboard. The right hand screen is a situation display divided into two graphics areas. In simple Cartesian coordinate format, they display amplitude against frequency and bearing against frequency. The amplitude/frequency area is used to set up the warner channels and thresholds. Twenty four emitters, with six modes each, can be handled, ie 144 warner emitter modes. Every pulse detected is displayed in real time and the persistence can be adjusted to allow the operator to watch a growing accumulation of pulses move towards the warning threshold. A threshold crossing automatically triggers visual and audible warning. (Figures 7.6, 7.7)

ANTENNA MASTHEAD UNITS

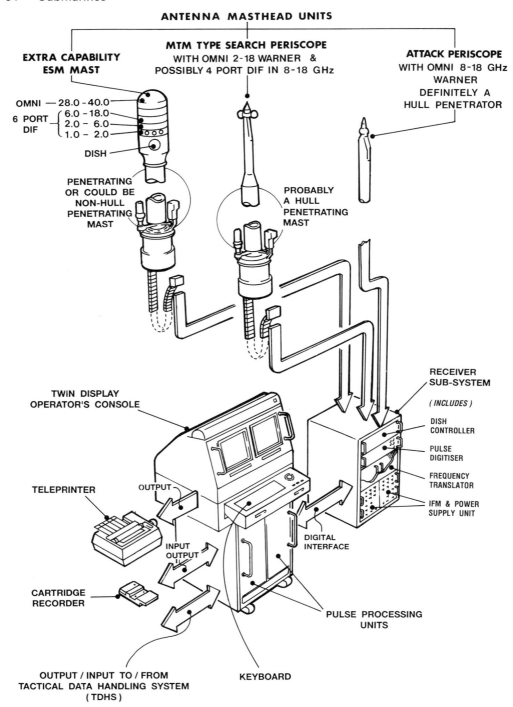

EXTRA CAPABILITY ESM MAST

MTM TYPE SEARCH PERISCOPE
WITH OMNI 2-18 WARNER &
POSSIBLY 4 PORT DIF IN 8-18 GHz

ATTACK PERISCOPE
WITH OMNI 8-18 GHz
WARNER
DEFINITELY A
HULL PENETRATOR

OMNI — 28.0 - 40.0

6 PORT DIF
- 6.0 - 18.0
- 2.0 - 6.0
- 1.0 - 2.0

DISH

PENETRATING
OR COULD BE
NON-HULL
PENETRATING
MAST

PROBABLY
A HULL
PENETRATING
MAST

RECEIVER
SUB-SYSTEM

(INCLUDES)

DISH
CONTROLLER

PULSE
DIGITISER

FREQUENCY
TRANSLATOR

IFM & POWER
SUPPLY UNIT

TWIN DISPLAY
OPERATOR'S CONSOLE

TELEPRINTER

OUTPUT

INPUT
OUTPUT

DIGITAL
INTERFACE

CARTRIDGE
RECORDER

PULSE PROCESSING
UNITS

OUTPUT / INPUT TO / FROM
TACTICAL DATA HANDLING SYSTEM
(TDHS)

KEYBOARD

FIG. 7.3   One possible MANTA configuration

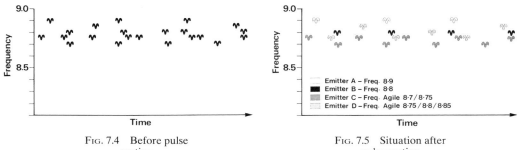

FIG. 7.4   Before pulse
sorting

FIG. 7.5   Situation after
pulse sorting

FIG. 7.6   MANTA operator's display console (*Photo: Thorn EMI*)

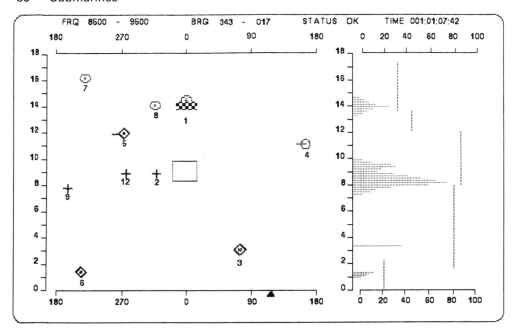

FIG. 7.7   MANTA X tactical situation display (left) and warning display (right)
(*Drawing: Thorn EMI*)

The bearing frequency area of the situation display is used to present the over-all real time tactical picture, to which synthetics are added as analysis is generated by the processor. Colour is used to distinguish hostiles, friendlies and unknowns, symbols to designate emitter types. Congested parts of the screen can be enlarged: for closer examination, to distinguish between radars adjacent in bearing, and to select targets. (Figs 7.8 a and b)

Individual contacts can be trapped with a size-adjustable, roll ball-moved box cursor; and their radar parameters called up in various alphanumeric pages on the left hand screen. An analysis results page shows side by side detailed radar parameters of the best library match, and up to five other possible matches in descending order of probability, giving a good basis for dialogue with the command. (Figure 7.9)

Another page is called up to establish the Emitter Report, on which data is manipulated before being sent to the command and the CEP. Contacts and suggested identifications can be arranged in several ways, (Figures 7.10 & 7.11)

▶ Order of first detection

▶ All hostiles, then all unknowns, then friendlies

▶ Order of seriousness of threat—or

▶ However the customer specifies.

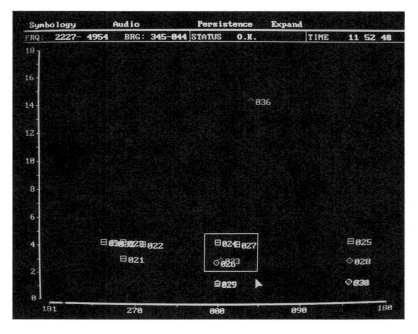

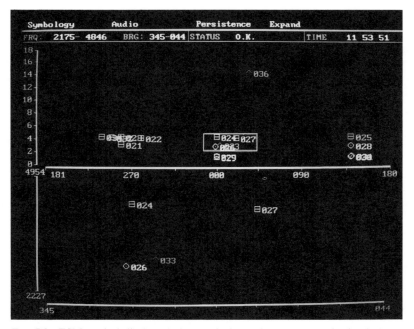

FIG. 7.8   ESM tactical display—before and after enlargement   a. (*top*) Display before enlargement   b. (*bottom*) After enlarging the area trapped by the box cursor. Main screen compressed into upper half. Cursor area in lower half.
(*Photos: Thorn EMI*)

ANALYSIS RESULTS

	TRACK	OTR	TC	BRG	AMP	FREQ	PRF	NAME	CN	TYPE	TIME
	4	8	1	166	35	11000	136,48	TEST05	26	F	LB	117

			ACTUAL	LIBRARY		NAME	SPOT	COPFN	CNF
FRQ	MAX	(MHz)		11000		TEST05	*00005	AAAZZ	26
	MEAN	(MHz)	11000						
	MIN	(MHz)		11000					
	MOD	TYPE	STABLE	STABLE					
	AGIL	TYPE	STABLE	STABLE					
	SPRD	(MHz)		1,0					
P-P	SPRD	(MHz)	1,0						
PRF	MAX	(Hz)		137,000					
	MEAN	(Hz)	136,480						
	MIN	(Hz)		136,000					
	JITTER	(%)	0	1					
	STAGGER		NO STAG	NO STAG					
PW	MAX	(uS)		1,890					
	MEAN	(uS)	1,894						
	MIN	(uS)		1,870					
SCN	MAX	(SEC)		0,000					
	MEAN	(SEC)							
	MIN	(SEC)		0,000					
	TYPE		UNEVAL	UNKNOWN					
AMP	PEAK	(dB)	30						

▶▶

| NEXT | | IDT | | OVR | | STG | | RTN |

FIG. 7.9   MANTA X—Analysis results page (*Drawing: Thorn EMI*)

EMITTER REPORT   9   TRACKS

	TRACK	OTR	TC	BRG	AMP	FREQ	PRF	NAME	CN	TYPE	TIME
	4	8	1	166	35	11000	136,48	TEST05	26	F	LB	109
▶	1	4		000	17	14500	204,69 S	TEST02	41	F	AI	109
	2	3		311	9	9114	3600,84		?		??	1
	3	3		062	7	3010	4960,12	TEST03	52	H	SU	1
	4	8	1	166	35	11000	136,48	TEST05	26	F	LB	109
	5	6		308	12	10603	301,48	TEST06	31	H	LB	2
	6			225	1	1500	8743,13	TEST08	60	H	SU	2
	7	7		222	29	1600	10000,00 S	TEST07	31	F	SU	109
	8			314	13	14200	9743,21	TEST04	43	F	SU	6
	9 L			205	14	7800	17841,31			?	??	17

▶▶

| SHOW | REP | OTR | STB | SYS | | DEL | | CLR | | PRG |

FIG. 7.10   Emitter report page (*Drawing: Thorn EMI*)

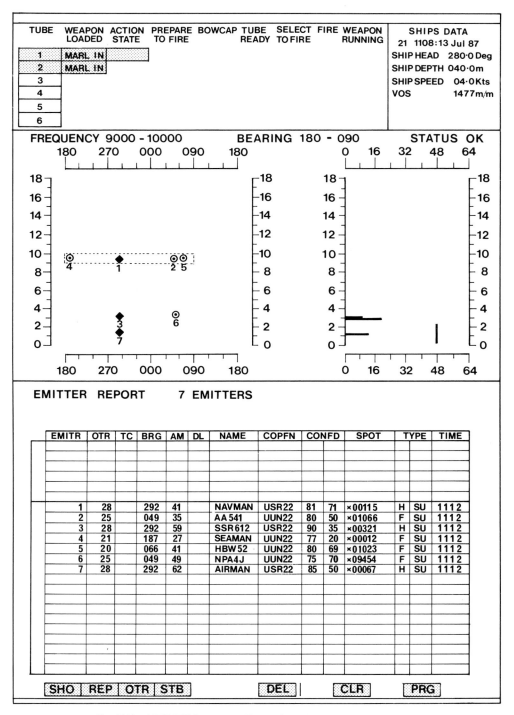

TUBE	WEAPON LOADED	ACTION STATE	PREPARE TO FIRE	BOWCAP	TUBE READY	SELECT TO FIRE	FIRE	WEAPON RUNNING
1	MARL IN							
2	MARL IN							
3								
4								
5								
6								

SHIPS DATA
21 1108:13 Jul 87
SHIP HEAD 280·0 Deg
SHIP DEPTH 040·0 m
SHIP SPEED 04·0 Kts
VOS 1477 m/m

FREQUENCY 9000 - 10000 **BEARING 180 - 090** **STATUS OK**

EMITTER REPORT 7 EMITTERS

EMITR	OTR	TC	BRG	AM	DL	NAME	COPFN	CONFD		SPOT	TYPE		TIME
1	28		292	41		NAVMAN	USR22	81	71	×00115	H	SU	1112
2	25		049	35		AA 541	UUN22	80	50	×01066	F	SU	1112
3	28		292	59		SSR612	USR22	90	35	×00321	H	SU	1112
4	21		187	27		SEAMAN	UUN22	77	20	×00012	F	SU	1112
5	20		066	41		HBW52	UUN22	80	69	×01023	F	SU	1112
6	25		049	49		NPA4J	UUN22	75	70	×09454	F	SU	1112
7	28		292	62		AIRMAN	USR22	85	50	×00067	H	SU	1112

SHO REP OTR STB   DEL   CLR   PRG

Fig. 7.11   MEL ESM report on Ferranti FISCS Command Display

The basic 2000 mode library can be extended in 1000 emitter mode steps, providing flexibility for different national needs and the two screens are completely interchangeable, which is good for redundancy. Moreover, the symbols are independent of the use of colour, which allows the system to be fitted in submarines, whose ESM operator has to work within the combat centre red, or other colour, night lighting. The whole system is compact enough to be fitted in either an SSN or an SS.

RECORDER

Submarine ESM mission libraries are loaded and unloaded either using a disc or cartridge recorder, which is programmed with a well thought out selection from the national EW data base. Not less than 5 per cent of the available radar mode library space should then always be set aside for use as a special operator's library. In this will be recorded significant contacts detected in the patrol area, with their exact parameters, ensuring that they are instantly recognised when they reappear. The system also needs a high speed, high quality tape recorder, for downloading interesting new radars, for analysis in depth back at base.

SSNs and modern diesels spend much of the patrol time well below periscope depth. Time deep offers excellent opportunities for recording equipment to double as a tool for injecting training tapes into the system. These raise operator classification and platform correlation skills, useful when forced to identify deliberately detuned and other difficult radars.

SUMMARY

Submarine ESM has four roles: warning, identification and tracking, passive targeting and gathering ELINT. Warning is often the most important but some intelligence must first be collected, to establish a national EW data base.

Warning is based on the principle of reciprocal intercept and the crossing of established amplitude thresholds. It requires continuous all round coverage, which can only be supplied by an omni antenna, or multiple fixed array, if a bearing is needed.

Rapid identification depends heavily on two technological advances: the IFM and the use of microprocessing: to establish radar pulse trains and carry out library matches. ESM can also refine tracking accuracy and help to shorten the engagement by providing long range passive targeting. Both require a dish aerial.

Two displays are needed: one to show the amplitude warning channels and general tactical picture; the other to exercise choice of target identities and manipulate target data before sending an edited report to the command—a process in which the operator still has an important part to play.

8
Sonar

During the Second World War, although very short range sonars were fitted in submarines of all nations, the periscope remained their most important sensor, because surface ships, including surfaced submarines, were their targets. Three factors, one political and two technological, changed this situation.

When NATO was formed in 1949, as a defensive alliance to contain an expanding Stalinist USSR, it faced a navy which already possessed 260 submarines. Between 1950 and 1957 the Russians built 236 more, all of them ocean-going, in an impressive construction programme, which at its peak turned out five new boats per month. These submarines were seen as a serious sea denial threat to Alliance ability to reinforce European NATO from the Americas. So, priority was put on improving the anti-submarine capability of all NATO submarines.

Meanwhile, invention of the snort apparatus put paid to any hope of finding enemy boats surfaced, so they had to be detected, identified and tracked by sonar. Direct drive diesel submarines were certainly noisy enough for this to be a practical proposition, but early attempts to exercise submarine versus submarine tactics were dominated by two problems: the good fire control solution needed to achieve success with a narrow spaced anti-submarine salvo of straight running torpedoes took time to derive; yet, all attacks had to be completed quickly, whilst a target was still snorting, otherwise there would be no knowing the depth to set on the torpedoes. Invention of the homing torpedo eased the first problem and solved the second. With it, an attack could always be carried out, once an enemy was confirmed within weapon range, provided sonar still had good enough contact to give the torpedoes steerage, or target an air flight missile.

It took some years to achieve tactical competence in the new role but very much better NATO sonars were already being fitted by the late 1950s, including early varieties of modern line arrays. However, in some navies, notably the Russian, there was no comparable political impetus to improve sonar, until a need arose to seek out enemy and defend friendly SSBNs.

Only in 1968, did the first Russian boat appear which showed clear signs of being designed for anti-submarine operations. This was the VICTOR class, a second generation SSN, whose bow sonar seemed to be loosely based on that in first generation British SSNs, a known intelligence target of the spies Houghton and Gee, who were working inside the UK Admiralty Underwater Weapons Establishment at Portland. Even with this help, the Russians have remained some years behind on sonar technology; but they have closed the gap considerably on noise reduction, which is the other side of the sonar equation. (Figure 8.1)

Fig. 8.1   VICTOR Class Russian SSN after collision with a tanker in 1984.
Conformal bow sonar staves can be seen under the crushed shutters of the six
torpedo tubes (*Photo US Navy*)

SONAR TYPES

Pages of sonars are listed in open literature and many more are in development but they all fall into one of two broad categories:

▶ Passive or listening systems

▶ Active systems

In passive listening systems, hydrophones are used to monitor the one way passage of sound unintentionally emitted by the target. In active systems, electrical energy is used to excite a transducer, the array elements of which project sound waves. When these strike an object they echo back to a hydrophone and establish an echo range, sometimes called the ping range. The transmitting transducer may also act as the receiving hydrophone, as it did in UK Type 2001, or be separate, the arrangement in the French *Eledone* system. (Figure 8.2)

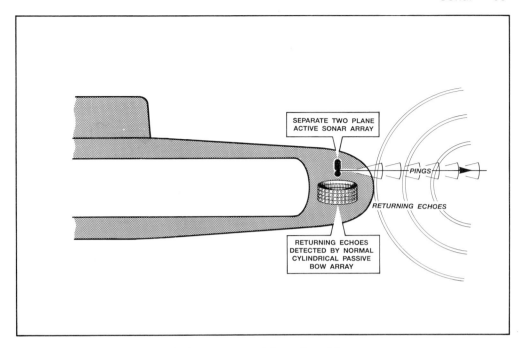

FIG. 8.2   Separate transmitting and receiving arrays

USE OF PASSIVE SONAR

Offensive sea control operations are often conducted entirely on passive sonar, because use of active at once forfeits the priceless advantage of surprise. However, sea water is an intractable medium. Sound travels through it at roughly 1500 metres per second, and to significant distances, but conveys only a rather vague impression of events going on around one, which takes time and much effort to clarify. For example, passive sonars do not detect automatically and certainly do not produce the sort of instant picture generated by a radar set. They rarely give a clear cut target identity. Indeed they do not even give a target range—just a bearing, and over time, a bearing movement. Also, approaching noise covers a wide range of frequencies, and travels towards one along many different paths, mostly bent. All must be monitored, as total data available is too poor to risk losing any of it.

One can only check out the whole noise frequency spectrum, and many ray paths, by fitting a large number of different arrays and by coupling them to very advanced processing systems. To convert bearings only information into ranges when holding several targets means manoeuvring the submarine and then analysing the apparent target motion of every contact. This also requires advanced computing. Whilst to get contact early, one needs several operators, using state of the art video/audio equipment, to pick out marginally detectable indications of fresh targets, from a highly confusing biological and oceanographical background.

Difficulties increase steeply when submarines have to act in the defensive sea control, escort role. To maintain station on a surface group, they must travel at speeds well over 20 knots, and ideally need a top sonar operating speed which matches their speed through the water. This aim can only be achieved by very good array designs and maybe reconfiguring the whole bow to reduce water flow noise. This may seem an extreme measure but a severe penalty has to be paid for leaving the difficulty unresolved. Once surface force speed goes above submarine sonar operating speed, the boat has to start sprinting and drifting, to create listening periods, which will get ever shorter as surface force speed creeps up.

Solving all these problems requires a substantial investment in research and development. It also means carrying a large number of sonar operators, who have to be fed and accommodated, which impacts on the size of the submarine, its capital cost and the cost of running it. Thus, one cannot have sonar on the cheap, but nor should one expect to. Once below periscope depth, the submarine is utterly dependent on sonar for safety and success.

This fact is well understood by the crew. Sound monitoring of the world around is a continuous thread running through their lives. They all contribute to its success, by making as little noise as possible. And, unless there are overwhelming reasons for behaving otherwise, their commanding officer, no matter what the operation, will always be looking for the best depth, best speed and best set of courses to optimise passive sonar detection opportunities.

Specific tasks for passive sonar are:

▶ Detection—Classification—Tracking

▶ Assisting TMA (*Target Motion Analysis*)

▶ Tracking own torpedoes

▶ Passive ranging

▶ Collision warning

▶ Torpedo alarm

▶ Collecting ACINT (*Acoustic Intelligence*)

Detection—Classification—Tracking

Ships, submarines and torpedoes all produce some noise. The first task of any passive sonar is to detect this radiated noise amongst the background of self noise and ambient sea noise which is always present. There are four categories of radiated noise which may be available for detection:

▶ Machinery noise

▶ Hydrodynamic noise

▶ Propeller noise

▶ Transient noise

Propulsion and auxiliary machinery noise do not vary much with target vessel speed but hydrodynamic noise and propeller noise are both speed dependent. Propeller noise consists either of cavitation or blade rate noise due to hull excitation (see Chapter 5). Hydrodynamic noise consists of water flow noise and various resonances set up as the water movement agitates hull fittings and cavities.

Even the best machinery still produces a low volume, broad band, continuous spectrum, due to liquid flow in hydraulic systems and mechanical friction in bearings. Such marginally audible noises are becoming more important as ships are quietened. Machinery may also produce *discrete frequence peaks* and their harmonics, which are detectable when passed through a narrow band filter, and will appear as darker lines on a spectrogram. They are caused by vibration of rotating and reciprocating machinery, which transfers to the hull through noise earths, via mountings and pipework. Spectrum lines become more marked when machinery is poorly maintained and out of true, or where its use involves repetitive engagements and disengagements, as occur in gear trains. (Figure 8.3)

At low target speeds, machinery noise peaks dominate the spectrum, mostly between 10 Hz and 1000 Hz. Certain combinations of lines are characteristic of ship classes, which aids classification. As target speed increases, a continuous spectrum of flow noise will appear, and if resonances are particularly bad, may add fresh peaks. Once cavitation inception speed is reached, there is a step change increase in noise levels over a broad continuous spectrum, and other classification clues become apparent, such as: number of propellers in use, number of propeller blades, and whether cavitation is suppressed, as it often is in a submarine running deep and fast.

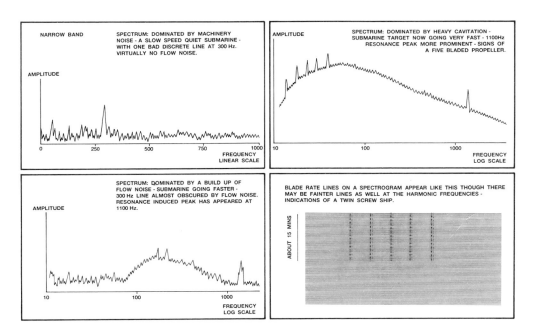

FIG. 8.3   Machinery-flow-cavitation-and blade rate noise

Transient noises are irregular and usually only noticed after contact has been established. They are valuable mainly as clues to target behaviour and vary in significance. The **curfuffle** of hydrogen being blown overboard from an atmosphere control system confirms that the target is unalerted to our presence. The **clunk** as a mast hits a badly aligned top bearing confirms that target is at periscope depth. Twenty **clongs** from an SSBN mean a full scale practice firing is in progress or the target is opening missile hatches to start a nuclear holocaust.

Once the target has become interesting enough to be tracked continuously, as opposed to just being reported regularly, the bearing accuracy required is better than +/- 1/2 a degree. It is essential also that any bearing movement be generated smoothly, because everything that is deduced about target position and movement depends entirely on quality of bearing information.

Target Motion Analysis (TMA)

It is a geometric fact that when a target maintains steady course and speed long enough for one's own submarine to carry out in succession, first one course and then another, also at steady speeds, two different target bearing movement rates will be generated and a unique solution for target course and speed become available—with qualifications. A historic range will also be available for the time when course was altered from one leg to the other. This TMA geometry is the basis for all submarine versus submarine, passive sonar only, attacks.

There are time and distance qualifications. Crossing legs must be maintained long enough to produce bearing movement input data good enough to make the computer-derived solution believable. As always, 'garbage in is garbage out,' and solutions based on legs of under ten minutes are probably suspect. When only prolonged crossing legs will make the bearing alter, the target has to be at long range. This is still a useful thing to know but it also brings into question whether the target has remained on steady course and speed throughout the time one's own submarine has been manoeuvring.

When the target and one's own submarine are moving in a similar direction, crossing legs can be executed again and again. A time against range plot, based on successive historic range estimates, will establish whether the range rate was opening or closing at the time of the last alteration of course. Sonar can also give more immediate warning if the target reverses course, or alters course radically to check for trailers, because it will cause doppler shift to occur on discrete frequency lines, a usable fact if they are stable enough for their movement to be meaningful.

Tracking Own Torpedoes

The sonar needs a good dynamic range, say 95 decibels, to be able to continue tracking the target, maybe only a tenuous contact, whilst also tracking own torpedoes, which will be loud by comparison when still close. If these torpedoes are wire guided, sonar will have an important continuing role to play, after their launch, to help keep them on a collision course with the target. Straight running torpedoes, whether nuclear tipped or not, also need monitoring by sonar, if only to ensure that they are still running straight!

Passive Ranging

Range often has to be determined purely by TMA but if the target does close to a distance of about 11 kilometres, where the length of the submarine hull would provide an adequate base line to establish range, the submarine sonar suite should be able to take advantage of the situation—either because it has a special passive ranging array, or can adapt parts of other arrays to perform the function. When accurate enough, a passive range on an unalerted target is much preferable to use of active ranging, which will instantly stampede the enemy either into flight or a pre-emptive torpedo launch. Passive ranging also helps to sort out the plotting when there are many close contacts.

Collision Warning

The most common occasion for collision warning occurs during a return to periscope depth from deep. Periscope visibility under water is only a few feet and the onus for safety has to rest with sonar. Two measures taken in the combat centre can help them discharge this responsibility more effectively. Since nearly all bow sonars have a blind stern arc, course is altered enough to inspect this arc before starting the ascent. Secondly, to keep reaction times as short as possible, any intermediate report filtering stage, such as a CEP, is cut out on the way up and the raw reports from the sonar operators put onto a loudspeaker.

Torpedo Alarm

Reaction to detection of enemy torpedo HE (*Hydrophone Effect*) will depend on capability attributed to enemy torpedoes: speed, range and depth floor, and own ability to: out dive them, out run them, confuse them with decoys, or possibly as a last resort in shallower water, lead them steeply down towards the sea bed, where they may not be able to pull up in time before suffering *bottom capture*. Whatever course is thought best, it will be a help to have an early detection, because the quicker we get moving ourselves, the further an enemy torpedo has to run. Also, if we fire back at them in the early part of their attack, we are more likely to disrupt it. The main need is for calm, regular and accurate reporting of the HE bearing and bearing movement. It is another occasion for having reports from sonar first hand.

Collecting Acoustic Intelligence (ACINT)

ACINT is a sensitive subject but, as with ELINT and COMINT, the purpose of collecting it, by whatever means and by whichever country, is to update a national data base. To obtain information good enough for this purpose two recordings are needed: one of target noise plus background and one of background noise alone, to establish a reference or absolute sound pressure level. Usefulness of the recordings depends on:

FIG. 8.4 Russian AKULA Class SSN—showing possible towed array sonar nacelle. (In addition to SNOOP PAIR/RIM HAT (not showing), this class has AMBER LIGHT, a dedicated ESM mast) (© *British Crown Copyright 1993/MOD*)

► Quality of sonar and recording equipment

► Range of target

► Effectiveness of self-quietening

► Ambient noise levels

For instance, there would be no point in a first generation Russian SSN taking recordings as a new Canadian Frigate passed 500 metres away, whilst off the Grand Banks of Newfoundland. There would be too much self-noise, the target would be too distant to get good recordings of individual noise signature components and everything would be drowned by the sound of billions of snapping shrimp.

PASSIVE ARRAYS

Modern sonar systems need arrays, beam formers and beam steerers, processors, displays, and some means of sending information to the combat centre and TDHS. Equipment for processing and displaying has similarities, whether one is analysing an incoming passive ray or a returning echo, so discussion of these aspects will be deferred until we look at active sonars. But passive arrays need considering separately.

The most useful combination of arrays, already fitted in American, British, French, Netherlands and probably Russian boats, and likely to become widespread in the 1990s is:

► Towed Array

► Flank (or Line) Array

► Bow Array (*may* also be active)

Towed Arrays

A towed array is a long length of neutrally buoyant wire with hydrophones embedded in it at intervals of up to 30 metres or more, which tows at the same depth as the submarine. The array may be kilometres in length. These large dimensions are needed to intercept the long wave lengths of the very low frequency noise spokes. For example, a 30 Hertz ray will have a 50 metre wave front. Early US arrays were streamed by flushing them out from a sheath but this limited their length to that of the submarine. Later ones were either clipped on with assistance from a tug or, more conveniently, unwound from a reel. It has been suggested that Russian VICTOR III, SIERRA and AKULA class modern SSNs dispense their towed array from a nacelle on top of the rudder stabiliser. If so, it is of the thin wire variety now usually found in US SSNs. (Figures 8.4 & 8.5)[1]

FIG. 8.5   Towed array construction (*Photo: Ferranti-Thomson*)

Advantages of a towed array are that it is well clear of submarine self-noise and can give very long range detections. However, it has limitations. The boat must be held on a steady course to keep the wire straight, the hydrophones have to be very small and therefore lack gain, and the wire can vibrate. There is ambiguity also about which side contacts lie, until two legs have been carried out; and, if poorly designed, it may be speed limited.

Towed array sonars such as the UK Types 2026 and 2046 are capable of receiving BB (**Broad Band**), NB (**Narrow Band**) or **DEMON**. They are most effective on *Demon* which is a system which demodulates the incoming signal and then puts the remainder through a spectrum analyser. The action is rather like removing the carrier wave from a radio signal. The band width of most interest to *Demon* is 0–2 kilohertz, where the machinery noise and flow noise induced spikes will lie.

Flank Arrays

Flank arrays are fitted on both sides of the submarine. The line cannot be as long as that in a towed array but the hydrophones are larger and closer together, giving a useful increase in gain for the detection of some frequencies. However, this may be offset by the interference which they suffer through proximity to the hydrodynamic self-noise outside the hull. The environment within the still waters of a main ballast tank, in a slow moving SS is quite favourable. It is much less so when the array is embedded in the outer skin of a fast moving, single hulled SSN.

Early systems were fixed beam and to use them involved sinuating or circling,

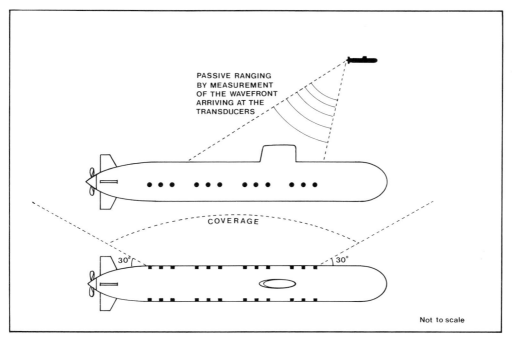

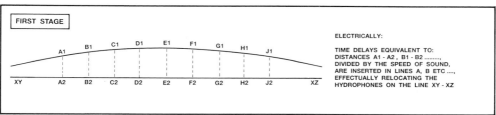

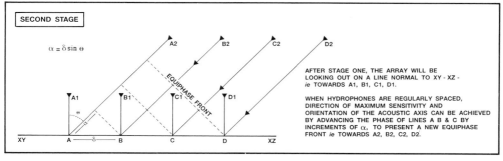

FIG. 8.6   a. Flank array arrangement
b. Beam steering a flank array

with the whole submarine acting like a very slowly rotating radar aerial. Modern systems, such as UK Type 2007, employ digital beam-forming and beam-steering techniques, which give accurate bearings to within 30 degrees of the bow and stern, without having to use such tactics. This makes it much easier to obtain a steady flow of data from targets on bearings forward of the beam whilst closing them, and reduces the blind stern arc problem created by some bow arrays.

Flank arrays also are capable of detecting BB, NB or DEMON but mostly they are expected to produce long range, convergence zone detections of noisy targets, (see below). Type 2007 is one flank array sonar which can also give passive ranges, by treating the hydrophones, electronically, as if split into groups. (Figure 8.6)

The major technological problem with a flank array, lies in establishing the exact location of each measuring hydrophone, in relation to all the others. Beam steering is achieved by inserting phase delays (for NB), or very short time delays (for BB), which effectively reorientate the acoustic axis or direction of maximum sensitivity of the array. A large amount of software writing is needed, to bring all the hydrophones back to a universal base-line before this delay insertion work can even begin. Worse still, the relative positions of the hydrophones may be affected by hull flexing, which varies with depth, and the submarine may not fully regain

FIG. 8.7   Spherical bow array (*Photo: Raytheon Submarine Signal Division*)

shape after flexing—yet another reason for not making repeated excursions to safe depth. Flank arrays truly test design engineers to the limit.

Bow Arrays

The bow array belongs to the principal submarine sonar, the one on which contact is normally held by the time an attack is executed, especially by torpedo, and the one with best tracking capability. It has a large number of array elements, sometimes called staves. This gives it maximum gain when passively listening to weak signals and best possible signal to noise ratio, that is, ability to pick out targets from ambient noise. It is most effective at those higher frequencies, which have short wavelengths matching the array width. Three bow array configurations are commonly used: spherical, conformal and cylindrical.

Spherical Arrays   The best passive submarine sonar in the world is BQQ 5D in the US LOS ANGELES class SSNs. This is a sonar suite, which includes a very large spherical bow array, with nearly a thousand elements in it, arranged in eighteen horizontal rings. The golf-ball is right in the bow, well clear of the pressure hull, ensuring minimal self noise interference. It has an excellent upward and downward looking capability and a relatively small blind stern arc. (Figure 8.7)

Conformal Arrays   A conformal array is horseshoe shaped and wrapped around the bow, above or below the torpedo tubes. Although chosen mainly to optimise active sonar performance, conformal arrays in British sonars such as Types 2001

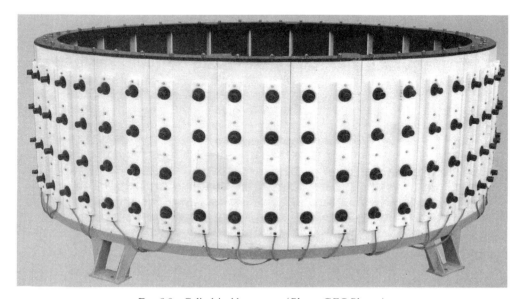

Fig. 8.8   Cylindrical bow array (*Photo: GEC Plessey*)

and 2020 still give a very good passive capability. They listen over a number of wide, say 20 degree sector widths, for high first detection gain; and track targets using narrow, say 10 degree electronically trainable segments for bearing accuracy. They have rather a large blind stern arc, but the effect of this is reduced by fitting a small passive array in the rear of the fin, and looking into the arc with the flank arrays.[2]

Cylindrical Arrays   Cylindricals may now contain 200 or more elements. *Triton*, produced by a Ferranti/Plessey/Marconi (USL) consortium, and fitted as Type 2051 in modernised British OBERON class SSs, uses such an array. It is put on top of the bow to give continuous 360 degree coverage. And provides good passive capability, (plus some active). There is slightly more flow noise than with a conformal array, but this is much less significant in an SS, which patrols at slow speed. The *Triton* array, and all the beam forming, beam steering and data handling techniques of a more modern sonar, which came with it, transformed the OBERON operational capability. (Figure 8.8)

SOUND PROPAGATION IN WATER

Before looking at active systems and the processing of all sonar information, we need first to consider how sound travels in water, because this has a profound effect on the performance of both types of sonar.

It would be convenient if it always moved through sea water at 1500 metres per second, along straight paths and all one had to consider was transmission loss due to **spreading** and **attenuation**. In reality, sound velocity increases with temperature, salinity and pressure (depth), producing refracting conditions; and whenever sound passes from one velocity level to another, the ray path is bent. The positions where the main bending occurs are called 'layer boundaries'. Sound may also be reflected off the sea bed, particularly when rocky, or the underside of the surface, and even more off the underside of flat ice. All these effects apply equally to the two-way travel of an active pulse or the one way noise path of a passive system.

Although salinity has a more marked effect in polar waters, temperature and depth are generally the main influences on velocity. One can be measured against the other by a device called a bathythermograph. Early 'bathys' were fixed to the submarine structure and could only measure as far down as the commanding officer was able to take the submarine. More modern, expendable bathys can measure much deeper without repeated excursions to safe depth, an important advance. (Figure 8.9)

Bathy data is used to construct an SVP (***Sound Velocity Profile***), which will depend on time of day, season of year and geographic location, but usually shows three distinctly separate water layers. They are named seasonal thermocline, permanent thermocline and deep isothermal layer. Thermocline means that temperature alters, usually decreases, with depth. Where there is no thermocline, water is said to be isothermal.

The seasonal thermocline extends, typically, down to about 60 metres, and is so called because in summer and autumn it warms up in the upper levels, to produce negative gradients, that is decreasing temperatures with depth. In winter and

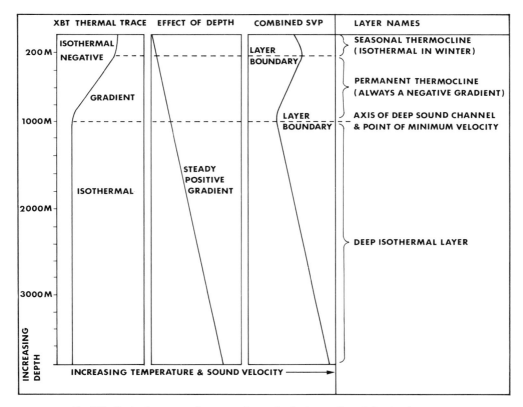

| XBT THERMAL TRACE | EFFECT OF DEPTH | COMBINED SVP | LAYER NAMES |

FIG.8.9   Bathythermograph trace and sound velocity profile—Atlantic winter.

spring, these disappear and the water is often isothermal all the way from surface to start of permanent thermocline.

This main thermocline does not alter much seasonally, though it can be quite different in a different ocean: for example, it is non-existent in the Arctic, which is uniformly cold right up to within a few metres of the surface. In the Atlantic, it is normally a steep negative gradient down to about 1000 metres. Below that, in the deep isothermal layer, temperature is a steady 2–3 degrees Centigrade down to the seabed and the dominant effect on velocity is the increasing pressure which occurs with depth.

Sound is refracted upwards wherever velocity is increasing, as it is continuously in any isothermal layer; and downwards when passing through a layer boundary from higher to lower sound velocities. If layer penetration does occur, the amount of refraction is given by Snell's Law, a simple cosine formula. Used in a computer, the formula allows one to trace out every possible ray path from a noise source placed at a selected depth. A much simplified ray path diagram for an Atlantic winter SVP is shown. (Figure 8.10)

In the diagram, the noise source is in the seasonal thermocline, which is isothermal. The upper section shows sound travelling in the surface duct, where it is being repetitively refracted upwards by the positive velocity gradient of

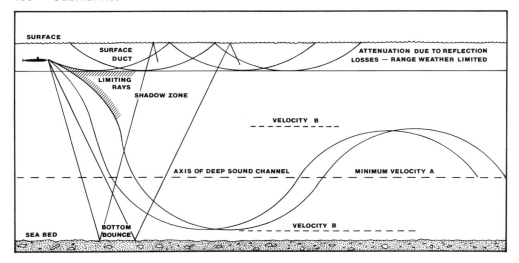

FIG. 8.10   Atlantic winter ray path diagram—submarine in surface duct

isothermal water and reflected downwards from the sea surface. The length of the surface duct is often limited by high ambient sea surface noise, but in the calm weather after a storm, it may be an excellent place to patrol when *seeking* contact.

Other rays, below the limiting ray, will penetrate the boundary into the permanent thermocline and be bent sharply downwards, creating a shadow zone below the layer boundary, which can be used when *avoiding* contact, to elude any active sonar operating above it. It was to overcome this defensive ploy that ships and helicopters started fitting VDS (***Variable Depth Sonars***) and long-cable dunking sonars, to operate under the boundary.

Some of the rays which penetrate the first layer boundary may also go on through the second, into the deep isothermal layer, where they will behave in one of three ways. Some go straight to the seabed and will reflect off it, back towards the surface, in an effect called 'bottom bounce.' This offers another means of calculating target range, provided: depth of water is known, the bottom is level and sonar can accurately measure the depression angle. The formula is:

$$R = \frac{4D}{\tan B} + \frac{d}{3000 \tan B} \text{ , where}$$

R = Range in kiloyards

D = Sounding in kilo-fathoms under submarine

d = Depth in feet of submarine below sea surface

B = Angle of depression

Example

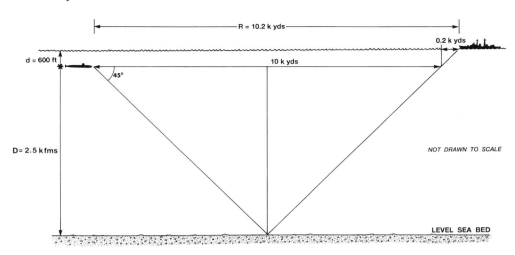

Fig. 8.11   Bottom bounce ranges

Thus, $R = \dfrac{4 \times 2.5 \text{ KFms}}{\tan 45^\circ} + \dfrac{600 \text{ feet}}{3000 \tan 45^\circ}$ and

Since tan 45° = 1, R = 10 + 1/5 = 10.2 Kiloyards.

When the submarine is at anything less than 600 feet, little d can virtually be ignored, since it will be very small in relation to the overall depth of the water.

Other rays may get trapped in the deep sound channel, the axis of which is the depth of minimum velocity on the SVP. Sound rays in the channel sinuate between depths of equal maximum velocity either side of the axis and because they are never reflected, only refracted, suffer minimal transmission loss. Consequently, they may travel many thousands of miles, especially those close to the axis, which undoubtedly is the optimum position to have a sonar system, if it can be put there.

When the SVP is steadily negative down to the point of minimum velocity and then steadily positive below that in the deep isothermal layer, conditions are sometimes created which allow the upper maximum velocity point of the deep sound channel to be quite shallow. If the water is also deep enough to allow the equivalent lowest ray in the sinuation to refract before it hits the bottom, (ie probably at least 2000 metres), the channel can produce convergence zones. In the zones, sound is intensified by partial ray focusing close to the surface at the top of the sinuation. (Figure 8.12)

The first three convergence zones occur at about 60, 125 and 190 kilometres, and are not more than 5.5, 12.5 and 18 kilometres wide respectively. Increase in noise when targets enter a zone can be very abrupt and focusing results in a noise level about 15 decibels above that to be expected at the same range after normal spreading and attenuation losses.

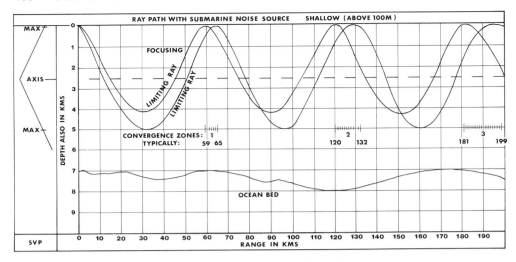

FIG. 8.12   Convergence zone formation

Any increase in target noise is always a help but convergence zone detections are particularly useful for SSNs with weapons able to exploit them immediately, and for SSs cooperating with other forces, because it enables engagements to take place well away from the detecting submarine.

USE OF ACTIVE SONAR

Long range, high power active submarine sonars are normally only used in SSNs, though they might be fitted in SSBNs for commonality reasons and because, in effect, an SSBN becomes an SSN once all its ballistic missiles have been launched. Only a nuclear reactor can produce enough power to operate such a sonar, so it is not an option for an SS or SSG.

The main reason for continuing development of such sonars is to insure against the possibility of targets becoming much quieter. However, even today, active sonar may be used by SSNs whilst they are in the defensive sea control role, either before the force being supported leaves harbour, or whilst acting as escorts during the passage. There are three possible modes of operation, all of which carry some risk:

► Independent area clearance

► Distant support

► Close support

Independent Area Clearance

The most favourable circumstances for use of active sonar occur during independent area clearance of home waters, because the SSN is under no pressure to make distance. Often, several days can be allocated to search important areas about to be used by own forces, or where there has been evidence of an enemy submarine on patrol. Full advantage can then be taken of bottom contours to make every active period on a course that will optimise sonar detection opportunities. The resulting, slow, methodical saw-tooth patrol pattern across the search area will have a good chance of flushing out an enemy. For example, in one night during an exercise west of Ireland in 1969, HMS *Warspite* found two SSs. One was HMS *Oracle*, who knew that an SSN was looking for her; the other, a rather startled intelligence collecting Russian SS, who did not! (Figure 8.13)

Distant Support

Escorting SSNs out in the deep field are likely to be more effective against enemy submarines when operating sonar passively. However, it is always an option to put one SSN still further out, and order it to use active sonar as a deliberate ruse, to draw enemies to the wrong area. Whilst doing so, it may well achieve detections, as operating conditions will be quite favourable, once well clear of noise interference from other ships of the force.

Close Support

Conversely, if close to the force, a powerful SSN active sonar acts as a beacon, directly drawing intrepid enemy commanding officers towards their prey. Meanwhile, noise from the ships nearby provides poor operating conditions for the SSN's sonar. Worse still, a useful surface ship escort has to be wasted acting as link ship for the SSN, to give it orders from the Force Commander, and to pass its contact data to everyone else. (Figure 8.14)

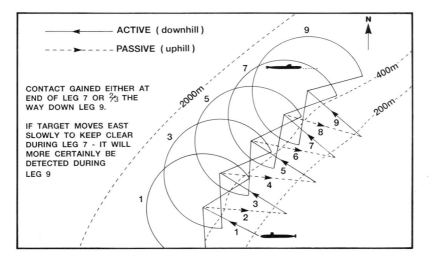

Fig. 8.13   Independent area clearance

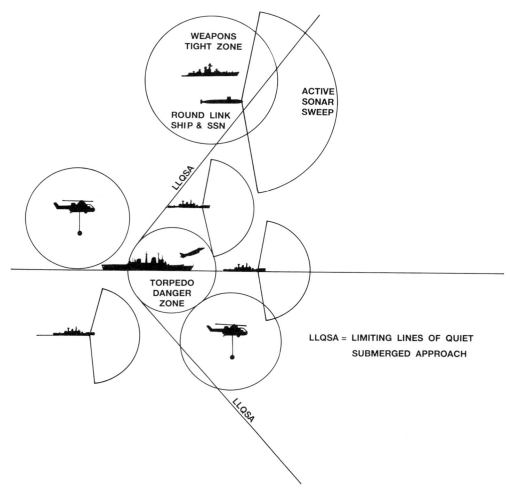

FIG. 8.14   SSN in close support

Risk of Counter Attack

Use of long range active sonar carries with it risk that an enemy submarine, or more likely two, will use sonar interceptions to mount a counter attack on the SSN. Two submarines can do this by exchanging fire control data on underwater communications systems. To frustrate such an attack, here again an SSN has to adopt a sprint and drift mode of operation, ensonifying the water ahead whilst at slow speed, then sprinting for about two thirds expected, effective sonar range distance, before making the next set of transmissions, thereby remaining in the swept water. Ideally, a substantial alteration of course should be made before the sprint, so that each period of active sonar use begins from a slightly surprising position. The faster a force proceeds, the less scope there is for taking these precautions, and the more important it becomes that data rates of active systems be kept high.

A slow rate of progress makes independent area clearance less dangerous than passage escort duty, but it is never without risk, since the enemy submarine may have a weapon range greater than the searcher's effective sonar range. Current weapons can throw an explosive charge to 54 kilometres and next generation systems are likely to have a throw of over 1800 kilometres, to match the much longer detection ranges of some passive sonar systems on some targets. (See Table 9.1)

By comparison, active sonars probably cannot achieve much more than 50 kilometres in good conditions. Therefore, the operational requirement for future active systems has to concentrate on giving them the lowest possible probability of exploitation by the enemy. The alternative, of trying to disguise from an enemy that someone is putting a lot of power into the water, is probably impossible; though enemy recognition of being illuminated might be postponed by making transmissions resemble as nearly as possible the ordinary biological noise in the sea.

ACTIVE ARRAYS

The best long range, high power submarine active sonar in the world, now in service, is the Type 2020, fitted in the British TRAFALGAR class SSNs. In this type of sonar, and its ancestor Type 2001, conformal array elements are normally grouped into segments or sectors, and sound is transmitted in one of three ways: Ripple, Sector or Broadcast. In ripple, power is sent through each segment in turn. In sector, a single arc is illuminated. In broadcast, an omnidirectional pulse is emitted. Each has its tactical uses: ripple for initial detection, sector for tracking and broadcast for close range melée situations. (Figure 8.15)

Amount of power put through an array determines ranges to be obtained, but in practice is limited by two effects: *cavitation* and *interaction*. Boiling cavitation bubbles, forming on the face of elements at limiting power levels, reduce sound generating efficiency and may cause wasting of array metal. Interactions between adjacent, closely packed elements, subjected to very short high energy pulses, will make some of them absorb rather than radiate sound. This too reduces efficiency and can cause physical damage; but the obvious resort, of moving elements further apart, itself worsens array performance.

Rippling is one solution to interaction effect, but it produces very slow data rates. Modern systems, like Type 2020, use broadcast as their normal operating mode and overcome interaction effect by spreading a large energy build up over a long, one second, pulse. This creates ambiguity of target range within a 1500 metre bracket, which is resolved by steadily altering the note of the pulse throughout its length. The note at the time of receiving an echo then establishes the target position within the bracket. Sound signals emitted by a bat for navigational purposes are structured in the same way. It is also the basis of deliberate FMOP (*Frequency Modulation on Pulse*) in radars. (see Chapter 7) (Figure 8.16)

ACTIVE PROCESSING AND DISPLAYS

Operators need different sorts of help, depending on whether they are manning an active or passive sonar. On an active, the main problem is *data shock*. Just

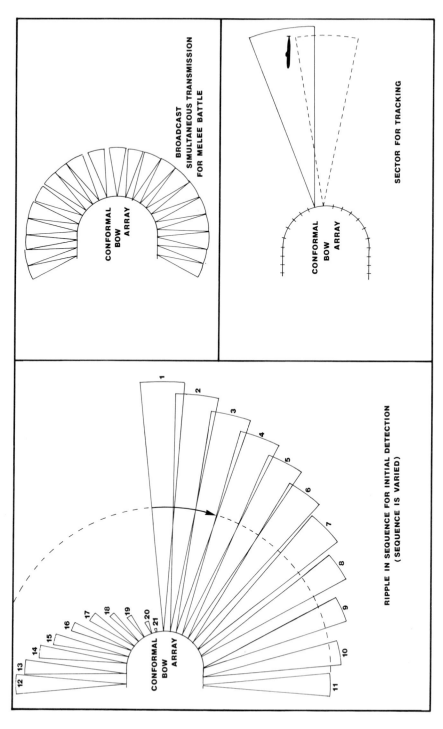

FIG. 8.15   Ripple Sector and Broadcast

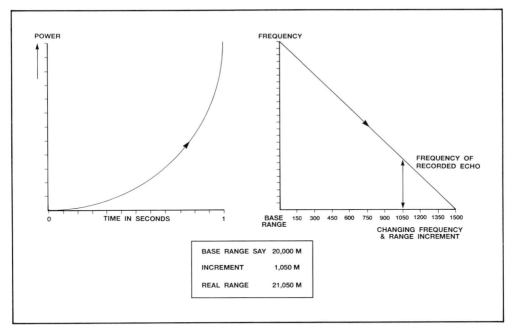

FIG. 8.16   Long pulse transmission

about everything in the sea sends back an echo. The processor must filter out obviously spurious contacts. For instance, biological contacts like fish and plankton do not usually echo on every ping. So contacts failing to appear say three times are ignored. Bearing in mind that the processor may be counting to three, on thousands of possible contacts, this alone is a big task.

Even with such filtering, operators are still kept very busy at their displays, finding real target echoes, and discounting those created by surface reflections, tide rips, and sea bottom crags. One reason for conducting active search patterns from shallow towards deep water is to help reduce the bottom reverberations.

Various ways of presenting data are shown. In the illustration, seven contacts are being tracked and the trackerball, (the + at 267 degrees, range 10010), is being moved to investigate a promising looking eighth at about 252 degrees. The arrow is the shipshead marker and the thinnest display shows the nature of the returning pulse. Using FMOP techniques, it may indicate target size, therefore add or subtract credibility. (Figure 8.17)

PASSIVE PROCESSING AND DISPLAYS

On a passive set, the operator needs help to find anything at all. Therefore, analysis of incoming information is normally carried out in at least two bands. Otherwise, all self noise is always present. By contrast, when listening on the HF band of a Type 2001 Sector system component, LF noise could be completely excluded from contaminating the HF reception.

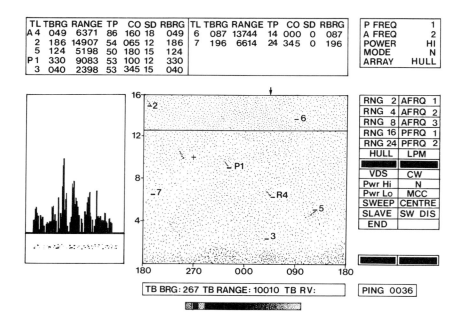

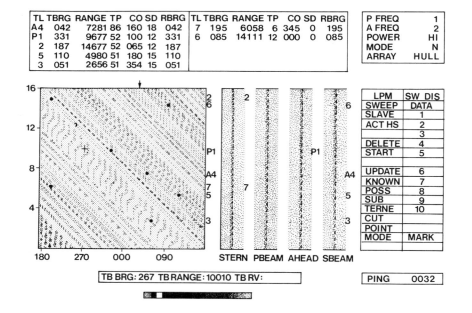

FIG. 8.17   Active sonar displays

Unlike ESM, sonar normally follows a two-times band rule. Therefore, *octaves* are 1.5–3.0 Kilohertz and 3.0–6.0 Kilohertz. Alternatively, if the whole 5 octave usable spectrum must be handled, they can be 0–2, 2–4, 4–8, 8–16, and 16–32 Kilohertz.

Distinguishing targets from background noise requires good cross-correlation, that is monitoring and comparing the output from all the array elements, to find the unidirectional, coherent target signal, amongst the multidirectional, incoherent noise. Of course, processing is never that simple. At long range, where detection is most difficult, multiple ray paths will ensure that the signal is anything but unidirectional, and ambient noise is seldom completely isotropic.

Narrow band and DEMON signals are sorted out by phase difference as they arrive, because they are single sine wave signals. Broad band signals are multi sine wave and have to be sorted by the time of arrival of the peak signal. Since some targets radiate over a wide enough noise spectrum to be detected by towed array, flank array and bow array simultaneously, further processing and cross correlation is needed to build a composite picture.

In modern sonars, much more processing is carried out immediately behind the array, rather than close to the display; and their pedigree lies in the software algorithms rather than in the fitting of new hardware. These two facts make possible a major shortening of time scales for the introduction of, so called, new systems, from about ten to about two years, and partly explain the proliferation of new type numbers.

For example, Types 2001 and 2020 were quickly given an improved look down/look up, passive capability, somewhat similar to that available in the BQQ 5, by applying beam steering techniques vertically over part of the otherwise essentially horizontal bow array. The resulting equipment, called Type 2027, can also accept details of the sound velocity profile from the TDHS, calculate the bottom bounce and surface reflection ray paths, and give a range estimation. It is not really a new sonar, just a use of new algorithms to create a clever new capability.

After processing has done its best, operators still have to find genuine passive targets amongst background noise. For the bow sonar, they need two different sorts of display. One must show bearings against time, with north always in the middle and a ships-head marker which moves. Due to the pattern which this movement produces, it is often called a waterfall display. On 2020, operators use a roll-ball on the display to choose arcs for aural examination, either in a trainable, wide beam, high gain, manual crude bearing mode (HF or LF band); or in a narrow beam, MAB (*Manual Accurate Bearing*) mode, also HF or LF band. (Figure 8.18)

Bow sonar operators also need a frequency against amplitude display, for viewing the filtered, narrow band target noise spectrum. In Type 2020, it can be expanded and contracted electronically, comparisons can be made with library signatures and hard copy can be taken of the picture being displayed.

Further displays are needed for the towed array and flank array information, though these are often combined, since both require a time against bearing format and use of a video-graphic, or continuous roll of sensitised paper, for the DEMON picture. Similarly, the 2027 vertical sonar can share displays with the 2020.

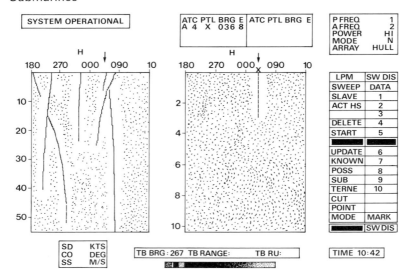

Fig. 8.18   Time Bearing displays

OUTPUT TO COMMAND SYSTEM

Once initial detection is made, the operator's task is to send bearing cuts of contacts to the command team, via the TDHS, and range cuts also when the contact is held on an active sonar. In early systems, bow arrays were mechanically trained and all contacts had to be followed manually throughout. This gave slow data rates and low target handling capacity. Moreover, the bearings cut through to the combat centre were neither accurate enough, nor smooth enough in their movement, to be used directly for deriving bearing rates in a submarine versus submarine attack. To make them usable, they were reverse plotted on the back of a glass TBP (*Time Bearing Plot*). Fair curves were then drawn through the raw bearings, on the front of the glass, and the slope of the curves gave the rates. (Figure 8.19)

Steerable-beam fixed arrays produce much better bearings. For example, a passive bearing cut from the MAB (HF) part of Type 2020 will be as good as any that could be taken through the periscope. Thomson CSF claim one tenth of a degree for the passive side of Eledone. Automatic tracking is also possible on many modern sonars such as Type 2020 and TRITON/Type 2051, once the operator has firm contact—an enormous advance.

Auto track systems are capable of holding about sixteen active and/or eight passive contacts. The rate of updating each one varies, depending on the priority given it by the combat team. Calibre of tracking can be judged from the illustration. Reproduced on the combat centre displays of a system like Ferranti DCH curves of this quality would themselves be a completed TBP, from which bearing rates could be measured, if this were not already being done by computer. (Figures 8.20 and 8.21)

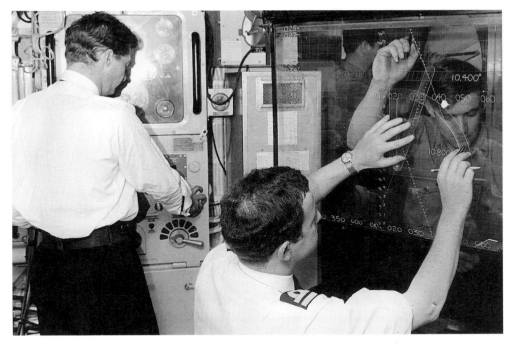

FIG.8.19   Time Bearing plotting—old style. Trailing with closing range rate
(© *British Crown Copyright 1993/MOD*)

OTHER USES OF SONAR

There are four other uses of sonar, which often require fitting of specialised equipment:

▶ Short range active

▶ Passive intercept

▶ Underwater communications

▶ Cavitation monitoring

Short Range Active

Several types of short range active sonars are fitted in submarines, for self protection and to bring the enemy to action more effectively, once an engagement has started. For example, some downward-looking E/S (***Echo-Sounders***) are needed for safe high speed navigation in unfamiliar or poorly charted waters; and others for accurate bottom contour map following, when wishing to avoid all use of masts for navigation. Upward-looking E/S are equally important: to establish thickness of ice overhead, by subtracting recorded distance from known submarine depth. These 'discreet sounders' work on very high frequencies, around 50 Kilohertz, to prevent them producing side lobes. They have a pencil thin beam,

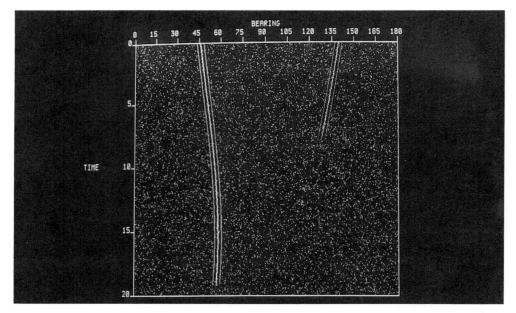

Fig. 8.20   Automatic tracking (*Photo: GEC Plessey*)

usually about 1 degree wide. They are operated at minimal power, which is then slowly raised until an echo can just be obtained. Displays are in the navigation centre. (Figure 8.22)

Forward-looking, short range active sonars are also needed to give warning of dangers ahead, such as ice bergs or ice keels and moored mines. And all-round-looking, short range, high frequency, high data rate, active sonars may be required, to cover the close quarters, dog-fight situation, by any boat whose bow sonar is passive only. Wherever it is derived from, the melee picture must be put on a circular Plan Position type display in the combat centre, as commanding officers need immediate hands-on control for this sort of battle. (Figure 8.23)

Passive Intercept

Intercept systems are designed to obtain information when an enemy uses active sonar, and can be regarded as the underwater equivalent of ESM. Anything they detect will always help data fusion at the CEP. And when one is trying to avoid, or fighting to shake loose, determined ASW opponents, the clarification of the tactical situation provided by regular and accurate information on enemy sonars may be vital.

Systems like *Paris* have a multi-band cylindrical array, fitted within a stream-lined dome. It is put on top of the casing, even in SSNs, to ensure continuous 360 degree coverage of enemy transmissions. All five octaves should be covered, since one is interested in everything: from powerful, low frequency, long range, surface and submarine systems; through the range of frequencies used by air dropped

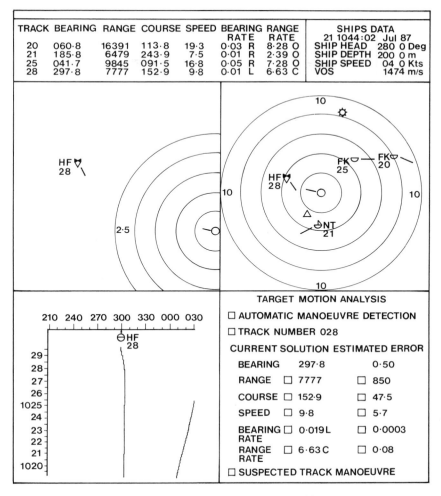

TRACK	BEARING	RANGE	COURSE	SPEED	BEARING RATE	RANGE RATE	SHIPS DATA 21 1044:02 Jul 87
20	060·8	16391	113·8	19·3	0·03 R	8·28 O	SHIP HEAD 280 0 Deg
21	185·8	6479	243·9	7·5	0·01 R	2·39 O	SHIP DEPTH 200 0 m
25	041·7	9845	091·5	16·8	0·05 R	7·28 O	SHIP SPEED 04 0 Kts
28	297·8	7777	152·9	9·8	0·01 L	6·63 C	VOS 1474 m/s

TARGET MOTION ANALYSIS

☐ AUTOMATIC MANOEUVRE DETECTION

☐ TRACK NUMBER 028

CURRENT SOLUTION ESTIMATED ERROR

BEARING 297·8 0·50

RANGE ☐ 7777 ☐ 850

COURSE ☐ 152·9 ☐ 47·5

SPEED ☐ 9·8 ☐ 5·7

BEARING RATE ☐ 0·019L ☐ 0·0003

RANGE RATE ☐ 6·63C ☐ 0·08

☐ SUSPECTED TRACK MANOEUVRE

Fig. 8.21   DCH picture just before attacking

active sono-buoys; to the high frequencies used by torpedo active homing heads. (Figure 8.24)

Much like an ESM equipment, sonar-intercept sonars need good sensitivity for early detection, and enough sensing array elements to provide bearings of near tracking quality accuracy. The minimum additional data needed is frequency and signal amplitude. Ideally, one also wants pulse analysis, allied to quick library search, to achieve rapid identification. And it helps if the system is well integrated with the rest of the passive sonar suite.

Underwater Communications

In sonar communications systems, commonly termed UWT (*Underwater Telephones*), both units must be able to send and receive. The combined

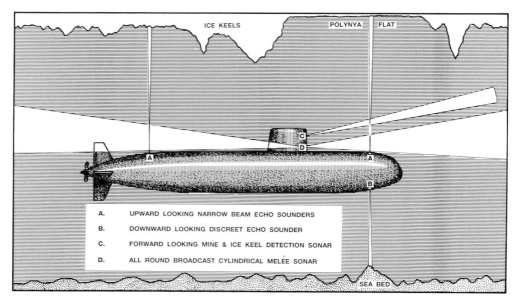

FIG. 8.22   Short range active sonars

FIG. 8.23   Russian TYPHOON Class SSBN with paint coming off the staybright
panels in the forward edge of the fin, covering her short range active sonars
(© *British Crown Copyright 1993/MOD*)

FIG. 8.24 HMS *Trafalgar*—showing intercept sonar dome. (Note also conical spiral communications aerial and search periscope with 4 port ESM antenna and communications aerial) (*Photo: VSEL*)

transducer/hydrophone is used like a radio transceiver. Main use of UWT is to exchange tactical data with other submarines in coordinated operations, or with surface ships during trials and exercises. The system needs to have all round listening coverage but the transmissions ought to be made more directionally. Even then, like any other communications, they should be encrypted, especially when being used to pass trials data, as they are by no means secure from unwanted listeners.

Cavitation and self noise monitoring

Submarines often have special passive sonar hydrophones fitted close enough to the propeller(s) to give immediate warning of cavitation inception. Throttle watch-keepers can see the associated monitors and are told to make any increase in speed gradually, thus preventing cavitation from developing, unless ordered to go to the new speed as fast as possible. Combat centres need their own monitors.

Other hydrophones are used to monitor machinery noise. Resultant spectra are then compared with ones made during static noise trials, hopefully eliminating self generated information from narrow band and *Demon* displays; since few things are more annoying than to spend all night at battle stations—only to discover that the submarine has been attacking its own refrigerator! (see Chapter 12)

MANNING

Not more than three operators and a supervisor are likely to be available continuously in an SSN, less in an SS. It is almost inevitable, therefore, that other men must be closed up to support watch-keepers, when all the equipment mentioned in this chapter is needed simultaneously, in a battle situation. (Figure 8.25)

Fig. 8.25   USS *Topeka* (SSN 754). Operators watching video screens and listening to audio. The system shown is AN/BSY-1 action data automation. This handles navigation and fire control for torpedoes and missiles, in addition to its sonar function
(*Photo: YOGI INC 1992*)

SUMMARY

Sonar is the prime detection system, not just tactically indispensable when bringing an enemy submarine to action, but vital also for own submarine survival, every day, in war or peace. Once below periscope depth, no other sensor is available.

To achieve surprise, most systems in a sonar suite act passively, but such sonars: do not detect automatically, only yield data slowly, give no instant identification, and initially provide just target bearing. Often, not even an approximate range is available until a target has been held for a minimum of twenty minutes, during which the submarine must be manoeuvred.

To cover every possible sound propagation path and the five octave frequency range of the enemy's unintentionally radiated and deliberately transmitted noise spectrum, a wide variety of arrays is required, including intercept equipment. Design is complicated by the need to achieve a high sonar operating speed in SSNs acting as escorts.

Good processing helps, but it is operators who find target signals amongst a background full of oceanographic and biological noise. However, thereafter, electronic beam steering and auto tracking do greatly improve bearing accuracy, which is the key to good target motion analysis, whether attacking or trailing.

The trend is towards all passive sonars being able to contribute something to all the tasks: broad band, narrow band, DEMON, passive ranging, and intercept. There is a move also towards greater integration of their data and a smaller number of displays, all multi purpose and able to present waterfall or spectrum analysis type data. This is badly needed to reduce operator numbers.

High power active sonars are fitted because the enemy might get much quieter. Meanwhile, they can be used for independent area clearance, and in a long range, distant support escort role—but not without some risk. Here too, operators need processing help, and intelligent handling of the submarine, to reduce spurious echoes.

Even submarines without long range, first detection, active sonars, need a short range active capability, mainly to handle a melee situation—but for mine and ice keel detection too.

A sonar suite also includes underwater communications equipment, upward and downward discreet echo sounders, and means for cavitation and self noise monitoring.

So much equipment makes for an ever changing scene, but this need not be a problem. As was shown with Type 2027, the pedigree of modern systems lies in the quality of their software algorithms. These can always be altered, provided designers build in capability upgrade potential.

9
Weapons

The diversity, long reach and powerful nature of modern submarine weapons were mentioned at the very beginning of this book and we saw in Chapter 3 that their number, size and complexity very largely determine the tonnage, and sometimes even the shape of the submarine itself. It is time now to look at their technical specifications, and think how best to use them. There are rockets, air breathing missiles, torpedoes, mines and ballistic missiles to be studied—and some pre-launch considerations.

ASW ROCKETS

First generation anti-submarine rockets, US SUBROC and Russian Starfish, were originally designed to give SSNs an anti-SSBN capability, when outside torpedo range. They are fired from a torpedo tube and consist of two parts bolted together, a rocket and a very powerful depth charge called an NDB (*Nuclear Depth Bomb*). The rocket motor ignites underwater, and the weapon travels level for a short distance before turning up towards the surface. Once in the air, it accelerates to supersonic speeds and heads for the target. At a preselected moment, the rocket is slowed down and the bolts sheared. The NDB then continues to the re-entry point, controlled by its own vanes. It is exploded by a hydrostatic fuse when it has sunk to the chosen underwater depth. (Figure 9.1)

These early systems are very noisy when they light up underwater and not very accurate in hitting their aiming mark. Second generation systems, such as US Sea Lance and Russian Stallion, are potentially better in both respects, provided the TMA solution of the target position is good. They also are launched from a torpedo tube but the rocket and payload are contained in a lightweight watertight capsule, which is pushed relatively quietly towards the surface. When in the air, the capsule is discarded, the fins deploy and the rocket boosts the weapon into a ballistic trajectory to the target area. After slow down and rocket separation, the torpedo payload makes a rather more accurate arrival in the believed target area and starts its own search and homing pattern. (Figure 9.2)

The comparative performance figures for the US and Russian systems are shown on page 127.

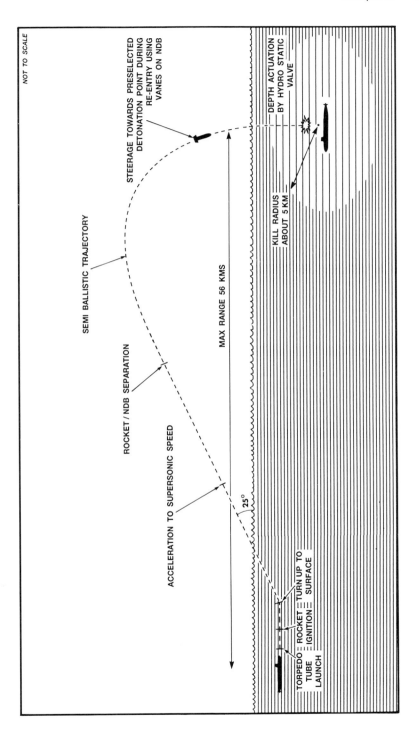

Fig. 9.1   SUBROC flight pattern

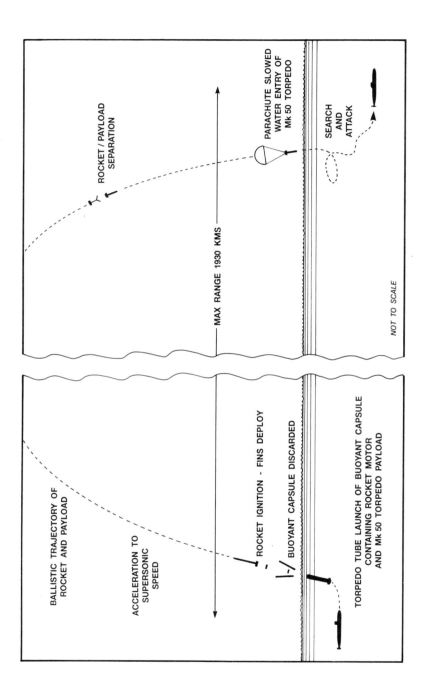

BALLISTIC TRAJECTORY OF
ROCKET AND PAYLOAD

ACCELERATION TO
SUPERSONIC
SPEED

ROCKET IGNITION - FINS DEPLOY

BUOYANT CAPSULE DISCARDED

TORPEDO TUBE LAUNCH OF BUOYANT CAPSULE
CONTAINING ROCKET MOTOR
AND Mk 50 TORPEDO PAYLOAD

ROCKET / PAYLOAD
SEPARATION

MAX RANGE 1930 KMS

PARACHUTE SLOWED
WATER ENTRY OF
Mk 50 TORPEDO

SEARCH
AND
ATTACK

NOT TO SCALE

Fig. 9.2   SEA LANCE delivery system

TABLE 9.1

Submarine Launched A/S Rockets

Nation	US	US	Russian	Russian
Weapon	SUBROC UUM-44A	Sea Lance	Starfish SS-N-15	Stallion SS-N-16
Range	56 Km	1930 Km	45–50 Km	92 Km
Payload	NDB	Mk 50 Adv Lt Wt Torp	NDB	Homing Torpedo
Warhead	Probably same as Starfish	45 Kg HE Shaped Charge	200 KT	150 Kg HE
Launched from	533 mm Torpedo Tube	533 mm Torpedo Tube	533 mm Torpedo Tube	650 mm Torpedo Tube

AIR BREATHING MISSILES

All submarine air breathing missiles have a common ancestor in the Second World War V1 flying bomb, which had a simple ram-jet aero engine attached to a stub winged fuselage. It was slow, relatively short range, and needed a long launch ramp. (Figure 9.3)

The first practical SLCM (***Submarine Launched Cruise Missiles***) were Regulus I, which entered service in USS *Tunny* in 1954, and the SS-N-3 Shaddock which became operational in converted Russian WHISKEY class boats in 1958. These were strategic deterrent land attack weapons, before the days of Polaris ballistic missiles. Both US and Russian missiles were powered by turbo-jet, a system missiles still use, in which gas energy produced by a turbine driven compressor is directed through a nozzle to produce thrust. It avoids the need for an extended ramp, though Shaddock does use JATO (***Jet Assisted Take Off***) boosters.

The main difference between the systems was that Regulus was housed in a hangar which preserved submarine shape but meant people coming up onto the casing to rig the launcher and missile, an awkward task in bad weather. Whereas, Shaddock was stowed in tubes which could be hydraulically elevated to provide their own launchers and its missile wings deployed automatically once clear of the tube, both very useful improvements. However, the tubes badly upset submarine streamlining in the early WHISKEY class conversions, a problem still not entirely overcome when Shaddock was deployed in the SSG JULIETT and SSGN ECHO II in 1962. (Figures 9.4 and 9.5)

Once Polaris ballistic missiles were in service, the United States stopped work on air breathing missiles, and did not come back to them again until they produced Tomahawk, and then Harpoon, in the 1980s. Meanwhile, the Russians maintained a continuous programme of SLCM development over the years. Shaddock was successively improved into the SS-N-12 Sandbox and SS-N-19 Shipwreck, long range anti-ship missiles. Russia was also the first nation to produce a sub-surface launched, autonomous, tactical, anti-ship cruise missile, the SS-N-7 Starbright, which appeared with the CHARLIE I class boats in 1967, another major advance

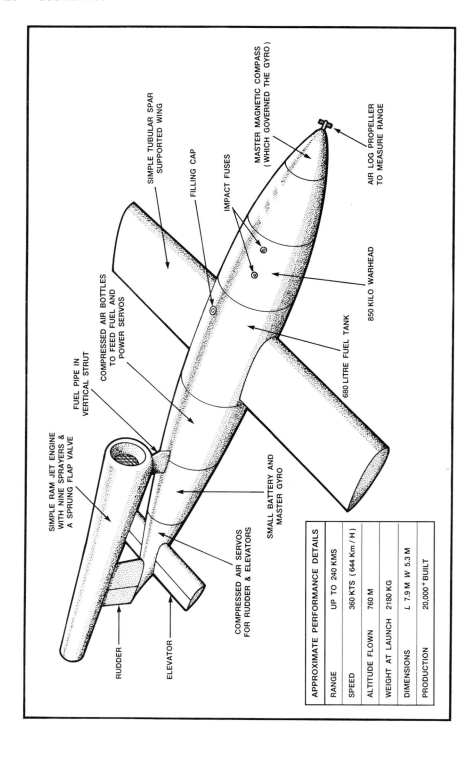

SIMPLE TUBULAR SPAR
SUPPORTED WING

FILLING CAP

IMPACT FUSES

MASTER MAGNETIC COMPASS
(WHICH GOVERNED THE GYRO)

AIR LOG PROPELLER
TO MEASURE RANGE

850 KILO WARHEAD

680 LITRE FUEL TANK

COMPRESSED AIR BOTTLES
TO FEED FUEL AND
POWER SERVOS

FUEL PIPE IN
VERTICAL STRUT

SIMPLE RAM JET ENGINE
WITH NINE SPRAYERS &
A SPRUNG FLAP VALVE

RUDDER

ELEVATOR

COMPRESSED AIR SERVOS
FOR RUDDER & ELEVATORS

SMALL BATTERY AND
MASTER GYRO

APPROXIMATE PERFORMANCE DETAILS	
RANGE	UP TO 240 KMS
SPEED	360 KTS (644 Km/H)
ALTITUDE FLOWN	760 M
WEIGHT AT LAUNCH	2180 KG
DIMENSIONS	L 7.9 M W 5.3 M
PRODUCTION	20,000+ BUILT

FIG. 9.3   The German V-I. Forerunner of all cruise missiles

Fig. 9.4   Russian JULIETT Class SSG 1991—showing missile launchers (© *British Crown Copyright 1993/MOD*)

(see Figure 4.4). They have also quickly copied the US Tomahawk example, producing two powerful, long range, terrain following cruise missiles: the SS-N-21 Sampson and SS-NX-24, to rearm early SSBNs, when ballistic missiles are removed as arms treaty reductions. Vital statistics of Russian missiles are given in Table 9.2; those of Harpoon, two versions of Tomahawk and French Sub-Exocet in Table 9.3. (Figure 9.6)

Flight Profile

Apart from more speed and longer range, modern missiles have other advantages over the V1. For example, they either follow sea skimming flight profiles just above the surface, using an extremely accurate radio altimeter; or high up and over profiles, which end in a steep, maybe 85 degrees terminal dive onto a ship. Both are harder to intercept than the V1 medium altitude approach. Low level causes late detection. High level passes above many defensive weapon engagement envelopes, and is only within the others for a short time, due to the Mach 2/Mach 3 speeds possible at high altitude. (Figure 9.7)

Guidance

Unlike the V1, which was simply aimed down a bearing, modern missiles can have either command guidance during flight or inertial guidance. In command guidance, the submarine establishes a data link with the reconnaissance aircraft and continues to view its missile through the eyes of the aircraft's radar. Once it has both missile and enemy group in sight, the boat selects a target and gives final missile guidance. This is the system used by ECHO II and JULIETT class submarines.

In inertial guidance, a missile is fed with: latitude and longitude coordinates of the firing position; a target future position, provided by shore command, or derived direct from a satellite picture; and any intermediate, dog-leg positions through which it is to pass. The missile's inertial navigation system will then take it through the selected positions. Anti-ship Tomahawk uses this system.

FIG. 9.5   Russian ECHO II Class SSGN—showing how streamlining was broken up
by missile launchers (© *British Crown Copyright 1993/MOD*)

FIG. 9.6   Tomahawk cruise missile launch from USS *La Jolla* (SSN 701)
(*Photo: US Navy*)

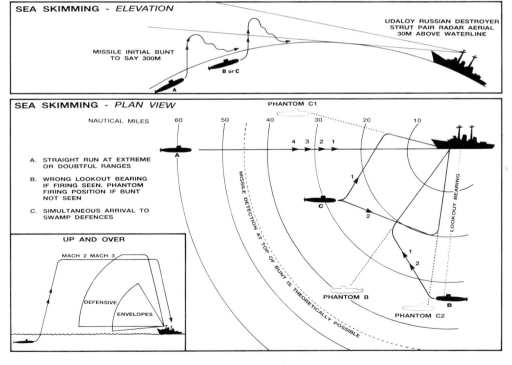

FIG. 9.7   Missile flight profiles

When an HE warhead Land Attack Tomahawk is employed against very precisely defined targets, a DSMAC (***Digital Scene Matching Area Correlator***) is used. This contains a miniature TV camera which constantly video records the passage of known landmarks, matches them with a sequence of images stored in its computer memory and adjusts the inertial navigation system to put its missile back on route for the target.

Homing

Intelligent homing is the third huge improvement over a V1. Ingenious terminal homing devices now available for use in missile heads include active radar, anti radar, home on jamming signal, infra red heat homing, select by T/V picture of target and, in the future, fire down on specific magnetic signature. The degree of combination of these methods which can be fitted in any one homing head is limited by space available and cost. However, some combinations, such as active radar and home on jam, are very effective ***force multipliers***.

TABLE 9.2

Russian Air Breathing Missiles

Missile Code-name	Range km Speed M	Guidance Homing	Warheads (HE & Nuc)	Subms (Nos) Mis⁸ Carried
SS-N-3C Shaddock	460 1.1	Command Radar	1000 kg HE 350 KT Nuc	J(4), E2(2) 4 ea, 8 ea
SS-N-12 Sandbox	550 1.7 +	Command Radar	1000 kg HE 350 KT Nuc	J(8), E2(12) 4 ea, 8 ea
SS-N-19 Shipwreck	620 1.6	Command Anti Radar	HE or Nuc	OSCAR 9 24 each
SS-N-17 Starbright	64 0.9	(Aimed) Radar	500 kg HE 200 KT Nuc	C1(8) 8 each
SS-N-9 Siren	110 0.9	(Aimed) Radar & IR	500 kg HE 200 KT Nuc	C2(6) 10 each
SS-N-21 Sampson	2000 0.7	Inertial T/V match	200 KT Nuc (CEP 150m)	Y-Notch(3)[1] Nos Vary[2]
SS-NX-24	4000 2.0	Inertial T/V match	1 MT Nuc Only	Y-Convn(1)[3] 12

Notes 1 Sampson also carried by 3 SIERRAs, 9 AKULAs and 26 VICTOR III class submarines.
2 Fired from 533 mm tubes. Number embarked depends on torpedo/missile mix.
3 Prototype for new class of submarine.

TABLE 9.3

Non-Russian Air Breathing Missiles

Missile Role	Range km Speed M	Guidance Homing	Warheads (HE & Nuc)	Submarines Carrying
Tomahawk Land Attack	2500 0.7	Inertial TAINS[1]	Various HE 200 KT Nuc	US 637 & 688 Class SSNs[2]
Tomahawk Anti-ship	460 0.7	Inertial Radar & Anti-Radar	454 kg HE	US 637 & 688 Class SSNs
Sub Harpoon Anti-ship	130 0.9	Inertial Radar	227–258 kg	US 637 & 688 Class[3]
Sub Exocet Anti-ship	50 0.9	Inertial Radar	165 kg HE	French[4]

Notes 1 TERCOM (Terrain Contour Matching) Aided Inertial Navigation System—using TV camera.
2 There are 33 STURGEON (637) class & 49+ LOS ANGELES (688) class capable of launching either type of Tomahawk missile from their 533 mm torpedo tubes. All since SSN 719 have also had 12 vertical external launch tubes fitted for the land attack version.
3 Harpoon is in 83+ US SSNs, 12 UK SSNs of SWIFTSURE & TRAFALGAR class and SSs of Australia, Greece, Israel, Japan, Netherlands and Pakistan. Turkey will have it in their new boats. Italy and Taiwan may fit it.
4 SM 39 Exocet is in all French nuclear submarines and in the AGOSTA class SSs of both Spain and France.

TORPEDOES

Post war development, from crudely aimed weapons to guided intelligent weapons, also occurred in the torpedo world. But underwater weapon designers did not start with such a clean sheet. Torpedoes were complex even in 1945, and improvements had to be won without losing gains already made. For instance, weight and hydrodynamic lift must balance, but adding capabilities often increases weight. So when Tigerfish became heavier than water, it had to be given deployable wings for extra lift whilst running at slow search speeds. However, wings increase flow noise, and Marconi have designed Spearfish to run with its body at a slight angle to the line of travel. This gives enough lift without wings, even though Spearfish is heavier than Tigerfish and has 30,000 components. Just one of the many problems to be overcome in a long, expensive development programme. (Figure 9.8)

The Basic Components

The modern dual purpose, anti-ship/anti-submarine homing torpedo can be divided into five separate components:

▶ Brain

▶ Warhead

▶ Power Plant

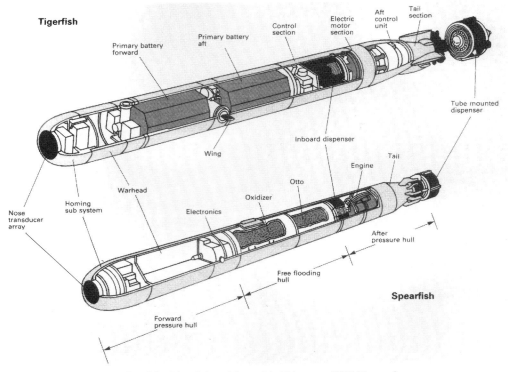

Tigerfish

Spearfish

FIG. 9.8   Tigerfish and Spearfish (*Diagram: GEC Marconi*)

▶ Control Surfaces

▶ Umbilical to submarine

Brain   The torpedo brain is in the nose and consists of a ring of micro-processors. Its first task is to *receive* commands from the submarine at the ***enabling point***, where the warhead is armed and homing logic circuits switched in; and subsequently to apply the impact and influence fuse settings. Instructions may also be received to change speed up or down, to alter the search depth and to stop the torpedo. The brain then sends back data to the fire control system in the submarine, on weapon course, speed, depth and distance run. Given this 'tellback', a combat team can recompute the fire control problem on a display showing torpedoes and target, then give fresh steerage.

The second task is to run the torpedo acoustics and, when contact is obtained, switch between passive and active search, and high and low speed, as needed to hold contact and complete a homing, reporting the action taken. The brain is programmed to spot and ignore any acoustic decoy met during the approach. If in a stern chase, it will order a pull out to one side before the final run in, pick the most deadly place on the enemy vessel and then hit it, whilst on a track broad enough to ensure maximum effect. The brain will also organise any re-attack needed and energise the firing circuits at the right moment when using proximity fusing. (Figure 9.9)

The third task for the brain is giving the up-down, left-right signals to the control surfaces at the rear of the torpedo, needed to carry out the intentions of the reasoning part of the brain. Sometimes a separate set of microprocessors is used for this function but it is best integrated into one package, if only to save space badly needed to keep the warhead as large as possible.

Warhead   The warhead comes immediately behind the brain. It has a main charge, a primer and detonators, usually not wound into the primer until enabling is ordered. The main charge must be man enough for the job but a balance has to be struck between volume and weight of warhead, range the weapon has to run, and space allocated to brain and wire dispenser. If the weapon must fit into an unaltered 533 mm tube, it is difficult to achieve both Second World War sized warheads and the longer ranges now needed.

In 1945, US Mark 14 and UK Mark 8 torpedoes had main charges of 300 and 340 kilogrammes of torpex explosive. They ran at 46 knots to 4.11 kilometres. Both had slower running modes, out to greater distances, but they were rarely used because the chances of hitting anything at over 4 kilometres with an aimed salvo were too small to justify wasting torpedoes. Table 9.4 shows that modern dual role homing torpedoes are expected to run out to much greater distances, and at higher speeds, but some carry only 45 kilogrammes of HE. Such small warheads

FIG. 9.9   The Brain—Homing sub-system (*Photo: GEC Marconi*)

use a combined blast and directed energy, shaped charge design, to produce a hot drive through bolt effect. Sea pressure does the rest. They should penetrate most hulls when a good angle of attack is achieved, but torpedo designers must not be complacent. A bit more explosive would be no bad thing, when coping with large twin hulled submarines.

Power Plant   First generation anti-submarine homing torpedoes were all electric, using power from high capacity silver zinc batteries to turn two contra-rotating propellers. They were a lot quieter than Second World War torpedoes, essential for the SSK role, and were quite adequate to deal with any diesel submarine. In improved versions, many are still in service. However, 40 knot SSN targets and much longer sonar detection ranges call for torpedo performance beyond anything achievable with a battery.

The new need will be met by torpedoes like Spearfish, undergoing trials in the UK, and could be met by some variety of the US Mk 50 Barracuda, just completing development. This sort of torpedo uses a non-stop, closed cycle Rankine steam turbine system, whose thermal energy is generated by chemical reaction between a liquid metal fuel and gaseous oxidant, supplied from separate tanks. After light up, high pressure water pumped into a mini boiler produces superheated steam; which drives a turbine, connected to the shaft via a gearbox. Spent steam goes through a condenser and, under pressure, is recycled to the boiler by a feed pump. Also on the shaft is an alternator, which in Spearfish generates several hundred kilowatts, ample to operate brain and advanced acoustics. A pump-jet propulsor is used, to halve gearing requirements, and to reap the benefits noted in Chapter 5. It is quiet and variable speed, both good for sonar performance. It is also insensitive to operating depth. The ranges and top speeds shown in Table 9.4 speak for themselves. (Figure 9.10)

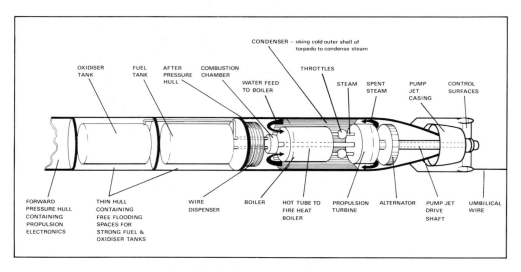

Fig. 9.10   Rankine steam turbine system

Control Surfaces   All torpedoes have *vertical and horizontal rudders*, just as an SSN has cruciform control surfaces. In fact, a torpedo is a miniature submarine. Vertical rudders are free from the moment of firing but horizontal rudders are usually held with slight dive on them until well clear of the boat. This is to prevent an immediate upward sheer, which might cause the weapon to broach when firing from periscope depth. In Spearfish, small control surfaces are mounted in the efflux of the pumpjet and make the torpedo particularly agile, a great help in the last stage of an attack, and when re-attacking. (Figure 9.11)

The Umbilical   Both torpedo and submarine have to manoeuvre after weapon launch. So wire must be unleashed from at least two places, one being a reel in the torpedo. In Tigerfish, submarine movement is made possible by using a hosepipe dispenser. This is a big advance on earlier systems, which involved towing an unstable reel through the water, often a source of trouble. The hosepipe principle was simple but the engineering was not. Complex mechanical and hydrodynamic forces had to be balanced, wire coating and lubrication technology

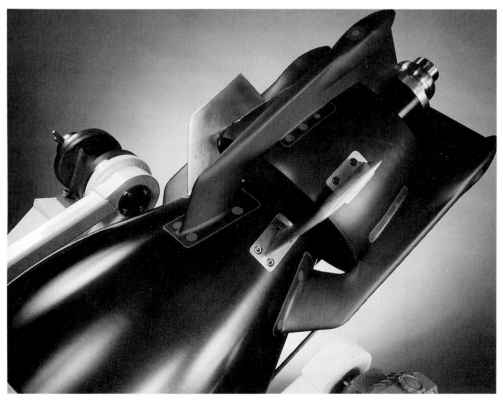

FIG. 9.11 Spearfish tail—showing pumpjet casing and control surfaces (*Photo: GEC Marconi*)

developed, and critical shear pin pull-off levels found. All involved exhaustive trials. (Figure 9.12)

Excellent as the system now is, boats should still be manoeuvred gently when possible during early stages of an attack, at least until enabling has taken place. After that, if the wire breaks, the torpedo will go on to the target area with whatever instructions it had at the time. This is a good reason for getting it onto an interception course as soon as possible, if it has been stepped aside to help sonar.

TABLE 9.4

Wire Guided Dual Role Heavyweight Torpedoes

Nation	France	Italy	Russia	UK	US
Model	F-17	A-184	53	Spearfish	MK 48 ADCAP
Range km	20 or 25	10 or 25	Max 20[1]	40 or 65	38 or 50
Speed kts	40 or 35	36 or 24	Max 46	70 or 60	55 or 40
Engine & Power	Electric (Ag Zn Battery)	Electric (Ag Zn Battery)	Probably Conventl Steam	Turbine Engine Thermal	Piston Engine Gas[2]
Length mm	5406	6000	7270	6000	5800
Diam mm	533.4	533	533	533	533
Wt kg	1360	1300	1610	1850	c 1600
Warhead kg	250	250	400[3]	45 (DE)[4]	267

Notes 1. By contrast, the 650 mm externally housed anti convoy torpedoes can carry a nuclear warhead to 100 km @ 30 kts/50 km @ 50 kts (approx). They too are probably turbine engine thermals.
2. Mk 48 ADCAP uses a pump jet propulsor and is a good half way stage to the US Mk 50 Barracuda.
3. 15 KT nuclear in big bang straight run version.
4. Estimated figure. A 45 kg directed energy head is also used in the Swedish TP 43X0.

MINES AND MINELAYING

Submarines can lay moored mines, tethered mines or ground mines and are themselves vulnerable to all three sorts. All are shaped for discharge from a 533 mm torpedo tube but differ in their mode of operation. A moored mine leaves the tube in one piece but is made up of two parts: a 'sinker' or anchor, and the mine itself. Once on the seabed, after a preset delay to let the submarine get clear, the buoyant mine separates from the sinker and floats up to a set height above the sea bed on the end of a mooring wire, whose selected length will depend on the depth of water and whether a surface or submarine target is sought. Detonation occurs on contact or on sensing an enemy magnetic/acoustic signature, unless inhibited by arming delays or ship count mechanisms. (Figure 9.13)

The US Type 57 Mod 0 moored mine contains 154 kilogrammes of HE and can be laid in depths of up to 350 metres. Being 3000 millimetres long, the mine occupies only half the rack space of a torpedo. Therefore, a LOS ANGELES class submarine, with 4 tubes and 22 racks, could theoretically carry 44 + 4 = 48. However,

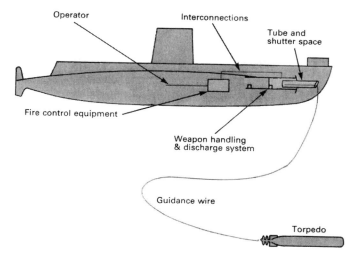

Operator

Interconnections

Tube and shutter space

Fire control equipment

Weapon handling & discharge system

Guidance wire

Torpedo

Tigerfish weapon system

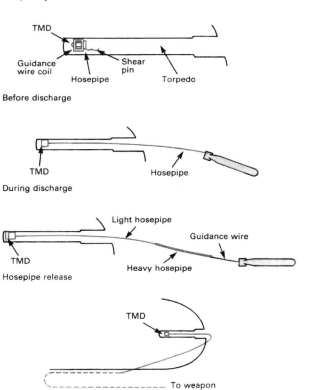

TMD

Guidance wire coil

Shear pin

Hosepipe

Torpedo

Before discharge

TMD

Hosepipe

During discharge

Light hosepipe

Guidance wire

TMD

Heavy hosepipe

Hosepipe release

TMD

To weapon

Steady tow

Tube mounted dispenser (TMD)

FIG. 9.12   Wire dispensing system (*Diagram: MUSL*)

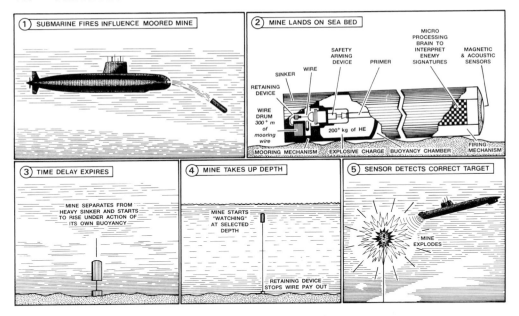

FIG. 9.13   Laying a moored mine

the submarine will want to have available two defensive salvos of torpedoes, so the maximum field which it can sensibly be expected to lay is 44 mines.

Tethered mines are laid and made to watch like moored mines; but when actuated, instead of exploding where they are, they release a homing weapon, which carries the HE charge to the target. For example, US CAPTOR releases an encapsulated Mk 46 torpedo and Russian Cluster Gulf sends up a rocket propelled torpedo body, a rising mine, when the target is in the weapon's vertical attack zone. The Russian mine, and probably CAPTOR, can be laid in up to 2000 metres of water. However, CAPTOR's 3700 millimetre length is likely to restrict stowage to one per rack, or a total lay of 22 for a 688 class submarine. Such small loads are best saved for those fields most under enemy surveillance and areas where other minelayers cannot easily reach, say under the ice.

Ground mines are sometimes known as influence mines because when first introduced they were the only ones not actuated by physical contact. They can be *submarine* laid in depths between 25 and 200 metres. The British Aerospace Sea Urchin is fairly typical. It actuates on sensing magnetic and acoustic signatures, or fluctuations in water pressure made by deep draught and fast moving ships. Configured as illustrated, with two 350 kilogramme warheads, it is still small enough to occupy only half a rack, so HMS *Upholder* could lay 26. (Figures 9.14 and 9.15)

Ability to distinguish very precisely between one target and another, a feature of modern mines, calls for complicated circuitry and has only become possible since the introduction of microprocessing. However, mines have a long shelf life; and clever actuation packages, once invented, can be back-fitted in many old submarine mines.

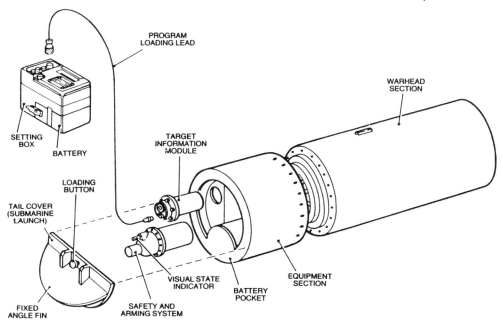

FIG. 9.14   Ground mine configuration (*Diagram: British Aerospace Military Aircraft Ltd*)

FIG. 9.15   Sea Urchin with double warhead (*Photo: British Aerospace Naval Weapons Division*)

Laying ground mines close inshore, in a shallow water area where the enemy is active, is a demanding operation. Even with power loading and six launch tubes available, several separate runs will be needed. The mines must be laid accurately, so that one's own forces know where they are, and cross tide, to make mine clearance harder. This calls for very adroit navigation, usually in daylight, but with the periscope used sparingly, or counter detection will take place. Loading and prompt launching of numerous mines calls for slick drill by weapons crews. It can also cause temporary trimming upsets, which tax a ship control team to the limit, since the boat will have very little water under the keel and an urgent need not to broach. Finally, there is the unwelcome but imperative duty to break radio silence to report the lay, a subject discussed more fully in the next chapter.

BALLISTIC MISSILES

SSBN operations are covered in Chapter 14 but to complete the weapons picture, it is necessary here to speak briefly of SLBM (*Submarine Launched Ballistic Missiles*). The data relates generally to American, British and French systems but some details of Russian missiles and the boats which carry them are available for comparison in Chapter 3. (Table 3.1)

SLBMs are stowed in upright launch tubes and require sophisticated handling systems, as is clear from pictures of weapons being embarked at Trident bases. They are launched sub-surface from a range of depths, the main requirement being a hovering or very slow speed submarine, with not too much rolling motion. They are positively ejected by separate expanding gas systems, and their first stage rocket ignites, once clear of water and submarine. It is discarded after burn out, and second (and third) stage rockets take the missile exoatmospheric, on a long ballistic trajectory to the target area. (Figure 9.16)

Missiles can deliver their RVs (*Re-entry Vehicles*) in a number of ways. In general, longest range is obtained by using a single RV; and greatest survivability against ABM (*Anti-Ballistic Missiles*), by maximising the number of incoming threats. For example, Trident 2 (D5) missiles in US OHIO class SSBNs have a maximum range of 12,000 km but at lesser ranges can deliver up to 12 nuclear warheads from a MIRV (*Multiple Independently targeted Re-entry Vehicle*) system. Each RV is ejected towards a different target and the defence problem can be made worse by using Penetration Aid Packages, which create a large number of false RVs. If not hardened, they burn up on re-entry but the defence, which should fire two ABMs at everything approaching, (to cover a malfunction), must start the engagement whilst RVs are still exoatmospheric, or it will never intercept everything in time. This overloading of the ABM system is known as 'winning the exchange ratio battle.' Defences will be further stretched by introduction of MARV (*Manoeuvring Re-entry Vehicles*), designed to evade ABMs. (Figures 9.17 and 9.18)

Details of US, UK and French systems are at Table 9.5.

FIG. 9.16   USS *Pennsylvania* (SSBN 735) embarking D5C (TRIDENT II) missiles
at the Explosives Handling Wharf, King's Bay, Georgia (which is also used by UK
VANGUARD Class SSBNs). The loading canisters are placed over the tubes with
a huge crane (*Photo: YOGI INC 1992*)

TABLE 9.5
Ballistic Missiles in Western Submarines

Missile Code-name	Poseidon C3	Trident 1 C4	Trident 2 D5	Polaris A3	SNIAS M4/TN 71
Rocket	2 Stage	3 Stage	3 Stage	2 Stage	3 Stage
Fuel Type	Solid	Solid	Solid	Solid	Solid
Range in kms [1]	About 3,600	About 7,200	About 7,200	About 3,600	About 3,600[2]
Delivers each of	14 MIRV[3] KT range	8 MIRV[4] KT range	12 MIRV[5] KT range	3 MRV KT range	6 MRV KT range
Carried by SSBN Classes	2 of US MADISON & BENJAMIN FRANKLIN[6]	12 of US MADISON & BENJAMIN FRANKLIN, 8 OHIO[7]	4+ OHIOs and to be in 4 UK VANGUARD	Current 3 UK R Class	Current 5 French SNLE

Notes   1. Ranges vary with numbers of MIRV deployed.
   2. LE TRIOMPHANT class SNLE-NG (Sous-marines Nucleaires Lanceurs d'Engines—
       Nouvelle Generation) will get new 11,115 km missiles.
   3. Accuracy CEP 450 m.
   4. Or 6 MARV, accuracy CEP 450 m.
   5. Or 7 MARV, accuracy CEP 100 m (using astro-navigation observation to correct flight
       path).
   6. The C3 fitted boats are being withdrawn.
   7. These first 8 OHIOs will not be backfitted with D5 unless Russian threat worsens again.

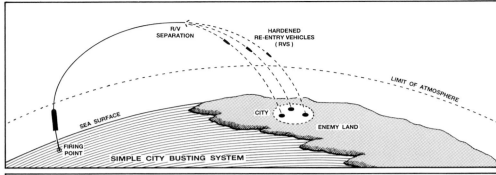

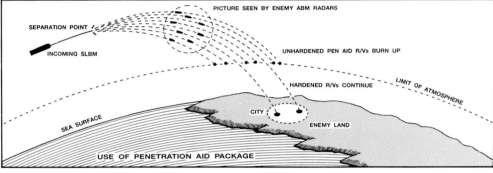

Fig. 9.17   Submerged Launched Ballistic Missile (SLBM) flight path

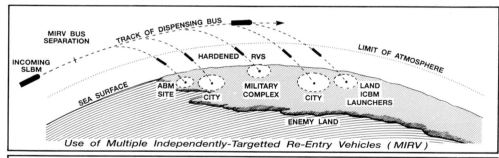

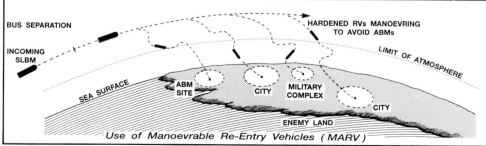

Fig. 9.18   MIRV and MARV

PRE-LAUNCH CONSIDERATIONS

Before any sort of submarine weapons are launched at any type of target, the commanding officer will run through his mind a sequence of questions in roughly the following order:

▶ Do ROE (*Rules of Engagement*) allow an attack?

▶ Should fire be withheld for some reason?

▶ What is the best weapon for this target?

▶ From what position should I aim to engage?

▶ Is the target already within best weapon range?

▶ If so, how bad are the TMA errors—(see Figure 8.21)?

▶ Is there a good enough probability of hitting?

▶ How many weapons should I fire?

▶ Is the launch system yet in the Action State?

▶ When am I going to open the bow caps/front doors?

This is not meant to be an exhaustive list but it does provide a few subjects which require discussion.

To Fire or Not to Fire

All warships operate under ROE. These consist of broad directives: to escalate, de-escalate or maintain the *status quo*; and a large number of individual, numbered, actions, which are either permitted or not permitted. Clearly, they must be unequivocal. And, for submarines, at a time of high political tension, the method as well as the circumstances in which 'weapons tight' ROE are going to be changed to 'weapons free', (allowed to attack), ROE, need especially careful thought. SSNs trailing important enemy units deploying at high speed cannot also be in constant satellite communication with base from periscope depth, awaiting a Government change of mind. Once use of weapons is authorised, all submarines need a fixed area, or ***moving haven***, in which they are free to attack any ship or other submarine found, safe in the knowledge that friendly units will be kept clear of them.

Even when fire is permitted, one must also consider whether overall operational aims will be furthered or prejudiced by attacking the particular target in prospect. For example, when short of weapons, one may have to save them for more important targets; and, when waiting for a key enemy unit known to be approaching, it is a bad error to disclose your presence prematurely. Moreover, there may be times when reporting enemy forces has to take priority over carrying out an immediate attack—perhaps to alert other members of a pack.

Weapon Choice Versus Ships

Against a single, unarmoured surface warship almost any air flight missile will create severe damage, particularly if it hits the ship broadside on. Many warships have side plating that is little more than 1 centimetre thick and missiles move at a minimum speed of 0.7 Mach. Even without a warhead, they release a lot of kinetic energy on impact, and their unexpended fuel is almost bound to start a fire, which is then spread by the warhead detonation, itself a cause of further damage. It may not always be a ship killer, but a hit from a missile does a lot of disabling, even when it is not nuclear tipped. (Figure 9.19)

FIG. 9.19   Ship after a missile attack (© *British Crown Copyright 1993/MOD*)

Weapons such as Sub-Harpoon are particularly suitable for use when marking a fast moving enemy surface group. Their relatively long range and short time of flight ensure a quick response once the signal to engage is received, and remove the need to run up into a more favourable position before firing, which so often delays and increases the risk of an attack with torpedoes against this type of target. Moreover, once settled at sea skimming altitude, such missiles are hard to detect in time, even when an AEW (*Airborne Early Warning*) aircraft is available to the defence.

However, a homing torpedo is a better weapon to use against any surface target which must be sunk at the first blow, (not just disabled), or whose sides are armoured. It is also the best weapon to use against super tankers, which often suffered only minor damage from missile hits during the Iran/Iraq war, due to a combination of heavy hull plating, shock absorbing by the liquid cargo and the deadening effect of an inert gas on top of it.

A torpedo will either strike well below the waterline, letting in a lot of water; or it will detonate immediately under the hull, creating a huge ball of upward moving gas, enough to break the back of the largest ship. Torpedoes have the additional advantage of being harder to decoy than missiles, largely due to the extra space in their homing logic which can be devoted to cleverer counter counter-measure algorithms. (Figure 9.20)

Weapon Choice Versus Submarines

Enemy submarines below the depth floor of one's own submarine's torpedoes, can only be destroyed by a nuclear warhead. It can be delivered by rocket or a straight running, 'big bang' torpedo, assuming such weapons are authorised for use. Both need to be well aimed shots, difficult to achieve at long distance.

Fig. 9.20   The backbreaking effect of a Tigerfish torpedo (*Photo: MUSL*)

However, a submarine hull, already under great stress from external water pressure at extreme depths, is not likely to survive an NDB (**Nuclear Depth Bomb**) explosion inside about 5 kilometres, so there is some room for error.

For all other submarines, the weapon to use is a dual speed, passive-then-active homing torpedo, either steered out towards the target by wire, whilst the boat maintains sonar contact on the target and weapon, ie Spearfish; or, at long range, delivered to the target vicinity by rocket and then able to search autonomously, ie Sea Lance.

Giving torpedoes like those shown in Table 9.4 a dual purpose, anti-ship/anti-submarine capability is certainly sensible. Both tasks need good hull penetration warheads, and flexibility of employment eases the stowage and reload problems produced by having several different sorts of weapons. (Figure 9.21)

Attacking Surface Ships and Land Targets

When attacking a surface force, particularly a fast moving one, a torpedo firing diesel electric SS often has to concentrate almost entirely on closing the DOT (*Distance Off Track*) enough to get off one shot before the enemy has again moved out of range, never to reappear. The faster the surface force and the shorter the effective range of the submarine weapons, the more restrictive will be the LLSA (*Limiting Lines of Submerged Approach*). (Figure 9.22)

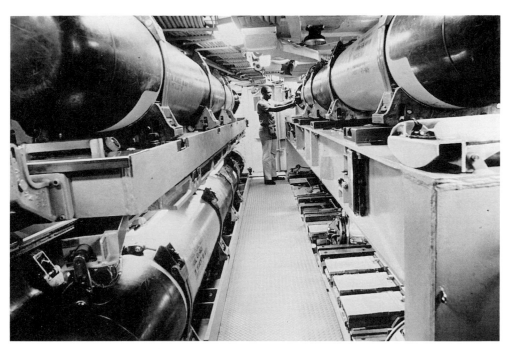

Fig. 9.21   The Torpedo Room of USS *Omaha* (SSN 692). Checking the securing of
Mk 48 torpedoes on their hydraulically operated traversing racks
(*Photo: YOGI INC*)

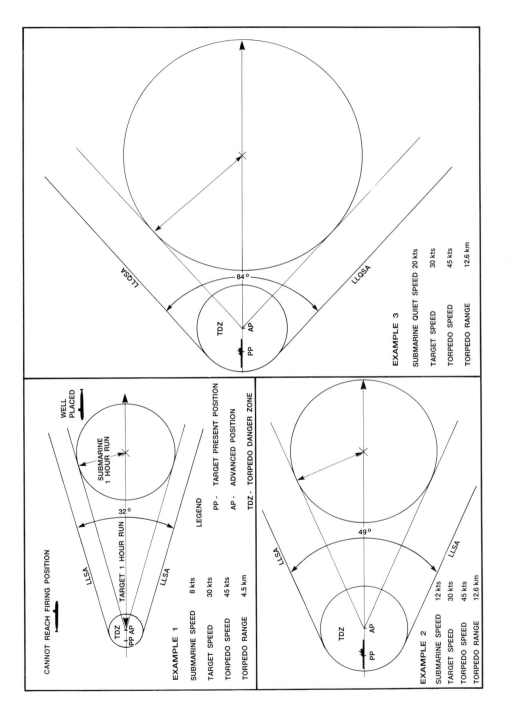

FIG. 9.22   Limiting lines of submerged approach

The situation is eased for an SSN. Unworried by battery conservation considerations, and unaffected by the factors which delay surface forces, such as replenishment operations, turns into wind for flying, bad surface weather; it can remain in contact for a long time, maybe days, and approach from a variety of different directions, at moments of its own choice. But the first requirement of any attack position is still the same, to be within weapon range. The other two needs are for a good probability of achieving a hit and to remain undetected during the approach, at least until weapons are fired and well on their way to the target.

Using Missiles   Sea skimming missiles describe a high initial 'bunt' on first breaking surface (see Figure 9.7) and the firing position should be far enough over the horizon to conceal it. If the top of the bunt cannot be hidden, weapons should be programmed to do a dog leg en route, so that the enemy are looking out on the wrong bearing, when trying to reacquire them on radar. Late acquisition will greatly increase the probability of a missile hit. When the initial bunt is unseen, weapon dog-legs also deny the enemy an obvious investigation bearing for counter detection of the submarine; and introduce the possibility, when firing salvos, of simultaneous arrival of weapons from different directions perhaps 90 degrees apart. (Figure 9.23)

FIG. 9.23   HMS *Courageous*—Salvo launch of Sub-Harpoon, the weapons setting off in different directions (© *British Crown Copyright 1993/MOD*)

When external assistance is needed to target long range missiles like the Russian SS-N-19 against ships, attack success depends entirely on the technical ability, and perhaps bravery, of the third party. If RORSAT (**Radar Orbiting Satellites**) or EORSAT (**Electronic Orbiting Satellites**) are used, they may be interdicted by the enemy, using a low yield nuclear weapon or an SDI (**Strategic Defence Initiative**) type damage laser, perhaps even before hostilities have begun; so nations like Russia have kept long range reconnaissance aircraft in their order of battle. These aircraft also are very much at risk. To get a clear enough picture of enemy force disposition to achieve target selection, they must close to ranges where they are liable to counter detection and then interception by defending aircraft. Assuming they have managed to establish data link communications with the submarine, and it can be frustratingly difficult at times, they may then have to fly on a steady course for twenty minutes or more, whilst passing the link picture. If an air intercept radar is detected on ESM in the meantime, the pilot needs an heroic temperament to keep flying straight and level for the benefit of a submarine!

The outcome is less doubtful when firing terrain-following cruise missiles such as US Tomahawk, or Russian SS-N-21 Sampson, at fixed land targets, because details of overland routes to be followed by missiles can be garnered by satellite well in advance of hostilities and a variety of flight programmes stored ready for use. Best of all, no third party is needed when firing; though external assistance would be required to use such weapons against moving ship targets.

Using Torpedoes   Latest homing torpedoes, like US Mk 48 ADCAP and UK Spearfish, have ranges of 50 to 60 kilometres and high enough speeds to overtake a surface force, if fired from not too far astern. However, it does not follow that an SSN torpedo attack should always be made from the rear. If the enemy force is moving fast, neither submarine nor torpedo can overhaul it quickly, so both are liable to detection over a much longer period during their approach. Moreover, many shorter range, slower torpedoes will remain in the inventory for years, and these are best brought into action by working round an enemy force inconspicuously, and then making a high closing rate approach from a bow or beam sector. (Figure 9.24)

Although there are no limiting lines of submerged approach for an SSN capable of greater speed than the force to be attacked, there are limiting lines of quiet submerged approach, depending on the SSN's maximum quiet speed. It must be a calculated decision, based on the strength of the opposition and sonar conditions on the day, how far, if at all, to exceed this speed during the final approach to the firing point. A bold fast run in, to a relatively short range firing position may well pay off. The fire control solution could be better and the main target have less time to react once the weapon is running. It would certainly be the best way of tackling a large convoy, spread out in an anti-nuclear formation.

However, if one very distinct sonar contact is held, representing an important but heavily defended warship unit, it may be preferable to fire from well outside the escorting ships and rely on a carefully guided, long range, fast running torpedo, or the kill radius of nuclear warheads, which make very precise fire control solutions less necessary.

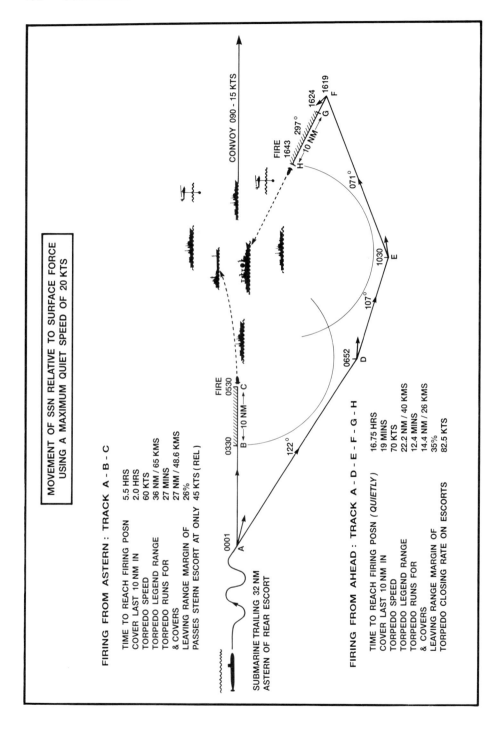

FIG. 9.24   Running into position for a torpedo attack

MOVEMENT OF SSN RELATIVE TO SURFACE FORCE
USING A MAXIMUM QUIET SPEED OF 20 KTS

CONVOY 090 - 15 KTS

FIRE
1643

297°

1624
1619
F

G

H ← 10 NM →

071°

1030
E

107°

0652
D

122°

FIRE
0530
0330

B ← 10 NM → C

0001

A

SUBMARINE TRAILING 32 NM
ASTERN OF REAR ESCORT

FIRING FROM ASTERN : TRACK A - B - C

TIME TO REACH FIRING POSN	5.5 HRS
COVER LAST 10 NM IN	2.0 HRS
TORPEDO SPEED	60 KTS
TORPEDO LEGEND RANGE	36 NM / 65 KMS
TORPEDO RUNS FOR	27 MINS
& COVERS	27 NM / 48.6 KMS
LEAVING RANGE MARGIN OF	26%
PASSES STERN ESCORT AT ONLY 45 KTS (REL)	

FIRING FROM AHEAD : TRACK A - D - E - F - G - H

TIME TO REACH FIRING POSN (QUIETLY)	16.75 HRS
COVER LAST 10 NM IN	19 MINS
TORPEDO SPEED	70 KTS
TORPEDO LEGEND RANGE	22.2 NM / 40 KMS
TORPEDO RUNS FOR	12.4 MINS
& COVERS	14.4 NM / 26 KMS
LEAVING RANGE MARGIN OF	35%
TORPEDO CLOSING RATE ON ESCORTS	82.5 KTS

Attacking a Submarine

Attacks on another submarine must always be regarded as a race against time, with victory going to the boat which detects first, identifies first, solves the TMA problem first, fires first, conceals the moment of fire best, and uses the most effective weapon.

One way to get off the first shot is to launch a fire and forget, rocket delivered NDB, using US SUBROC or Russian Starfish, before the enemy is close enough to fire any sort of torpedoes. However, when these weapons are fired at their extreme ranges, it is difficult to get an accurate enough forecast of present and future enemy position, except when the other submarine is making a fast and noisy run. On the other hand, if fire is delayed until TMA can be refined with a bottom bounce range, (see Figure 8.11), the weapon launch may be detected, and use of active sonar certainly would be. Both will cause the enemy to start taking evasive action.

Homing torpedo payloads on the rockets, as in the US Sea Lance or Russian Stallion, will allow for rather more error in calculation of enemy present and future position. However, the weapons are potentially being fired over much greater distances, especially Sea Lance, again raising the probability and degree of error.

Moment to fire   Wire guided homing torpedoes can be fired as soon as the enemy is within weapon running range on calculated intercept course and should be fired as soon as possible after that. However, to reduce interference on sonar, they may have to be stepped to one side after launch and only brought back towards the target bearing when they have run some distance. Allowance must also be made, when firing from abaft the beam, for having underestimated target speed and for the possibility that the target will, at some point during weapon run, wake up to what is happening and put the torpedo into a stern chase, which means overtaking an enemy going at maximum speed before torpedo fuel is exhausted. Scope is also needed for a re-attack, if the first pass by the weapon misses. All these requirements add to the distance through the water which the torpedo may have to travel, and therefore are possible deductions from its ***legend range*** when considering the target range at which to open fire. That said, one must not over provide for all possibilities, or the enemy will fire first. (Figure 9.25)

Number of Weapons to Fire

Missiles   Assuming all have similar terminal homing systems and the target ship has deployed no counter-measures at the time, if the first missile of a stream salvo locks on, the chances of it hitting are better than 90 per cent. If it misses, the chances of the second missile hitting are still around 70 per cent, whatever the enemy has done meanwhile. By the time number three arrives, it has rather less than a 50 per cent chance, and a fourth only about 20 per cent unless the earlier missiles have already seriously reduced the target's defensive capability. If several hits are needed, or target ECM capability is high, or AEW aircraft are present, then a variety of terminal homing methods must be used to

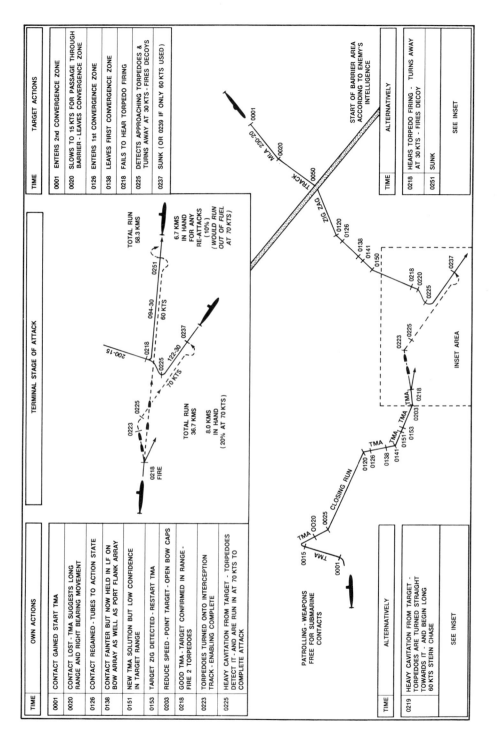

FIG. 9.25   Anti-submarine attack

ensure getting through the defences. When one hit will do, it is probably best to make a number of two-missile attacks, inserting dog-legs, as already described, if the enemy's position is accurately known.

Torpedoes   Firing against surface ships in the days before homing weapons, the number of torpedoes used depended first on how many hits were needed to sink the ship and secondly on the number of extra ones needed to spread the salvo, so that it covered possible inaccuracies in estimating enemy course and speed. One hit was considered enough for a merchant ship or destroyer, two for a cruiser and a battleship needed as many as possible. Even allowing for the slightly smaller warheads in modern torpedoes, two hits are almost certainly enough for most ships around today. And since only those aimed to hit need be fired, when using homing torpedoes, a salvo of two is probably the best number. It also makes allowance for a single weapon malfunction. For the same reason, it is best to fire two torpedoes at a submarine target.

Assuming the Action State

To bring any launch system to the action state, space round the weapons is pumped up with water from a special tank, unless tubes are already flooded. Then pressure between tube and sea outside is equalised. Bow caps and front doors cannot be opened until this has been done. Weapons interface units must also be connected to the selected tube either by an order from a combat centre console or a local control panel. (Figures 9.26, 9.27 and 9.28)

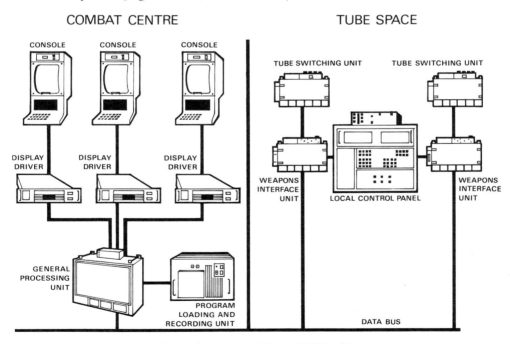

FIG. 9.26   Submarine Command System DCH architecture

Fig. 9.27   Two of the three DCH consoles in HMS *Opossum* (*Photo: Ferranti International*)

Tubes must be brought to the action state at the very beginning of an incident. It ensures being ready first, allows more time for any weapon preparation, and completes noisy activities whilst still at long range. But there are arguments for a delayed opening of bow caps. In many boats, once open, they increase water flow noise near bow arrays. And poor sonar contact hampers the TMA process. Moreover, whilst bowcaps are open, warheads on weapons are more vulnerable to counter mining by enemy ordnance, thus effectively increasing kill radius for badly aimed, NDB tipped enemy rockets. Conversely, a loud transient noise when opening bow caps and shutters with full hydraulic pressure just before firing will be a dead give-away to an alert enemy. (Figures 9.29 and 9.30)

In snap attacks, responding to enemy fire, quietness is less important, and two flooded tubes can be made ready in under a minute.

Launching the Weapons

Most second world war submarines had dual pressure compressed air discharge systems. Discharge pressure was set high enough to squeeze a torpedo out of the tube, and *impulse cut off pressure* was adjusted to ensure that only the torpedo left the submarine and not also a large bubble of air. The system worked well and is

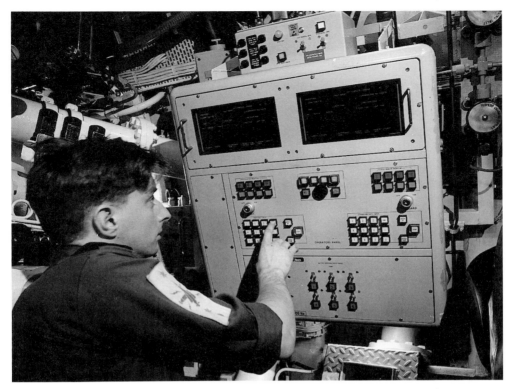

FIG. 9.28 HMS *Opossum*—Local Control Panel (*Photo: Ferranti International*)

still in service in some navies, but it is too noisy for a submarine versus submarine engagement.

Various alternatives have been tried. The US Mk 37 torpedo, now mainly useful as a mobile mine, starts up in the tube and then swims out. Other systems still use a positive discharge, but produced by a slug of water, either rammed into the tube hydraulically, or pumped into it by an ATP (*Air Turbine Pump*). Both are less noisy than putting compressed air directly into the tube. (Figure 9.31)

A positive discharge is important because, in a dog fight situation, one may have to fire whilst manoeuvring at speed with large amounts of rudder applied. Thus, the heart of an ATP system, is the PFV (*Programmable Firing Valve*). Control circuitry is programmed with weapon type and can sense a submarine's speed and attitude. It opens the PFV, delivering just enough energy to the pump to get the weapon clear of the boat, whilst keeping noise to a minimum.

Firing any weapon causes an imbalance in submarine trim, only partially offset by replacing it with a tube full of sea water. Therefore, all discharge systems have to include means for compensating for any net loss of weight. For example, when standard British torpedoes are fired from a 533 mm torpedo tube, an AIV (*Automatic Inboard Venting*) system on the tube remains open long enough, after the tube has refilled with water, to allow an extra 350 litres to flood into a special AIV tank.

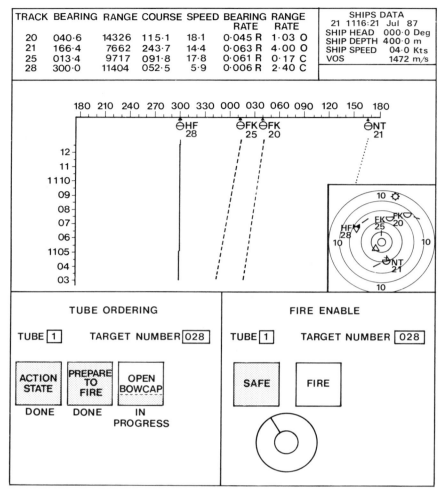

TRACK	BEARING	RANGE	COURSE	SPEED	BEARING RATE	RANGE RATE
20	040·6	14326	115·1	18·1	0·045 R	1·03 O
21	166·4	7662	243·7	14·4	0·063 R	4·00 O
25	013·4	9717	091·8	17·8	0·061 R	0·17 C
28	300·0	11404	052·5	5·9	0·006 R	2·40 C

SHIPS DATA
21 1116:21 Jul 87
SHIP HEAD   000·0 Deg
SHIP DEPTH 400·0 m
SHIP SPEED   04·0 Kts
VOS   1472 m/s

FIG. 9.29   DCH console—opening No. 1 bowcap. All data remain visible

SUMMARY

Submarines use five types of weapon. New since the Second World War is the air breathing missile, used for quick reaction, highly damaging, long range attacks on ships, and popular with nations who only have SSs, because it helps overcome the problem of limiting lines of submerged approach. It can be fired from sub surface, has very intelligent homing systems, and a land attack version can precisely destroy a parked aircraft 2,500 kilometres away.

Most traditional and most versatile is the torpedo. All submarines carry it for their own protection. It is now capable of engaging either submarines or surface ships at 65 kilometres after a 60 knot approach and a highly intelligent attack. It has a brain of enormous processing power and is the best weapon to use to sink a ship.

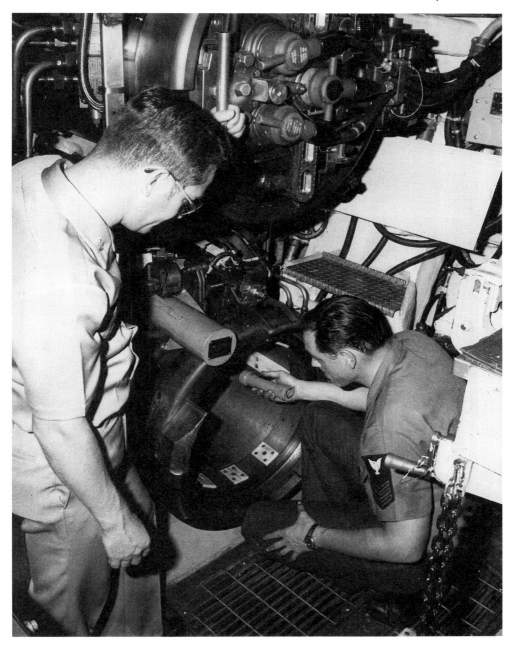

Fɪɢ. 9.30   USS *Los Angeles* (SSN 688). Torpedo tube rear doors, showing cable
connections (*Photo: US Navy*)

Bow cap

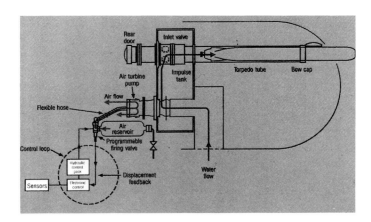

Weir's R.T.P. Pump

Programmable firing valve

FIG. 9.31   ATP discharge system (*Strachan & Henshaw*)

Rockets also are carried for use against other submarines. Originally, they delivered only a nuclear payload and were noisy. New versions are quieter in their launch and will take a homing torpedo to 1,930 kilometres, to exploit very long range sonar detections, but they still need a good datum position at which to aim.

Submarines can also be used to lay moored, tethered or ground mines, some capable of recognising individual ship signatures and others of laying in up to 2,000 metres of water. The laying operation does not require a special submarine but it does require practice, especially ground mine laying in shallow water. Finally, a special SSBN type submarine can carry the nation's strategic deterrent ballistic missiles and threaten to deliver an elusive collection of re-entry vehicles to ranges up to 12,000 kilometres.

Before any of the weapons are deployed, the command has a great deal to do. Attacking a surface ship, there is the need to achieve the optimum firing position. Attacking another submarine, there is the race against time. Always, there is the need to be sure that one is within range and that one is using the best tool for the job. Above all, when waiting for a change of ROE, or when using data from friendly forces, one must have good communications.

10
Communications

Submarine operations have always been critically dependent on reliable, secure, but slow, one way communications, for transmission of orders and information to boats at sea. Today, to take advantage of SSN rapid movement capability, they also need to be fast and sometimes two way. The role dictates which is used but both require good organisation and strict monitoring by whoever has OPCON (***Operational Control***). Usually, this is a shore based authority, (Flag Officer Submarines in the UK), but OPCON can be transferred to the senior officer of a seagoing force, with whom SSNs are cooperating, provided that his staff have been augmented with a submarine commanding officer to act as SEC (***Submarine Element Coordinator***).

DEPLOYMENT PATTERNS

Moving a large number of slow, diesel powered SSs to and from fixed patrol areas, with no mutual interference, nor cramping of surface and air operations, is a tricky water space management problem. It can be controlled with one way signal traffic, but only if a comprehensive initial deployment plan is drawn up, which will swing into action with minimal chatter. The plan must include a matrix of allocated patrol areas, transit routes to reach them and static ***safe havens*** where submarines can pause for a major hitch during deployment, without holding up other boats coming out behind them. En route, submarines must be assumed to be going at the routed speed quoted in their ***Submove*** signals and need ***moving havens*** established around them. (Figure 10.1)

A one way communication system is also used for SSBNs, who never transmit once on deterrent patrol, and is quite adequate to control SSNs in fixed areas. However, SSNs on offensive sea control operations, released from such areas to intercept or pursue specific enemy units, can cause problems. They need early clearance to use the water ahead of them, but their future position, now partly dependent on enemy movement, becomes less predictable. Nor can their protective moving havens be expanded unduly to cover this uncertainty, or large 'no go, weapons tight' areas will be created for one's own forces.

To strike the right balance between these imperatives, those controlling surface, ASW air and submarine units need to be in close touch, preferably collocated as they are at UK Fleet Headquarters Northwood. With good liaison and imaginative forward thinking, an SSN can be signalled its assumed location, about which it can stay silent if correct. Even then, pressure will grow for

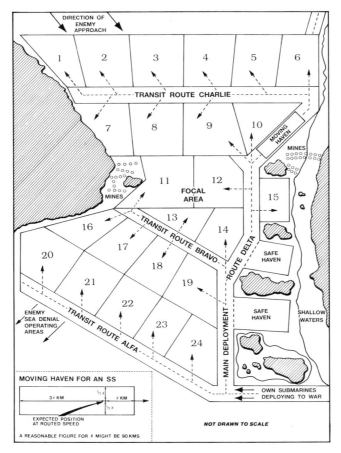

FIG. 10.1   A simple deployment matrix, showing use of transit routes and havens

submarines to report their positions positively, and either method eventually may oblige an SSN to transmit.

ONE WAY SYSTEMS

The heart of any one way communication system is a radio shore-to-submarine broadcast, keyed from the Submarine Headquarters, using digital and/or teletype multiplex signals. Primary transmission is normally at frequencies in the VLF band, (See Table 10.1), which can be received underwater by aerials at depths down to about 20 metres. Being a ground wave system, it does not use ionospheric reflection, so coverage is total out to the maximum range, which depends on radiated power. Early stations achieved 3000 kilometres with about 20 kilowatts. Those built in the 1980s radiate more than 600 kilowatts, to achieve substantially greater coverage.

Although the best available, VLF is not a perfect system. Shore stations have much above ground equipment, all vulnerable to pre-emptive attack, including

350 metre high aerials in some modern installations. Moreover, they are few in number and many have to go off the air completely for maintenance, which is clearly undesirable. Submarines almost always have to do something operationally limiting to read the broadcast: reduce speed, come shallow or steer certain courses. Transmission is restricted to relatively slow speeds, it does not always work very well through ice, and large areas of the world remain totally uncovered by VLF. These problems have produced many technical responses, some more successful than others. (Figure 10.2)

Broadcast Station Vulnerability

Credibility of any national strategic deterrent depends, in part, on convincing potential enemies that one can maintain continuous communication with missile forces. VLF station vulnerability is important mostly, therefore, because SSBNs will be reading the broadcast. Naturally, sensible military precautions must be taken, especially against trained sabotage groups, but one could never guarantee that so fragile an installation had been made immune to unheralded, precision, cruise missile attack, let alone a pre-emptive first strike with nuclear weapons. Instead, the enemy has to be convinced that alternative means of communication exist and will remain effective long enough to initiate a second strike. For example, until 1991 the US demonstrably ensured continuity of command by maintaining a force of aircraft, which trailed wires for VLF transmission. The Russians have several VLF stations, providing redundancy. More important, their SSBNs patrol relatively close to base and could use a back up transmitter working on the LF band, whose ground wave also has some surface penetration over short distances.

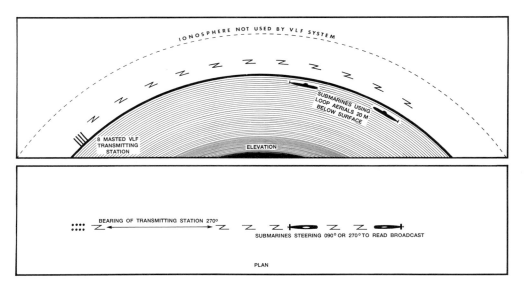

FIG. 10.2   VLF reception

Station Reliability and Efficiency

Modern VLF stations are more efficient, more reliable and can survive slightly better than their predecessors, mainly because they are built on modular lines. Instead of one long aerial, they have up to eight huge self radiating antenna masts, each fed by its own, say 100 kilowatt, transmitter power amplifier, via a dedicated tuning and phase shifting unit, located close to the mast. If transmission frequency is changed, the control system automatically retunes every aerial, and RF signals from all eight points are phased together. This means that the antennae are coupled by radiation, to give a single strong emission. (Figure 10.3)

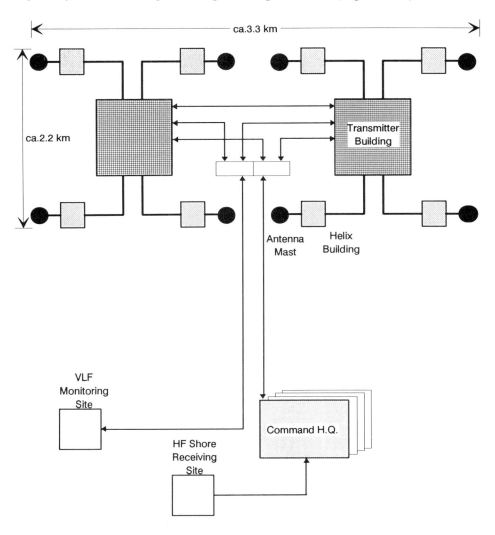

FIG. 10.3   Typical configuration of a VLF transmitter site (*Diagram: Telefunken Systemtechnik GMBH*)

The system is split into two units. Each has four power amplifiers, housed in a transmitter building which can be given some protection, and four associated masts. Any power amplifier can be connected to any antenna within its own unit. Used separately, either unit can handle the full station task, at a reduced radiated power, whilst maintenance, or quite major repair work, is carried out on part of the other unit. This high degree of redundancy, and the proven ability of the masts to withstand very severe weather conditions, gives an almost 100 per cent guarantee that some station capability will always be available.

An essential, and expensive, element in giving a VLF station high efficiency is construction of an underground base counterpoise, usually of copper cables, which extend radially from each mast for several hundred metres and have to be spaced all round it at roughly two degree intervals. Provided this is in place, about 80 per cent of the energy leaving the power amplifiers of a modern station is converted into radiated power, even after losses in the tuning and phase shifting units. Comparable efficiency in older stations would be about 20 per cent.

Another important part of any broadcast station is a monitoring unit, sited at least 50 kilometres clear of the main transmitting installation, from which the quality and field strength of the outgoing signal can be continuously sampled, to ensure that the submarines are receiving the best possible service. (Figure 10.4 a and b)

Submarine Operational Limitations

At the submarine end, two special aerials have reduced the pain of reading VLF broadcasts. Both can be used whilst the boat stays deep, perhaps to hold onto a promising sonar contact below the layer boundary, likely to be lost by going to periscope depth. One is a towed buoyant wire, the other a towed buoy. The aerial part of the wire breaks surface some way astern of the boat, and it can be slightly unnerving to see a line of seagulls standing on it, moving through the water sideways. However, on all but flat calm days it is completely inconspicuous, and gives better reception than fixed loops in the fin, especially at extreme ranges. It can also receive HF. The buoy too has positive buoyancy and is streamed up to just below the surface for VLF reception.[1]

Whilst useful, wires and buoys still impose limitations. Good reception on the wire is often only obtainable on a course close to the bearing of the transmitting station, or its reciprocal. Buoys, even when well shaped for steady towing, are often awkward to get in and out of their housing. So much so, that the Russians have had to fit special, deck level TV monitoring equipment. Both systems tie one to the use of modest speed whilst reading the broadcast, thus losing ground when trailing an enemy unit. It would be preferable also if both could be streamed from much deeper than at present but lengthening the towing wire is not a simple matter. Reels are limited to the size which will fit in the casing space, because it is highly undesirable to bring the wire through a hull gland. The only alternative, of making the wire thinner, reduces towing strength, hence speed, and produces an increase in noise signature, due to the thrumming of a thin wire. (Figure 10.5)

Fig. 10.4   a. The Antenna Tuning Elements (*left to right*): Switchable Helix Coil, Main Variometer and Coupling Variometer.   b. A single antenna compared with the tower of Ulm Cathedral (*Both Photos: Telefunken Systemtechnik*)

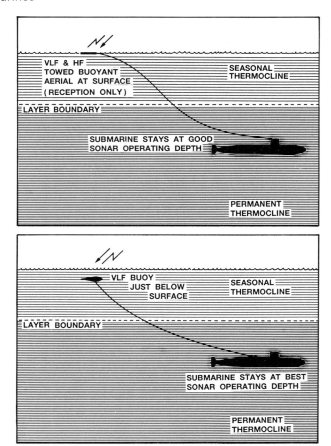

FIG. 10.5   Towed wires and buoys

Speed of transmission

The narrow bandwidth available at VLF frequencies makes the system inherently slow. So, although telegraphic message speeds have been raised from 75 to about 200 baud (bits per second), by increasing the number of channels on carrier frequencies, maximum VLF broadcast capacity has probably now been reached. However, the other one way systems examined below, either involve exposing a mast, or are even slower, ensuring the continued popularity of VLF.[2]

OUTSIDE VLF COVERAGE

In the many parts of the world still not covered by VLF, an HF or LF broadcast is used, though the information carried is now usually made available simultaneously, via satellite, on UHF and SHF. Satcoms are discussed more fully under two way communications, but here we need to note that they can only be received via an exposed aerial, on a whip or mast. This means coming to periscope depth

TABLE 10.1

Frequency Bands

Named	Frequency Band	Translation
EHF	30–300 GHz	Extremely High
SHF	3–30 GHz	Super High[3]
UHF	0.3–3 GHz	Ultra High
VHF	30–300 MHz	Very High
HF	3–30 MHz	High Frequency
MF	300–3000 kHz	Medium
LF	30–300 kHz	Low Frequency
VLF	3–30 kHz	Very Low
ELF	0.3–3kHz	Extremely Low

and risking airborne detection in good weather, albeit the hazard is reduced if receiver aerials are built into optical sensors and/or a main tactical mast, as we saw in Chapter 6.

ELF

In recent years, both the USA and Russia have set up stations for broadcasting on ELF, to back up their VLF systems. Finding a good location is not easy. The underlying ground forms part of the transmitting circuit and must be of geologically suitable rock. The above ground part of the circuit has to be many kilometres in length, to match the wavelength of emitted signals, and is unlikely to be a welcome newcomer in inhabited areas. The whole undertaking is vastly expensive, like so many communications projects, and the end result is a transmitted data rate of only a few bits per minute.

Despite all these objections, ELF is well worth the outlay. Its data speeds are quite adequate to send an executive signal for some action previously agreed, and it can always be used as a bell ringer, to call submarines shallow to read another broadcast. Meanwhile it confers much improved dependability. The wire/earth circuit produces an exceptionally strong ground wave signal which travels great distances. Unlike VLF, it is almost impervious to other electromagnetic activity, whether produced by the enemy or nature, and reliably penetrates ice. Moreover, it can be received much further below the surface, which allows submarines, particularly SSBNs, to stay deep at times of high political risk. It also helps anticipate a little, any improved capability to detect boats patrolling at shallower depths, perhaps by one of the non sonar methods discussed in Chapter 12. (Figure 10.6)

Broadcast Organisation

Since reading a broadcast so often imposes operational penalties on a submarine, messages must be vetted ruthlessly for relevance by the Submarine Headquarters Broadcast Controller, to minimise traffic volume. Those not sent may have to be held for some time, and long admin signals may be made 'basegrams' for receipt on return to harbour. Vetting is best done by another

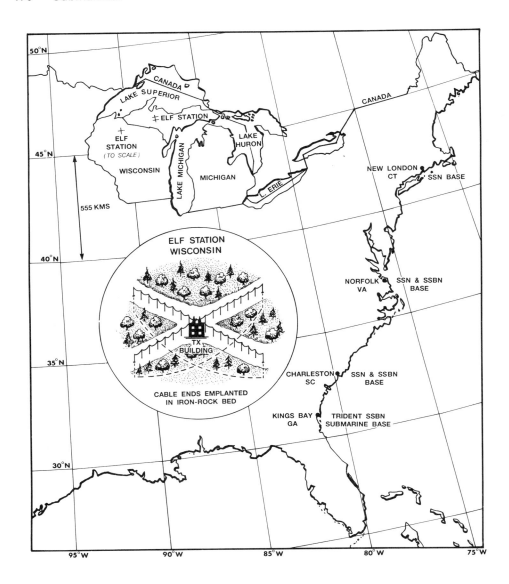

Fig. 10.6 ELF

submarine commanding officer, who will recognise rubbish instantly, and fully appreciate the significance of not receiving those messages delayed or treated as irrelevant.

Once released for transmission by the controller, messages are given a serial number and sent in batches at set times, known as 'routines' or 'schedules'. If very important, they will also be sent 'out of routine' as soon as received in the headquarters, against the possibility that the submarine is already shallow. All messages are then retransmitted on an agreed minimum number of succeeding routines. Vital messages, such as ordered changes of rules of engagement, may be made the subject of a separate series and sent out many more times.

All this retransmission gives one wide latitude, over when traffic is received. For example, SSNs instructed to read only the vital message series may not need to come shallow more than once a day, a great help, operationally, when deploying at high speed to a distant area. Time wastage is also reduced by starting every broadcast routine with a traffic list, that gives the numbers of new and old messages about to be sent, from which submarines can quickly see if they need to stay shallow.

The system is well proven in war but it does have a penalty. The larger the number of re-runs allowed, the greater the uncertainty over message receipt time. Ashore, it has to be assumed every one is read on its last re-run, because acting on any other assumption might put two boats in the same water. Therefore, it is still difficult to redispose submarines in a hurry, even in an age when they can be routed at high speeds.

TWO WAY COMMUNICATIONS

Submarines sending traffic to shore, normally use a channel of communications on which two way working occurs. Minimally, it means the authority first contacted by radio acknowledging safe receipt of the submarine message. When cooperating with an aircraft or surface force, much longer two way communication may be needed, particularly at the time of weapon release, as was shown in Chapter 9.

Exceptionally, submarines may broadcast pre-programmed messages, using an expendable radio buoy, which can be sent up to the surface whilst the submarine remains deep. Though useful, it is not an ideal method. The number of buoys carried is limited and the authority addressed has to arrange for a message receipt to be sent on the submarine VLF broadcast. Where the addressee is afloat and trying to maintain a tight radio emission policy, this can be an embarrassing requirement. (Figure 10.7)

DECIDING TO TRANSMIT

A modern international crisis can produce a complex and fast moving political scene, sometimes with uncertainties even regarding who is fighting who. And timing may be everything. Any SSN involved in managing such a crisis must be under very positive control, and inescapably this means rapid and frequent two way communications, to keep abreast of events. Moreover, the SSN may well have to ask permission to engage—as HMS *Conqueror* did in 1982.

In war too, there may be problems regarding neutrality status of certain nations, but enemy identity is usually clear cut. Then, boats only transmit in situations where it is obligatory, or when possible operational advantage outweighs risk. Mandatory reasons include the need to report: movement of key enemy units or Task Groups, with any action results; enforced departures from an assigned moving haven, and successful completion of a mine-laying mission. A mining report has to include exact positions for each mine laid, which for good reasons

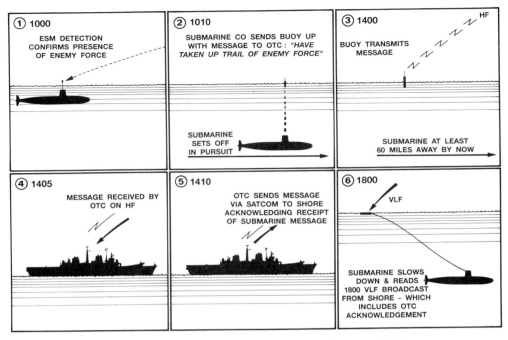

Fig. 10.7   A fairly typical sequence of events when using expendable buoys

are often not the ones envisaged before sailing. It must be sent as soon as clear of the laying area, to ensure that Headquarters have the details before the submarine can become a casualty.

The risks to be considered when transmitting are: mast detection by enemy radar, message decipherment by enemy cryptologists and the fixing of a submarine's position by enemy DF networks. One can never afford to be complacent about any of these dangers. However, much improved ESM warners and adoption of the main tactical mast concept do reduce risk of mast detection to quite an acceptable level, except perhaps when right on the enemy's doorstep. Modern machine ciphers and wider use of on-line cryptographic techniques have also largely stopped decipherment, which so fatally compromised German U-boat operations for much of the Second World War. But DF, another major cause of their undoing, is still a problem, particularly for navies who continue to make heavy use of HF transmissions, which an intercept network now virtually never misses.

SATELLITE COMMUNICATIONS

The best way to send messages in the 1990s is by SATCOM (*Satellite Communications*) using UHF or SHF. It means coming to periscope depth and exposing a mast mounted conical spiral antenna, but simultaneous, two way business is conducted at data handling speeds. Indeed, data itself could be sent, on EHF, using a dish aerial, a mast need identified in Chapter 6.

A good worldwide system can be built with four or five satellites held in geostationary orbits, whose combined 'footprints' will cover most places between latitudes 70 degrees N and 70 degrees S. NATO submarines depend largely on US FLTSATCOM (*Fleet Satellite Communications*), which is such a system. The United States own most NATO satellites and run the allocation of FLTSATCOM channels. One of these is permanently dedicated to SSIXS (*Submarine Satellite Information Exchange System*)—which will also broadcast non-US NATO submarine traffic.

The messages go to the satellite via an up-link and are stored in priority order. Like VLF traffic, they are then broadcast at set times, but the boat can also interrogate the satellite. Often, in seconds, all outstanding broadcast traffic is requested and received out of routine; a couple of messages are transmitted; Shore Headquarters, or the OTC afloat, is given an updated position, and maybe even persuaded to alter the moving haven, if duty officers are alert; and the submarine is heading back down to her best operating depth. (Figure 10.8)

Such flexibility is excellent. SATCOM also provides one of the most secure means of sending a message from the submarine. Not only does it enjoy on-line cryptographic protection but, usually, it can only be intercepted by a third party who is situated close to the line of sight between the two communicating units.

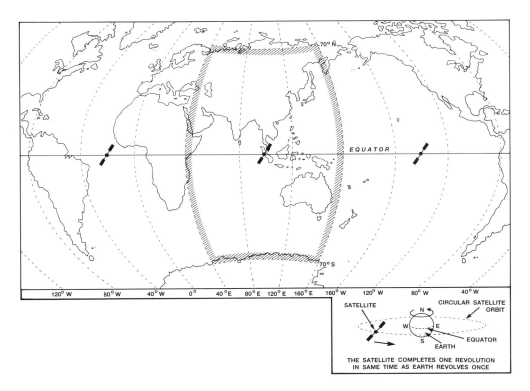

FIG. 10.8   Footprint of a single satellite placed over Sumatra (The world can almost be covered by three 'birds' but, in practice, a fourth is needed and one must have some redundancy)

The one worry is the thought that satellites have been known to break down, cannot be replaced in a hurry and, in a major war, could be removed by enemy action. Therefore, they are not entirely reliable and one must have alternative channels of communication available.

USING HF

The normal back up for SATCOM, and the only form of submarine-to-shore communication for many navies is HF, which has to be made to work as well as possible. For example, short range DF risk can be reduced by giving expendable buoys the ability, when necessary, to delay the start of their transmission for several hours. This is a great help to an SSN able to distance itself from the launch position at a quiet speed of 15 knots or more.

Most of the problems suffered by HF, including its vulnerability to D/F, are due to use of sky wave reflected off the ionosphere. If this hops several times, it may be received almost anywhere, though not necessarily where most required. Conversely, there are areas in the world, often a long way from base, from which it is notoriously difficult to establish HF communications with anybody. The effects may be seasonal and it is always important to be using the right frequency for the time of day; not only to have the best chance of gaining contact but also to avoid making transmissions which could still give bearing lines to an enemy, with no possible compensating gain to us.

The HF propagation problem is compounded in submarines by relatively low power transmitters and the sea level sited aerials. These combine to produce a rather fainter signal than can be expected from a surface ship. Unless warned that there is some submarine emergency in progress, shore stations tend to set the receiver gain to accommodate the average incoming signal level. Often, this will barely be high enough to pick up an SS on its calling frequency. The problem, mainly a training one, existed even when the United Kingdom had a global system of radio stations. Now, no nation has a really good, worldwide HF network entirely under its own military control.

When finally, an HF signal is received ashore, it has to be re-routed to its destination, using fixed service communication links. This adds to delay. Moreover, the number of powerful fixed link stations, has also shrunk over the last thirty years, reducing the reliability of any service which had to be continued from places far afield after a removal of all satellites. Yet, despite these many shortcomings, submarines may have to use HF. So all nations are fitting it in their new boats.

Most submarines also have at least two HF aerials, and no longer need a portable spare. The important drill of rigging emergency aerials has by no means died, however, because an emergency SATCOM aerial could be badly needed if the top of the HF mast is damaged. (Figure 10.9)

AVOIDING THE USE OF HF

Boats involved in SUBAIR cooperation, during offensive sea control operations, have always had the option of sending their traffic for shore on UHF to the friendly aircraft; which then, either retransmits the traffic on HF when well clear

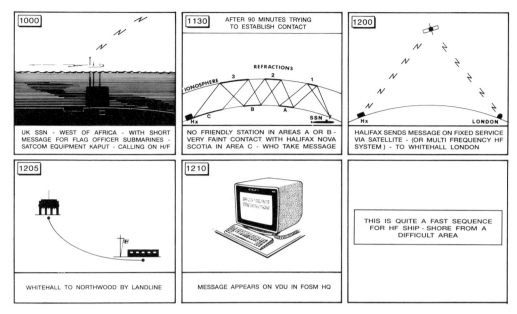

FIG. 10.9   HF ship-shore

of the submarine position, or holds it until arrival at base. Both provide more security than use of HF by the submarine and should be used if available.

USE OF NON RADIO METHODS

We have already discussed, in Chapter 8, the use of sound underwater for communicating between two vessels at sea, using underwater telephones. Sound can also be used, in a crude way, to send a message to shore. To work, the boat must be in an ocean area covered by friendly monitoring, either SOSUS or TASS (**_Towed Array Surveillance Systems_**). Then, when the shore headquarters wishes a submarine, usually an SSN operating outside fixed areas, to acknowledge receipt of a message, or to indicate its location, it orders it to 'Rumble' at a given time. When this moment arrives, the submarine will deliberately cavitate for a very short spell, giving the alerted intercept stations the required information. Clearly, there is some risk of an unalerted enemy also noticing cavitation; but in an SSN trailing a high speed enemy at extreme sonar detection range, this may be less worrying than the many penalties of using an HF, or any other, radio frequency band. (Figure 10.10)

CHANGING ROLE OF THE OPERATOR

In the 1950s: senior radio operators had to be able to retune the HF transmitter, which lived in a cage at the back of the tiny radio room; all operators sent and received hand keyed Morse at an impressive rate, requiring much training to achieve; and off line encipherment of individual messages, by methods like

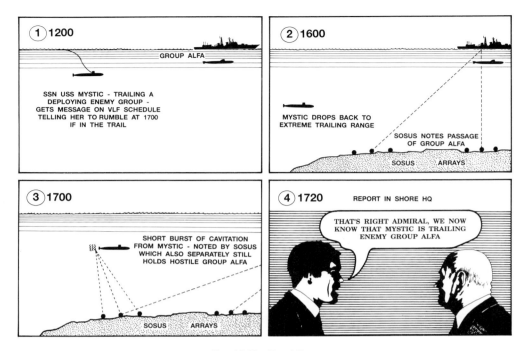

FIG. 10.10   Rumbling

double subtraction frame, was often laborious and complicated enough to need the attentions of two off watch officers.

The advance of technology has simplified every aspect of this scene. HF transmitters now have automatic tuning and the whole HF circuit is protected by EDC (**_Error Detection and Correction_**) equipment, as are SATCOMS. Encrypted broadcast messages, whether received through a SATCOM transceiver, or the towed buoy, are automatically machine decoded and then spewed out as read-able plain language text by teletype machines. Tending several of these machines whilst continuously monitoring a multi-channel broadcast in an SSBN is a busy and very important task—the next message might be the alert signal—but it no longer needs a telegraphist. However, operators are still taught to touch-type, a useful ability when preparing outgoing messages, ready for transmission. They can be seen practising their skills in the spacious radio room of USS _John C Calhoun_ (SSBN 630), though they would be more likely to use them in an SSN.[4] (Figure 10.11)

Officers still train in cryptography, to break down messages internally coded, using off-line systems, to ensure that their text is given a very narrow distribution onboard, perhaps because they concern some family mishap. Operator training is still needed, to set up encode/decode machines correctly, to carry out the right procedures with satcom or HF, and often to do first line maintenance on the equipment. Also to perform many old tasks which have not changed, such as careful updating of communication publications. Nevertheless, there has been

Fɪɢ. 10.11   The spacious radio room of USS *John C Calhoun* (SSBN 630)
(*Photo: YOGI INC 1987*)

a marked and welcome reduction in the overall time it takes to train submarine personnel for communication tasks.

SUMMARY

Roles dictate whether communications remain one way or must include two way working. Both need good organisation and imaginative control by officers with submarine command experience. Continuous one way only is the rule for SSBNs, intermittently read one way the pattern for SSs, who break silence only to make important reports.

The SSN ability to move at high submerged speeds and work with other units poses a water space management and coordination problem that often forces a reluctant use of two way working. It is not a new problem. German U-boats ranging widely, on the surface, during the Second World War were controlled with two way communications, and paid heavily for reporting their positions on HF.

SATCOMS have made two way working a lot more secure and enable broadcast messages to be read at data handling speeds. However, satellite vulnerability and the need to be able to read broadcasts whilst totally submerged mean that both VLF and HF remain important, irrespective of the shortcomings of the latter, only partially eased by having expendable buoys.

VLF broadcasting is still the heart of the system, despite US and Russian introduction of ELF, to provide greater dependability and a deeper patrol capability, mainly for their SSBNs. Modular and unitised construction of 1990s VLF stations has made them efficient, reliable, and more survivable, if only due to better redundancy. Raising radiated power has increased range, putting in multiplex system keying has probably taken transmission speeds as high as they can be lifted, and it is difficult to see how the operator task could be made much easier.

However, more high power VLF stations are needed to increase world coverage, and there is room for improving the system operationally at the submarine end. A start has been made with towed buoys and wires; but it is not satisfactory that delays in receiving vital information from shore can still only be avoided by accepting speed, depth and course limitations.

Encouragingly, submarine communications development represents a much higher proportion of the total British naval communications budget than it used to ten years ago. This reflects the vast potential of SSNs, and the need for tight control of them in modern geopolitical conditions. Whenever submarine admirals and their staffs meet to confer, this subject is now always very near the top of the agenda. Indeed, communications is *the* growth area for submarines.

11
Navigation

Submarine navigation should be sound, safe, accurate and covert. Advancing technology has made a slightly mixed contribution towards promoting these aims. Introduction over the last forty years of inertial systems and a wide range of electronic 'navaids' has certainly done much to promote greater accuracy. Supply of bottom contour maps, drawn up with their special requirements in mind, has also enabled submarines to navigate more discreetly—in the areas covered. However, the huge endurance of SSNs encourages operating authorities to send them much further afield. Often, this means deployment into areas still not very well charted, even for surface ship navigation. Moreover, large hulls and high submarine speeds can greatly increase the severity of damage following a navigational failure. Therefore, the need to adopt sound practices, to use commonsense, and above all, for the commanding officer to give navigation his close personal attention, is as great as ever.

SOUND PLANNING

Sound navigation seeks to forestall the appearance of unknown dangers. It begins with a good operational plan, prepared with great care by the submarine operating authority. This is then treated with total scepticism by the submarine, who assume it has been put together by an idiot, and therefore needs checking from end to end, well before leaving harbour. Normally, nothing is wrong but misprints can occur and possible hazards have sometimes been forgotten. For instance, in 1973 HMS *Conqueror*'s orders for a Fleet exercise included instructions to patrol dived in an area close to the Bonifacio Straits between Sardinia and Corsica. The exercise planners had overlooked that this area, in which several British boats had been lost during the war, was still classified in Notices to Mariners as an uncleared deep minefield. Fortunately, the commanding officer remembered this warning. In all matters of submarine safety, the gods look after those who look after themselves.

In an earlier era, whilst carrying out one of the first submarine versus submarine exercises, HMS *Acheron* was less lucky. Proceeding as ordered, about 50 metres deep, she suddenly hit a granite pinnacle. At five knots, no great damage was done, but at SSN speeds it could have been a disaster. There was no sounding on the chart anywhere near shallow enough to account for the grounding, but the planners were at fault nonetheless. They had set the exercise west of the Hebrides in an area which was not regularly used by submarines, where soundings of any sort were then rather sparse, and craggy land nearby was clearly warning of an equally spiky sea bed, all good reasons for avoiding it.

In the past, hydrographers did not devote much attention to the bottom, anywhere, if it lay below 100 metres. This thought should certainly make an SSN commanding officer exercise moderation in speed, and come shallow in plenty of time, when approaching groups of islands or a mid ocean ridge. Even around the Azores, an area used by shipping quite regularly, and therefore reasonably well charted, rapid and unexpected shelving conditions have been noted on SSN echo-sounders, in places where there should have been over two thousand metres of water.

SAFE PRACTICES

Safe navigation of any vessel means taking adequate and timely measures to avoid known dangers. In this respect, a submarine is no different to other craft. Operational and navigational hazards are plotted on the chart, highlighted and given a wide berth. However, there are some risks which apply only to submarines, mainly due to their ability to pass under other vessels as well as round them. For example, commanding officers always have in mind a keel depth to which they are going to take the submarine if suddenly faced with a possible collision whilst at periscope depth. Small SSs in the 1950s were taken to 25 metres. Today, when very large submarines can meet ships of up to 500,000 DWT with a draught of 29 metres, one must go to about 50 metres, and do so earlier.

It is the advent of these very large ships, as much as the need to provide the safe operating envelope mentioned in Chapter 4, which makes it unwise to take big submarines regularly through shallow areas. Of course, home waters may be navigated submerged, with care, by SSBNs and SSNs making discreet departures, if the submarine base has been suitably located. Leaving the Clyde, one can dive once past the Cumbraes, thus avoiding the ubiquitous peacetime AGIs (*Intelligence Collecting Ships*) which remain outside the three mile limit off Northern Ireland.

Another hazard of operating in inshore waters is the trawler. Apart from expensive legal claims, not too much damage resulted to either party from encounters between small, slow SSs and fishing vessels who could easily cut free their gear. The situation is now much more serious. Higher speeds are used and trawl lines are as strong as tug-ropes. In November 1990, when HMS *Trenchant* snagged the trawler *Antares*, within seconds, she was on her side, and still attached to her gear when pulled under, just as *girding* can occur if a large surface ship starts towing its tug. In the open sea, submarines always should, and usually do, shape a course to avoid passing directly beneath any vessel with the noise signature of a trawler. When using ranges in confined waters, there may be little room to take such avoiding action. Then, the only sensible course is to slow right down, before getting to the CPA (*Closest Point of Approach*).

In the longer term, trawlers ought to be fitted with a distinctive underwater noisemaker, especially when fishing water clearly marked on the charts as submarine exercise areas. Such a bleeper would also be useful on oil rigs planted in regularly used submarine transit routes.

ACCURATE MEASUREMENT

Navigation is never 100 per cent accurate, no matter which method is used. It is not a question of preventing error from occurring, therefore, so much as recognising its likely nature, measuring it carefully whenever possible, and thereafter making allowance for it. An extreme example might be the moment in very high latitudes, during HMS *Dreadnought*'s 1971 North Pole trip, when her commanding officer wanted to know the ship's heading. At the time, one compass was showing west, another north and a third east. With only a small pause, the navigating officer confidently said: 'South Sir!' Making allowances for their differing rates of precession, which he had been monitoring, they were indeed all indicating that the ship was steering south. A well organised officer.

Some error occurs when taking observations, or 'fixing' as it is usually called, some when producing the DR (***Dead Reckoning***), that is direction and distance run since last fix, and some when adjusting the DR for currents and tidal stream to produce an EP (***Estimated Position***). The longer the interval between fixes, the more serious the effect of errors in deriving and adjusting the DR.

In the 1940s, everything promoted error. Offshore, submarines had to surface to take sun and star sights with a hand held sextant, a difficult enough business from a very low bridge on a rough day, without trying to do it in a hurry. Inshore, available tidal information was only an estimate based on historic data, distance run was measured by a propeller driven log that worked least well at the very slow speeds used in the patrol area, and strength of tidal stream often exceeded submarine speed through the water. Worst of all, in bad weather days might go by between fixes. After 72 hours at three knots, allowing only 5 per cent for errors, a modest figure, the submarine could be nearly 20 kilometres out of position, more if the original fix was suspect. It is against this background that technological achievements of the last half century must be measured.

The Modern Requirement

SSBNs, SSGNs and SSGs all have a need for high accuracy navigation. An SLBM can only follow the right trajectory if accurately programmed with latitude and longitude of target and SSBN at the time of firing. At worst, it will miss by the combined error in these two positions. There is no problem at the target end. Satellite reconnaissance of stationary objects can give coordinates to the nearest second of arc, that is to 30.5 metres. Precision to about 100 metres is indeed required to kill a hardened missile silo, hence the need for in-flight astral observation and adjustment of trajectory in the MARV. (See Table 9.5) Aiming at a city, however, accuracy of about 800 metres would be enough; and maybe twice this figure acceptable, since it is equally disquieting to contemplate an enemy air burst over Trafalgar Square or Victoria Station.

SSGNs and SSGs firing cruise missiles at an enemy unit at sea, must assume that a forecast position of a moving target, given to them by someone else, already contains a fair measure of error. Moreover, the terrain over which the missiles fly is featureless, so they cannot self-correct their programmed flight path. Therefore, it is always wise to fix shortly before firing, minimising DR component, and overall to aim for an own ship error of under 200 metres. In short, SSBN needs forced the fitting of better navigational equipment, but the needs of those launching tactical cruise missiles are now more demanding.

IMPROVED FIXING

Introduction of the following equipment has improved the accuracy of fixing:

- ▶ Periscope sextant
- ▶ MF/DF
- ▶ Hyperbolic Radio NAVAIDS
- ▶ Satellite Transit fixing
- ▶ NAVSTAR Global Positioning System

Periscope Sextant

The sextant is fitted as an integral part of the periscope and embodies a gyro stabilised artificial horizon. This allows a number of separate altitude angles and times to be read off in the comparative peace of the combat centre, whilst the submarine exposes only a single small mast. Readings are averaged and fed into a computer, already loaded with static daily nautical almanac data and a sight reduction programme. Position line details can be available in a few minutes and are capable of giving 800 metres accuracy fixes, provided the submarine is kept head to sea to reduce rolling and the sight taker is in practice.

Too much light is lost in periscopes to take stars, so only sun, moon and bright planets are available. Often, only one such object will be visible. This means taking a Sun-Run-Sun, or other 'running fix', which introduces DR inaccuracy and will not provide an observed position until the second sight has been reduced. These are very real disadvantages, but astro navigation remains paramount amongst the systems available, because it can be used anywhere in the world and all parts of it are either onboard the submarine or far enough out in the Universe to be beyond enemy reach.

Medium Frequency Direction Finding (MF/DF)

The system provides a submarine with bearings of shore stations, from which it can plot two, or sometimes three, position line fixes. MF/DF stations transmit omni-directionally, so a DF intercept aerial is needed. Unlike those from some of the earlier radio navaids, bearings of an MF/DF station are unambiguous and can be taken quite quickly, but their accuracy will not be better than 1 degree, which equates to a nautical mile of error for every sixty from the station. This is reasonable when patrolling just over the horizon from the coast, but when 1080 kilometres offshore, two bearings will produce a 'diamond of uncertainty' whose sides are all 18 kilometres long. In extremis, such a fix may be enough to keep one within the patrol area, whilst waiting for an astral observation, but it is no help to a missile firer. (Figure 11.1)

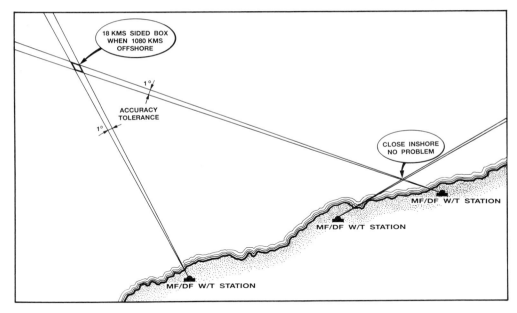

FIG. 11.1   Diamonds of uncertainty

Hyperbolic Radio Navaids

Hyperbolic systems all work on the basis of simultaneous transmissions from two widely spaced stations; a Master and a Slave. By noting which signal is received first, and the time or phase delay, before the other arrives, a system receiver can show that the observer lies on a specific hyperbola, (curved line). Another Master/Slave pair gives a second curved line. Using specially engraved charts, the lines are plotted and the submarine lies somewhere close to where they intersect. Diamonds of uncertainty can be quite small and are less sensitive to range than those produced by MF/DF fixes. (Figure 11.2)

LORAN was the first hyperbolic system to appear. It transmits synchronised pulses and uses time delay. The 1950s version worked at 2 Megahertz, had only limited ground wave cover and a sky wave often badly distorted at night, or when crossing intervening land. LORAN C, the present version, is much better. Lower frequency (100 Kilohertz), more stable signal propagation, and the very precise time measurement of atomic clocks, have combined to produce an accuracy of 400 metres at a distance of well over 2000 kilometres from the stations. This is good enough for use in resetting any DR system. The main shortcoming of LORAN C is that coverage is restricted to the northern hemisphere, and even there gaps exist, notably in the Barents Sea and Arctic Ocean. (Figure 11.3)

DECCA was the first of the hyperbolic systems to work on phase delay. The stations transmit different harmonics of a common frequency as continuous waves, rather than pulsed signals. It is essentially for use inshore, with fixes available 180 kilometres from the stations by night and out to 450 kilometres by day. When best placed between stations, a fixing accuracy of 400 metres is possible. At worst, a

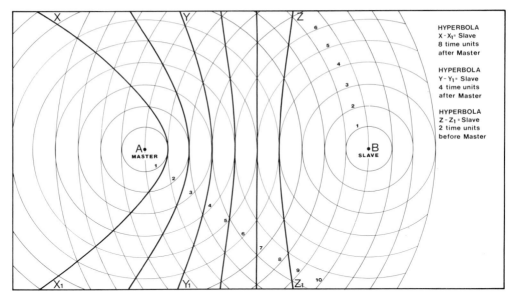

FIG. 11.2   Construction of a hyperbolic fixing chart

DECCA position will not be more than 3.6 kilometres out. It is a good local system, whose only real disadvantage has been the impossibility of making it worldwide. Its very limited spread can be seen from the coverage diagram.

OMEGA, a more recently introduced phase delay system, provides the worldwide service which DECCA cannot. Eight stations spaced round the world, synchronised by atomic clocks, emit simultaneously on VLF frequencies. Like DECCA, the transmission is continuous, not pulsed and the signals are coded to prevent ambiguity. Being VLF, they will penetrate sea water and can be read without raising a mast. Accuracies of 1.8 kilometres by day and 3.6 kilometres by night are achievable when stations lie no more than 3600 kilometres from the submarine. Though these figures are not good enough for missile firers, they are fine for ordinary navigation. The southern hemisphere stations are particularly helpful. The main problem with OMEGA is lack of redundancy. Interdiction or breakdown of one transmitter makes a huge hole in the coverage.

Satellite Transit Fixing

Navigational satellites were first established in the 1960s. The current system, called TRANSIT or SATNAV consists of five satellites in polar orbits, with Earth spinning inside them. The satellites are monitored from ground stations and made to transmit a fixed frequency note and a digital message, detailing any aberrations from their published orbits. The submarine SATNAV receiver notes the aberrations and measures the doppler shift of the received signal, that is the change in frequency from the fixed frequency note. This gives acceleration. Knowing speed and acceleration, the computer can use integral calculus to give distance.

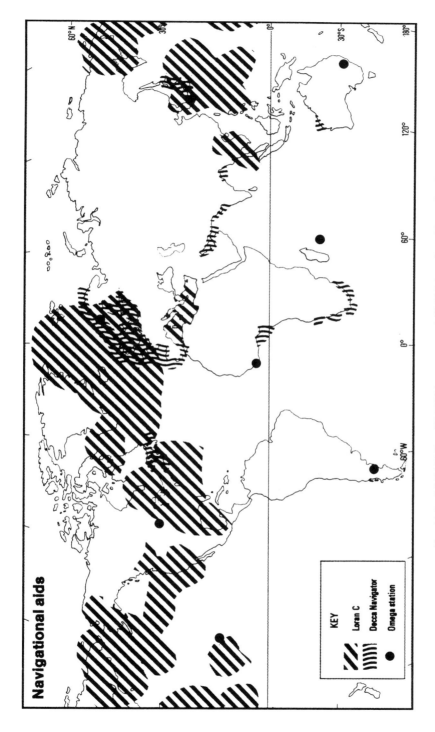

FIG. 11.3 LORAN C and DECCA coverage and OMEGA stations (*Reproduced from the Times Atlas and Encyclopedia of the Sea by kind permission of Times Books, a division of Harper Collins Publishers Ltd*)

The combination of the daily global rotation and the 108 minute orbits of the satellites provides at least four opportunities to fix on each satellite per day. In high latitudes, one can fix every half hour, but at the equator only every three hours, so DR inaccuracy does creep in. It is important also to discount contributions to doppler shift made by the submarine, since two knots of movement along the line of sight will add a kilometre of error to the position. Error can also come from small variations in satellite speed but 800 metres accuracy should always be available.

Apart from requiring more satellites, to shorten time between fixes, the only disadvantages of this very useful system are the need to raise a mast and, as with all satellites, vulnerability to enemy action.

NAVSTAR Global Positioning System (GPS)

The latest Navaid, now entering service, NAVSTAR GPS, uses both satellite and hyperbolic fixing technology. Eighteen transmitting stations circle the earth at a height of over 20,000 kilometres. Their signals are synchronised and their orbits so arranged that three or four of the transmissions are always available to the submarine, no matter where it is on the globe. Having the stations in orbit, creates three dimensional hyperboloids of revolution, in place of the two dimensional hyperbolas of static LORAN or DECCA stations. The onboard receiver, which automatically selects the most favourably placed stations, then has to synchronise its time clock with the satellites and solve three or four simultaneous algebraic equations. Variables in the equations are the two submarine, or three aircraft, position coordinates and a time dependent quantity, which relates the position of the hyperboloids to the spinning earth.

GPS should provide latitude, longitude and height above sea level anywhere on earth, at any time, to an accuracy of 10 to 20 metres, and a relative accuracy ten times better than that. This must make it the ultimate navigational system but its dependence on satellites and the raising of a mast are weaknesses. Moreover, the complexity of the four dimensional problems being solved by its high speed digital computer, make manual checking impossible. It is sensible, therefore, when using this or any other navaid, to know where you ought to be, before asking the system for a position. This is particularly true in submarines, which spend long periods deep. It means keeping a good DR, and checking systems against each other, rather than reading positions off one box on the bulkhead and blithely taking them as gospel. (Figure 11.4)

IMPROVED DEAD RECKONING

Replacement of propeller driven logs by instruments which electrically sense water flow past the vessel has greatly increased accuracy of distance measurement when at slow speeds. Ability to keep a true record whilst manoeuvring has also been improved by applying computer processing to the mass of data from compasses, logs and clocks, which establish direction and speed of movement over time, and thus provide the final position. (Figure 11.5)

Most significant of all contributions to DR accuracy, however, has been the

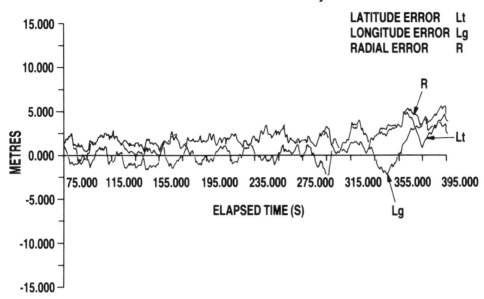

FIG. 11.4   GPS trials results (*Diagram: GEC-PLESSEY Avionics Graphs*)

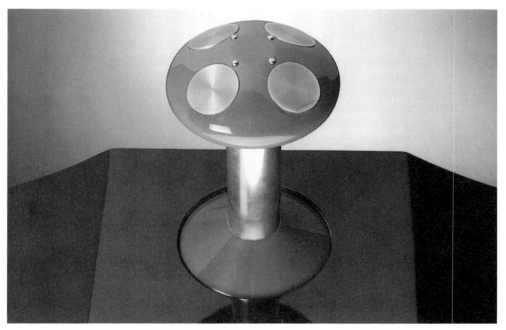

FIG. 11.5   *Aeronautical & General Instruments Ltd* Combined Doppler/Sonar
Electro-magnetic log sensor (*Photo: John Dodds Studios*)

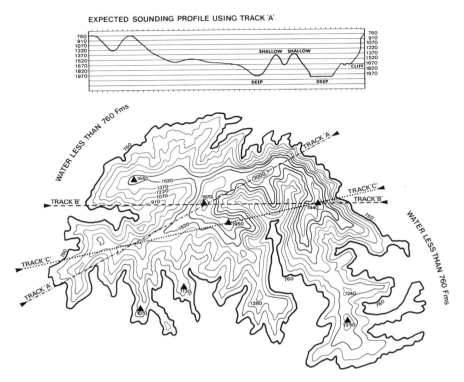

EXPECTED SOUNDING PROFILE USING TRACK 'A'

FIG.11.6   Bottom contour fixing using a typical chart

fitting of SINS (*Ships Inertial Navigation Systems*). The basic SINS component is a weight suspended in gimbals inside a container which is rigidly fixed to the submarine structure. The inertia of the weight tends to maintain it in its original global position but any acceleration applied to the submarine will try to move the container relative to the weight. The effort needed to overcome this relative movement, is measured electrically to give the accelerations along three axes, (north/south, east/west, up/down), which are fixed by gyroscopes. Outputs from the accelerometers, once integrated electronically, give three dimensional movement of the submarine from its original position.

SINS is particularly valuable because it allows for movement in depth as well as azimuth, and measures distance and direction travelled across the globe, not just through the water like most DR systems. Therefore, the recorded position already takes account of current and tidal stream. Indeed, comparing a normal DR position with a SINS position is an excellent method of establishing the stream in a given area. Over a long time, SINS error can build up, usually due to slight wandering of gyroscopes, whose performance should be monitored, like any other compass. However, when working well, SINS can still be within 2 kilometres of position after a 5000 kilometre Atlantic crossing, which has included a major NATO exercise. It is effective also in giving a good ship's heading in high latitudes, where other compasses have trouble.

COVERT BOTTOM CONTOUR FIXING

During periods of high international tension, submarine navigation, particularly in SSBNs, may have to become totally covert, which rules out even use of a periscope sextant. This means that position can only be established by using bottom contour maps and a discreet, narrow beam echo-sounder to locate particular features on the sea bed, known to exist in the patrol area, maybe a small deep hole or higher plateau. Once found, the position can be passed over at intervals to check that SINS is still accurately maintaining the DR. (Figure 11.6)

Bottom contour maps, already important aids towards using sonar effectively, as we saw in Chapter 8, all have their contours marked regularly and confidently like those on a land ordnance survey map, allowing lines of soundings taken by a submarine to be matched with contour crossings on the map. This makes them very different from ordinary charts, which only show the approximate position of the 100, 20 and 10 fathom lines, mainly for the benefit of ships making a landfall. Good maps may show features suitable for use as discreet navigation patrol points in considerable detail.

Not surprisingly in view of this use, such maps are highly classified. Care also has to be taken, when surveying any part of the world in enough detail for it to be used as an SSBN patrol area, to conceal the true nature of the work being performed, which will certainly be noted by intelligence collecting units. Thus, nations with SSBNs also have large fleets of survey vessels and employ them widely. This has provided much useful data to those nations who commissioned the work, but detailed surveying is very time consuming.

SUMMARY

Accuracy of submarine navigation has been transformed by an impressive list of technological advances. The periscope sextant is not the most complicated of these, but it is the most important, because the enemy cannot touch it.

Meeting the needs of missile firing submarines has been the main spur to greater accuracy. The latest navaid system gives 20 metre fixing anywhere, anytime, provided a mast can be raised and the mice have not got at the satellites.

Paradoxically, although submarines now know where they are very precisely, in some respects their navigation has become more dangerous; due to higher speeds, wider deployment and increased hazards in coastal waters. Sound plans, safe practice and use of commonsense therefore remain as important as ever.

The need for covert navigation has produced bottom contour maps, the first charts ever designed primarily with submarine requirements in mind. These are very helpful. However, surveying is slow work and nations obviously do not exchange those maps produced in enough detail to be used by SSBNs on patrol, further slowing dissemination of the most useful information. This is typical of the secrecy, which has to surround submarine activities, a subject explored in more depth in the next chapter.

12

Signature Reduction

Anyone watching nature programmes on television will know that small living creatures can be located in many ways. Their predators make passive detection by sight, smell, noise, and heat emanation. Bats can also obtain active detections, using high frequency sound. All these methods have had their counterparts in man made anti-submarine systems and most are still used. In addition, submarines can be found actively by radar when they are exposing masts, and passively by sensing various magnetic effects which they may produce, permanently or temporarily.

To carry out covert missions in peace and survive long enough in war to perform the tasks entrusted to them, all submarines must present a low profile, or 'signature' to each of these possible means of detection. Consequently, much time, cash and effort is spent on the submarine signature reduction methods examined below. Low signatures are particularly necessary for SSBNs, since the credibility of any submarine borne deterrent, in part, depends on unshakable conviction that an enemy cannot find our missile firers at will, in order to eliminate them as part of a pre-emptive first strike.

SIGHT

Flying over very calm water with the sun behind them, aircraft have spotted submarines as much as 46 metres below the surface. Danger of detection is greatest when there is a light coloured, sandy sea bed acting as contrast beneath the hull. To reduce visual signature, British boats in the Mediterranean during the Second World War were painted two shades of blue and those sent to patrol off the top end of the Malacca Straits were painted green. These colours matched sea water in the respective areas very well but most nations now use a uniform black worldwide. This is fine for North Atlantic conditions. However, those sent into clear waters should remember that they need to be well down to avoid risk of a casual air sighting whilst deep, especially when aircraft have already had their attention drawn to the area by some earlier incident.

Periscopes and masts are camouflaged (see Figures 6.1 and 6.9) but the best insurance against them being detected visually is to keep submarine speed below four knots whilst they are up, because it is the feather of spray that most often catches the eye of the observer, rather than the mast itself. Achieving such slow speeds in an SSN, in between bursts at higher speeds, requires tight ship control, that is hydroplane drill and trimming, and the patience to wait until logged speed has slowed down.

A periscope used within ten kilometres of potentially hostile surface craft, is normally raised for a very short time and only just far enough to get the necessary bearing and range information. However, when collecting photographic intelligence, a periscope has to be kept up long enough to allow water to drain off the top window before starting to take pictures, or nothing useful will be achieved. Moreover, to pick out fine detail, ships must be snapped from inside 1500 metres when using 6X magnification, and inside 800 metres for a submarine. Greater ranges can be used when equipped with 12X magnification but there will still be a high risk of counter detection. Hence, during covert operations, photography should be restricted to vessels showing something genuinely new, which means that all submarine officers need a very good knowledge of what is already in the national data base on other navies.

SMELL

SSs snorting for long periods in relatively calm weather can leave a plume of ionised exhaust gases behind them. To take advantage of this signature, some 1950s aircraft were fitted with equipment able to 'sniff' for the smell and follow it to its source, often making their final approach with radar strangled, hoping for a visual sighting. In the 1990s, snort periods are kept too short for significant diesel exhaust signatures to develop. However, it is still necessary to be alert for breakdowns which might create a trail behind the boat, say a cracked external fuel tank in an SS or leaking hydraulic system on a non-hull-penetrating mast in an SSN. (Figure 12.1)

NOISE

Machinery can be prevented from contributing to radiated noise signatures in three ways:

▶ Selective switch off

▶ Individual machine isolation

▶ Collective raft isolation

Selective Switch Off

Submarines, once dived, normally maintain one of a number of 'quiet states', which introduce progressively tighter curbs on the types of machine which can be run. The end of the line is UQS (*Ultra Quiet State*), which provides the minimum equipment needed to service passive sonars, support life, and keep control of the submarine, on the ordered course, at ordered depth, whilst deep. Anything less than this will be sustainable only for a limited time. Before listing machines for exclusion at any level of quietness, account is taken both of their contribution to radiated noise and the loss of operational capability which will be suffered by having them switched off. UQS is not known as 'ultra-nasty' for nothing. Operating with air conditioning and ventilation off in the tropics really is nasty,

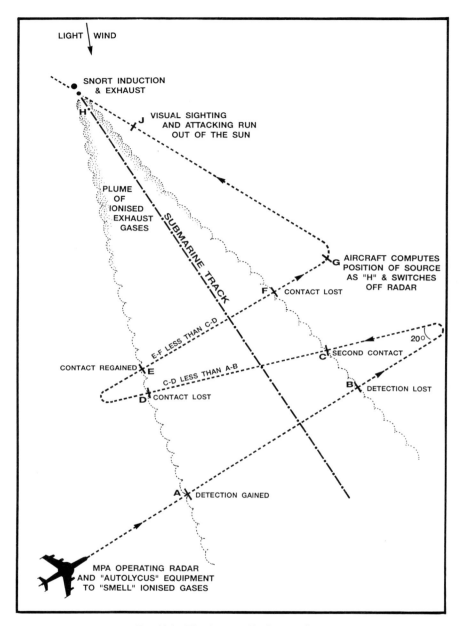

FIG. 12.1   The danger of laying a trail

and gains in quietness may be more than matched by decreased efficiency of men and equipment.

A command decision is needed to start a machine which has been excluded from use whilst assuming a quiet state but this is only to prevent casual use. Flexibility is required. If one has a good knowledge of noise trial data, and more recent upkeep history of individual machines, one can sometimes bring them back on with great gain and negligible enhancement of the signature on the bearing that matters. This is particularly true when the submarine has had an opportunity to establish a detailed polar diagram of its own radiated noise. (Figure 12.2)

Individual Machine Isolation

Single machines are isolated by placing them on resilient mountings and connecting all services to the machine: fuel, lubrication, coolant, through piping flexible enough not to transmit machinery vibration to the hull, and thence into the water. The system can fail for many reasons. The weight of some very large machines may be too much for their mounts, compressing them to solidity and allowing vibration through to the bedplate. Or oil and paint contamination may cause the mounting material to lose its resilience, with the same result. The machine itself may deteriorate and start producing more vibration than the mounting is designed to handle. In a confined space, some piece of thoughtlessly stowed portable equipment, like a toolbox, all too easily can create a noise bridge between machine and hull. Finally, the sheer number of machines, mountings and flexible connections to be monitored by the small 'acoustic housekeeping' team in the submarine, increases the danger of faults being missed.

Collective Raft Isolation

One way of reducing the supervisory task is to collect a group of machines onto a large raft. This can be acoustically isolated from the hull as a single unit by floating it on four or more hydraulic jacks. There is a penalty when using high speeds, because the raft will probably have to be locked, to prevent it developing dangerous accelerations. However, at that point the radiated noise signature is usually dominated by propeller and hydrodynamic noise, not machinery noise. (See Chapter 8)

The first rafts appeared in the second generation of American and British SSNs. They were quite small because they were fitted mainly to isolate steam turbines and gear trains from the hull, which they did very effectively. The main machinery spaces of later SSNs have much bigger rafts, able to accommodate a lot more equipment. This has further tightened control over the noise isolation process and has allowed very heavy machines, like steam driven turbo-generators, to be properly isolated for the first time. Given the money to do so, there would be merit in using rafts even more widely, to mount as much auxiliary machinery as possible in this way, and maybe put the whole living area into an isolated box, which would help cut off many transient noises at source. (Figure 12.3)

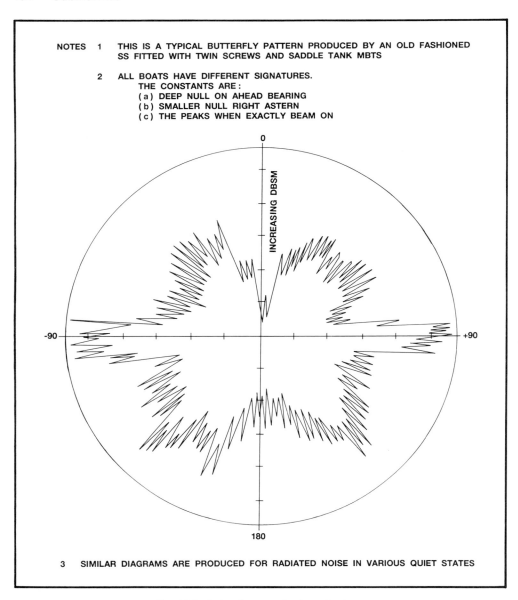

FIG. 12.2   Polar diagram of noise reflection

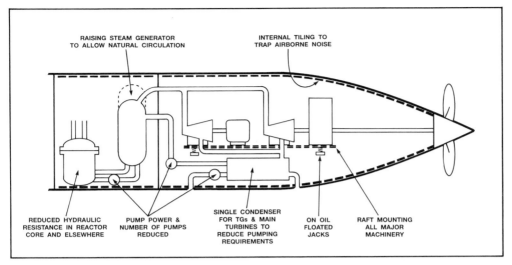

RAISING STEAM GENERATOR
TO ALLOW NATURAL CIRCULATION

INTERNAL TILING TO
TRAP AIRBORNE NOISE

REDUCED HYDRAULIC
RESISTANCE IN REACTOR
CORE AND ELSEWHERE

PUMP POWER &
NUMBER OF PUMPS
REDUCED

SINGLE CONDENSER
FOR TGs & MAIN
TURBINES TO
REDUCE PUMPING
REQUIREMENTS

ON OIL
FLOATED
JACKS

RAFT MOUNTING
ALL MAJOR
MACHINERY

Fig. 12.3   Possible noise reduction measures

Problem Solving

Submarine sound isolation is an activity in which the good intentions of the designer are very soon frustrated by a badly briefed, or confused, construction worker. At worst, quite serious errors may remain concealed until the first noise trials. For instance, when HMS *Warspite* was ranged in 1968, the trials officer reported, quite early on, that unlocking the raft did not seem to alter the signature being recorded, news almost guaranteed to ruin the day!

Such a major problem can only be tackled by methodically carrying out a 'pyjama cord test' on every machine on the raft. In this test, a continuous loop of cord is passed round the machine. Wherever it has to be cut and rejoined to pass a pipe connecting some service to the machine, that pipe is then traced and examined, to ensure that it is either going to another machine on the raft, or is flexibly isolated before being secured to the hull. Despite the fact that *Warspite* was in general a very well built submarine, there were twenty one direct noise shorts from the raft to the hull. It took sixty hours to find and fix them all. They were mostly the work of one man who had not appreciated which parts of the compartment were on and which off the raft, when clipping up pipes. This may sound absurd but in fact with everything painted the same colour it was quite difficult to tell the difference. Today, the shipyard deliberately paint raft components a distinctive colour to make such a mistake less likely.

Well conducted noise trials provide a wealth of useful data for making comparisons, when checking machines and overall signature later in the commission. Likely signs of trouble are more interference with passive sonar and raised vibration levels, with certain machines running. Vibration has always been checked periodically, during routine maintenance, but the real need is for something like a Ferranti-Thomson VIMOS (***Vibration Monitoring System***). Permanently installed and computer controlled, this detects, locates and quantifies vibration produced by machinery and transients, as they occur, using information from a set of accelerometers and hydrophones, widely distributed inside the hull. Displays present collated data in both graphic and text forms to stimulate immediate corrective actions, much as a remotely monitored burglar alarm does; and to help discount self noise lines on sonar Demon displays. The system weakness is that it can only monitor near field noises, but if the computer algorithms are well written, sometimes far field predictions of radiated noise can be made from such data. (Figure 12.4)

Casing Checking

It is not only machinery and transients which contribute to a radiated noise signature. Propeller and hydrodynamic noise also have to be minimised. Mostly, this

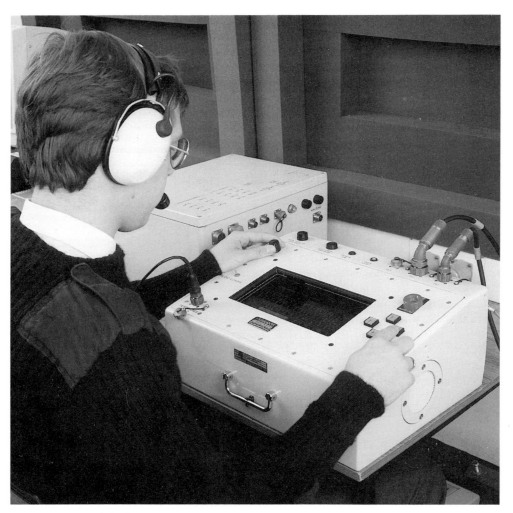

FIG. 12.4   Operator's desk unit of Ferranti VIMOS (*Photo: Ferranti Thomson*)

means using good hull and propulsor designs, as discussed in Chapters 3 and 5. However, radiated noise, and self noise interference on sonar, can be aggravated by vibration of badly secured portable fittings and rattling of metallic debris trapped in the Casing. Both are especially serious for SSNs, which expect to operate silently, with good results from sonar, whilst more than fifteen knots of water streams through their casing spaces.

Debris is most likely to accumulate whilst overhaul work is carried out. It is best removed by an industrial vacuum cleaner before leaving the dry dock, because it is more difficult to winkle out from the lower levels, once these are underwater again, with the submarine afloat. Checking for loose fittings needs to be delayed till just before sailing on patrol, but with enough time left to put things right. One US SSN always sent a team through the casing armed with rubber coated hammers, to obtain final proof that nothing could be worked free, a sensible idea.

HEAT

In theory, a submarine may be detected from the air or space, using infra red techniques: either because recent operation of masts on a flat calm day has left thermal scars on an otherwise unbroken sea surface; or because the submarine is heating up the water around itself.

Thermal Scars

In practice, the North Atlantic is at Wind Force 0 less than 5 per cent of the time. Indeed, Force 4, or stronger, winds blow over it 80 per cent of January, and about 50 per cent of July. So, the overall danger of detection of mast scars in such an area, year on year, is minimal. However, the discriminating ability of infra red equipment has now advanced to the stage, (< one tenth of a degree Centigrade), where such scars could be spotted if present. At the least, this provides SSBNs with another compelling reason for avoiding the use of any mast during periods of high political tension, especially if accompanied by flat calm weather.

Sea Warming

Warming of the area around the submarine occurs due to the action of the circulating water systems, which use the sea as their ultimate 'heat sink'. The problem is aggravated in modern SSNs, whose cooling water is pumped internally at near atmospheric pressures before being passed through a major heat exchanger close to the pressure hull. This very desirable arrangement lowers the number of hull openings and replaces a multiplicity of internal piping, all dangerously stressed to the full pressure of the sea outside, by one much safer system. However, it does also concentrate the warming action.[1]

Luckily, there are two factors which make it more difficult for ASW forces to exploit the phenomenon. The lack of a homogeneous thermal structure in the ocean means that the very small changes one would expect a submarine to produce cannot automatically be attributed to submarine activity. More important, submarines do not carry out slow tight circles or stay still in one place—certainly not at periscope depth—the only behaviour likely to make the warming conspic-uous. It is true, they can hover when deep, maintaining neutral buoyancy with special automatic pumping and flooding arrangements, but as they now nearly always have a towed sonar array and a communications wire out astern of them, there is already every incentive to keep under way, on steady courses. (Figure 12.5)

COLD   COLD   COLD
WARM SURFACE

ANY SUBMARINE USING MASTS
ON A FLAT CALM DAY - AND
LEAVING THERMAL SCARS

VERY HIGH SPEED SSN (40 KNOTS AND OVER)
LEAVING A MEASURABLY HEATED WAKE -
AS WELL AS BEING VERY NOISY

SLOW SPEED SSBN -
WASTE HEAT WARMING
OF SURROUNDING SEA

FIG. 12.5   Thermal scars and sea warming

REFLECTED SOUND

There are five ways to reduce the effectiveness of enemy sonars, that is their ability to obtain a meaningful reflected noise signature, or echo, from the submarine. The noise can be scattered or absorbed, the submarine can be manoeuvred to present a minimal echoing area, the signal can be diverted onto a decoy, and the enemy sonar displays can be jammed with additional noise.

Scattering and Absorption

Transmitted noise, like a radar pulse, is scattered most when it hits a well rounded hull, whose designer has avoided using flat surfaces on the fin, rudder and hydroplane stabilisers, and who has managed to abut adjoining surfaces without creating right-angled corners.

Noise is best absorbed by coating as much as possible of the hull, fin and control surfaces with anechoic tiles, which have the potential to knock 40 per cent off the signature. The size of tile and depth of absorbing material needed can be judged from the picture, as can the difficulty that nations have in getting tiles to stay put! (Figure 12.6)

There is also a potential conflict of interest, between sonar designers seeking the best site for flank arrays, and those trying to reduce echo signature. Clearly, the tiles will do little good if punctuated by a long line of large metal transducers. Since the flank array has a passive role only, the answer probably lies in adopting a form of hydrophone which works on the piezo-electric principle, rather than magneto-striction, and therefore can be made of a non metallic substance, whose absorption factor might match that of the tiles.[2]

Manoeuvring

Keeping the submarine bow on to the nearest source of sonar transmissions is one of the oldest methods of echo signature reduction, invariably used in the days when submarines had to penetrate a screen of escorts at slow speed, to attack a convoy or some major unit. It was particularly effective for SSs like the British 'A' class, which had length/beam ratios of 13:1 and beams of under 6.8 metres; but even in an SSN, it is better to present a beam of 9.8 metres to the enemy sonar, however remote, than a length of 85.4 metres (TRAFALGAR class). Incidentally, a few degrees either side of the bow also often represents one of the lowest nulls on the polar diagram of radiated noise. Meanwhile, one will be using the most effective area of the bow sonar, right ahead, and any torpedoes fired will have a minimum alteration of course to complete before settling on an interception track.

Use of Decoys

Whereas the first three methods of reducing enemy sonar effectiveness were designed to avoid contact, decoys are used as a means of *breaking* contact. The most basic sort are SBDs (**Submarine Bubble Decoys**): canisters launched from an SSE (**Submerged Signal Ejector**), whose chemical contents will give

FIG. 12.6   Russian OSCAR Class SSGN showing anechoic tiles missing—even in
1991 (© *British Crown Copyriqht 1993/MOD*)

off a large cloud of gas once exposed to salt water. During the Second World War, submarines also occasionally blew high pressure air out of their ballast tanks, with the vents open, to create a similar effect. The gas cloud acts as a more effective reflector of the sonar signal than the submarine, allowing the boat to slip away, whilst an enemy wastes time approaching the wrong contact. More complicated SSE launched decoys hover at mid depth, giving off strong acoustic signals, designed to attract homing torpedoes. However, like the SBD, they suffer from the serious disadvantage of remaining geographically stationary, which an efficient ASW plotting team will realise quite quickly, and a good torpedo brain ought to be able to work out. (Figure 12.7)

The most sophisticated decoys are torpedo-like in structure and mobile. They should be carried in their own specially fitted launch tubes, to ensure that they are always ready for use, without having to dedicate one or more of the few torpedo tubes to carrying them. Modern mobile decoys are capable of responding to active transmissions with a realistic echo and produce a noise signature with believable broad band, narrow band and demon characteristics, making them very hard to tell apart from real submarines. Inevitably, putting so much wizardry into decoys makes them expensive, and not many can be carried; but they may buy just enough time to allow the submarine to counter attack effectively, and survive, when no other tactic or device could do as much. Then, they will seem cheap at the price.

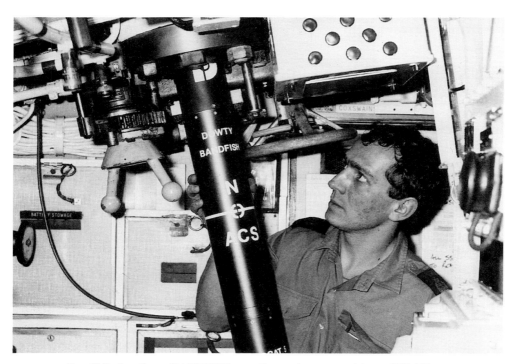

Fig. 12.7   Loading a BANDFISH acoustic countermeasure into an SSE (*Photo: Dowty Maritime*)

Jamming

In general, jamming is best done from off board, using a decoy, to avoid drawing more attention to the submarine. However, use of a surprise tactic whilst manoeuvring to break contact can sometimes be effective. It is perhaps worth remembering, therefore, that the displays of active enemy sonars operating at frequencies close to that of the **underwater telephone** (UWT) can be very seriously disrupted by training the UWT onto the bearing, increasing the volume to maximum, and feeding the noise of an electric razor into the mouthpiece!

RADAR REFLECTION

Mention was made whilst discussing ESM, (Chapter 7), of the increased warning time which can be obtained by coating all masthead areas with RAM (**Radar Absorbent Material**), a rubbery substance which reduces radar reflection. Flat surfaces and right angles must also be avoided, as they are when reducing sound reflection. To be effective, RAM has to be on everything exposed to radar pulses. This includes many areas inside ESM radomes, which by design are transparent to RF (**Radio Frequency**) energy. RAM must also cover all parts of the supporting mast which will be above the sea surface when the system is in use. This is not easily achieved on a stainless steel, hull-penetrating mast, most of which has to go down into a top bearing. It is a much simpler and cheaper task to give low signatures to non hull-penetrating masts, which can be made throughout of synthetic materials like GRP (**Glass Reinforced Plastic**), that already have a low index of reflectivity for RF energy.

MAGNETIC

The Earth is surrounded by a weak magnetic field, which has a vertical and horizontal component. These fields vary in different geographic areas, but in any one place provide a fairly constant background. The submarine is at risk as soon as its own magnetic field, or signature, is allowed to become strong enough to produce measurable distortions, or anomalies in this background; because these can be detected, from below by a magnetic mine, or above by an aircraft fitted with MAD (**Magnetic Anomaly Detection**) equipment. Both have become more sensitive and more discriminating in recent years; whilst submarines have become larger, increasing the physical and sometimes scientific difficulty of treating them. Thus, although covered last here, magnetic is now perhaps the most awkward signature to keep at safe levels.

The Problem

The signature is created from both types of magnetism, permanent and induced. Acquisition of permanent magnetism is an almost unavoidable side effect of many shipbuilding processes, such as cold working of steel. Once at sea, it can be made worse by compression and expansion of the hull during depth changing, in the presence of the Earth's magnetic field, particularly whilst making very deep dives with the boat on north/south courses. Clearly, submarines built with non magnetic titanium alloy hulls start with a very useful advantage, but hull magnetism is only one part of the problem.

There are varying degrees of permanent magnetism, from very hard, (that is hard to remove), to relatively soft, and all shades in between. Hull steel is unlikely to be the hardest onboard, because many machines in a submarine, and their steel components, have to be highly toughened to carry out their functions. Such physical hardening also instils very intractable permanent magnetism, and items given it can have an effect on the overall signature out of all proportion to their mass.

Induced magnetism can result from a wide range of intermittent and semi-permanent activities, inside and outside the hull, all of which cause electrical currents to flow. The list of contributors obviously includes every machine run on electrical power. Much less obvious, but certainly a possible culprit, might be electrolytic currents produced whilst providing cathodic protection to external metal fittings, such as propellers.[3]

Deperming

Permanent magnetism can be reduced by a process called 'deperming', sometimes shock or saturation deperming. It involves placing the submarine inside coils, through which high energy DC electrical currents are passed for quite short time intervals, first with one polarity and then the opposite. The currents create large magnetic fields, which shock ferrous metal molecules out of their existing alignments. After an initial shake up phase, the current pulses are gradually strengthened, until the metal is driven into magnetic saturation, then decreased again exponentially towards zero, to bring the signature below the required level. The magnetic state of the submarine is checked after each shock, by taking readings from magnetometers, fitted in lines beneath the deperming berth. (Figure 12.8)

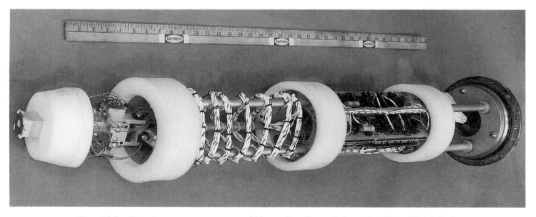

FIG. 12.8   Raytheon magnetometer (*Photo: Raytheon Submarine Signal Division*)

The influence of the Earth's magnetic field must be removed during the deperm, therefore, two sets of coils are needed. The most important and most numerous are the 'X' coils, which go round the boat laterally, like a solenoid, in the same plane as the bulkheads, and therefore work at right angles to this plane, producing a longitudinal magnetic field, which does the main job of shocking the submarine hull. A smaller number of 'Z' coils go round the submarine, parallel to the waterline, to create a vertical magnetic field, equal and opposite to the main component of the Earth's magnetic field, which is largely vertical in UK latitudes. To counteract the small horizontal component of the Earth's field, the 'X' field values are deliberately slightly biased against it during the treatment. In theory, 'Y' coils are also needed to compensate for misalignment between the fore and aft line of the submarine and the lines of force of the Earth field; but are unnecessary if the deperming berth can be roughly orientated on magnetic north. (Figure 12.9)

Until quite recently, the coils were close wrapped round the submarine, so none of the heavy copper cables could be lugged into place until the boat was in the berth, and progressive changes in the signature had to be monitored manually. As a result, a deperm took several days, and was always difficult to fit in. More serious, the treatment given tended to wear off quite quickly, probably because initial flux levels used were not high enough properly to saturate *any* of the steel

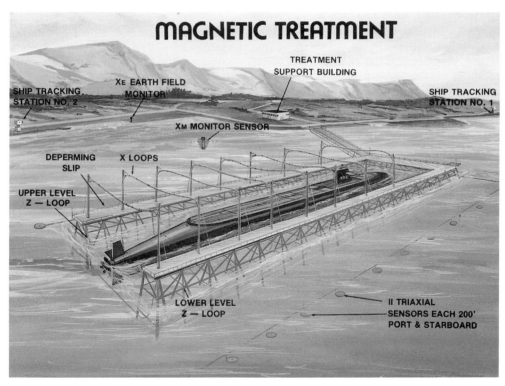

Fig. 12.9   Magnetic Silencing Facility (*Photo: Raytheon Submarine Signal Division*)

onboard, let alone the really intractable items. Some of these can only be brought fully under control with fields many times stronger than those needed for most hulls. Only partially treated, they go on producing signature distortions themselves and gradually restore magnetism to softer items. These programming and wear off problems alone always made it hard to keep all boats within tolerable signature limits. In addition, close wrapped cables may produce uneven hull treatment, leaving sinuations within the signature which clever modern mines can spot. (Figure 12.10)

A much better deperm is achieved with an MSF (***Magnetic Silencing Facility***). This consists of three jetties, joined into a 'U' shape, with 'Z' coils fitted around them and 'X' coils strung between the two long sides. The submarine drives into the box formed by the 'X' coils and is secured mid way between the jetties. With nothing to rig, and the signature changes computer monitored, the whole treatment process can be completed in a few hours. This encourages regular deperming and allows a surge requirement to be met during the run up to war. The permanent installation is safely able to handle the higher currents needed to produce adequate hull treatment fields, even though these must be larger still, once the cables are further from the submarine. Above all, the uniform field produced by the MSF, deals with the ends of the submarine properly for the first time, and will iron out sinuations in the signature, provided enough 'X' coils are used and properly spaced. (Figure 12.11)

Fig. 12.10   Close wrap deperming (*Photo: Raytheon Submarine Signal Division*)

FIG. 12.11   Submarine in MSF (*Photo: Raytheon Submarine Signal Division*)

This leaves the very intractable items, which can be handled in one of two ways. Either, the whole submarine must be subjected to fields large enough to guarantee bringing under control anything on board, no matter how hard, or all the very hard items must be identified and individually depermed in a smaller special facility, as part of the installation sequence. Although treating everything together, on completion of building or refit, would be better, there are practical difficulties. MSF field strengths could only be raised the necessary amount by huge increases in size and cost of all components; or by equally expensive, risky, time-consuming development of new technology, like super conductivity, to provide high currents through less massive cables. There may also be equipment onboard liable to erasure by high magnetic flux, just as a credit card can be wiped, which would have to be specially protected.

Individual pre-installation treatment requires tight control procedures, and might allow permanent magnetism to be reintroduced after installation. However, firm control over items is one of the great advantages of the modular assembly techniques now widely used; and very hard items, although they take a lot of deperming, once properly treated, also show quite strong resistance to any attempt to remagnetise them. On balance, therefore, individual treatment seems the most sensible way to tackle this difficult problem, certainly in the short term, and for those with limited budgets.

Degaussing

Induced magnetism is handled by installing coils inside the submarine, which when energised will cancel it. They are called degaussing coils and may be fitted around whole areas of the submarine or individual machines, or both. Degaussing coils are needed on all three axes, and the current in them must be adjustable, because the signature effects produced slowly alter with latitude, as the lines of force of the Earth's field go from near vertical in high latitudes to near horizontal at the magnetic equator. More immediate changes in coil currents are required as the ship alters course, because unusual effects on the horizontal component of the Earth's field will be detectable the moment the submarine ceases to be parallel to it.

The Ultimate Aim

The magnetic signature is so important and losing control of it so dangerous that the ultimate aim must be to have a quick reaction, closed circuit system. It would mean fitting magnetometers inside, and maybe outside, the submarine, and using their output to trigger immediate corrective action in coil current settings whenever any internal action of our own, or some unforeseen external action by the enemy, made the computed near field magnetic signature go outside limits.

SUMMARY

Submarines may be sought with many different sensors and a low signature has to be presented to each. A nearly invisible, odourless, silent, non-magnetic, non-heat-producing submarine, of many thousand tons, is a tough specification to meet. Ensuring that it can absorb or scatter half the energy directed at it by active sensors is no less challenging. The task is quite hopeless unless one begins at the building stage. Extensive raft mounting of machinery, hundreds of square metres of anechoic tiles and special mobile decoy launchers, cannot be tacked on later. They must be an integral part of the design.

When total blending with the environment has not been achieved, the usual situation, the submarine is operated to minimise the impact of those signatures which remain. By no means all the measures taken have been quoted but: strictly controlled quiet states for restricting the use of machinery; staying end-on at critical times to present minimum aspect; use of slow speed when a periscope is up; avoiding the creation of thermal scars on flat calm days; thoroughly checking out the casing for potential rattles; are good examples of actions which will make operations more discreet.

The most important signatures are noise and magnetic. Noise is doubly dangerous, helping enemy passive sonars and hindering our own. Magnetic is the most difficult to control, least well understood, and perhaps most rapidly growing in significance.

Both noise and magnetic signatures are checked intermittently, during static and underway noise trials, and by running over a magnetic open sea range. These checks are helpful in establishing base line data after building, and ensuring that everything is installed correctly, but the real requirement is for full time monitoring, not intermittent. So onboard instruments and computers are being fitted, to measure near field effects and convert them logically into predictions of the far field which an enemy might detect. Eventually, signatures like the magnetic, which can be corrected instantly without compromising operational capability, ought to be managed by a closed loop system.

13

Atmosphere Control and Health Physics

Nuclear powered submarines, patrolling for weeks without access to air from the surface, need efficient atmosphere control almost as much as low signatures. They must also have a totally reliable radiation monitoring system. A modern SS, whose successive snorting bursts can be days apart, and whose weapons might include nuclear tipped torpedoes, hardly needs less. However, SSNs and SSBNs can be given much better control machinery, because they have inexhaustible power to run it. By contrast, battery power is so precious in an SS, that any auxiliary machinery needing much of it would not be used, any more than it would be if it made a lot of noise. Thus, the equipment has to be quite modest.

THE GASES NEEDING CONTROL

Wartime submarines surfacing to charge batteries nightly, and 1950s boats snorting regularly, also pulled in enough air for their people, albeit some 60 minutes snorting was needed in British 'A' boats to make a complete atmosphere change. The main concern was that an enemy might keep the submarine deep, preventing surfacing or snorting. This could cause oxygen (O_2), which is vital to life, to be reduced; and carbon dioxide (CO_2), which is poisonous in quantity, to be increased; both to dangerous degrees—simply due to men inhaling one and exhaling the other. Since CO_2 is also much more prevalent than other noxious substances needing removal, O_2 and CO_2 remain the most important gases to monitor.

Batteries introduce two new concerns. They need their own special ventilation arrangements for pulling out hydrogen, which becomes explosive when it reaches a 4 per cent concentration. There is no room for bad design or operator error in this area.[1] Many SS battery ventilation systems also take extracted gas aft to engine rooms, for ingestion by diesels, via pipes running outside the pressure hull. All hull penetrations have isolating valves, and drains, to check external piping, but such systems increase the risk of getting salt water in battery cells, producing chlorine, a pungent toxic gas. The danger is most acute following mine, depth charge or torpedo explosions, which can fracture pipes and spring open shut valves by several turns. In SSNs/SSBNs, all ventilation runs are put inside the hull. However, batteries are still placed in sealed tanks or compartments, to prevent any accidental flooding, although it makes ventilation more difficult. (Figure 13.1)

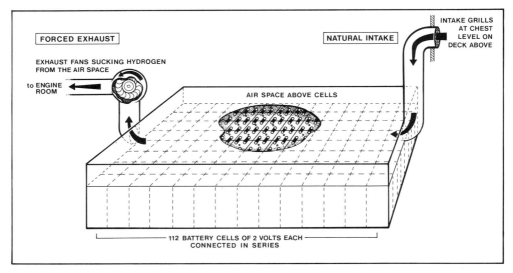

FIG. 13.1   Battery ventilation for cells in a tank—typical layout

Several other gases, only ever present in innocuous amounts when boats changed their atmospheres regularly, would become dangerous if allowed to build up throughout a long SSN patrol. Carbon monoxide, mainly from cigarette smoking; freon, from refrigerating and air conditioning plant; methane, from sewage tanks; and CTC (***carbon tetrachloride***), found in many cleaning products, all fall into this category, and provision has to be made for them.

Oxygen Supply

Nuclear powered submarines, being steam driven, have efficient evaporators, which are constantly converting salt water to fresh water, to replenish their feed tanks. Some of this pure water is treated by electrolysis, which breaks down H_2O into its component elements: oxygen for breathing, and hydrogen, which has to be eliminated.

Submarine electrolysers produce oxygen very efficiently, if allowed to settle down and run steadily; but they also make noise periodically when discharging hydrogen overboard. (See Chapter 8) The discharge can be delayed, but not for long, because one must minimise the possibility of an explosive recombination of the gases being produced. If the noise becomes an operational embarrassment whilst on patrol, it is best to turn off the machine altogether, and operate a back up system. Because, run intermittently for short periods, it may fail to give a reliable supply of oxygen. (Figure 13.2)

Most diesel powered submarines still carry strictly limited supplies of fresh and distilled water and cannot waste power running evaporators on patrol. Modern SSs, like HMS *Upholder*, have plenty of fresh water, produced by osmosis technology, but not enough spare power to run an electrolyser. (Figure 13.3)

Thus, all SSs are forced to revive their air supply by operating oxygen genera-

Fig. 13.2   Two high pressure (125 bar) Electrolysers—fitted in early UK SSNs and SSBNs [*see also Fig. 16.9*](*Photo: CJB Developments*)

tors. These are hollow cylinders, loaded with solid, 15 centimetre diameter oxygen candles, made of chemicals, say chlorates, that will give off free oxygen when slowly 'burned'. Oxygen generators also act as a back up system for SSNs and SSBNs, which carry a large outfit of candles. The time after shutting down an SS, (or switching off the electrolyser in an SSN/SSBN), at which to start burning candles, is usually laid down in tables. It depends on the submarine's internal volume and the number of people carried. Alternatively, it can be related to reaching a specific oxygen level, measured by monitoring equipment. (Figure 13.4)

Carbon Dioxide Removal

Although both should be done together, scrubbing carbon dioxide from small polluted atmospheres helps relieve distress for people living in them more quickly than raising oxygen levels. In submarines, CO_2 is removed by drawing foul air through liquids or granulated solids, which are highly absorbent to it. The primary systems in SSNs and SSBNs, use organic materials like MEA, (**Mono Ethanol Amine (C_2H_7NO)**, in cold solution, because, being hygroscopic, they dehumidify as well. They can also be continuously recycled by heat treatment, important for any system which has to be forever running.

The back up system in all boats, and primary system in most SSs, is a set of CO_2 absorption units, which can carry up to four canisters each of soda lime. The fans

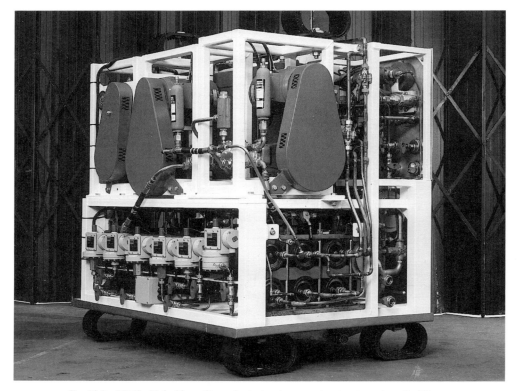

Fig.13.3   HMS *Upholder*—Osmosis technology water treatment unit (*Photo: Biwater Treatment Ltd*)

drawing foul air through the lime can be either electrically or hand operated. The atmosphere control tables mentioned above will also say when and how many canisters should be used. (Figure 13.5)

Carbon Monoxide Burning

Except in areas such as the combat centre, where it could decrease operator effectiveness, smoking is not normally restricted in nuclear powered submarines. Consequently, over a period of time, carbon monoxide steadily builds up, with surge increases during recreational activity times, especially film shows. Although SSNs and SSBNs do not charge their batteries to the gassing point whilst on patrol, there is also a small but steady increase in hydrogen levels. Both these gases can be contained by periodic operation of a CO and H2 burner. (Figure 13.6)

Freon Spotting

Freons are derivatives of methane (CH_4), in which hydrogen atoms have been replaced by chlorine and fluorine atoms, for example, Freon-12 (CCl_2F_2) and

Fig.13.4   Oxygen generator and chlorate candle (*Photo: Molecular Products Ltd*)

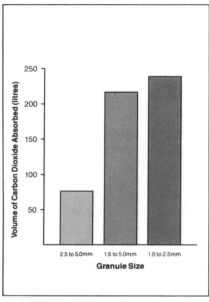

Graph   Effect of particle size on CO₂ absorption   Disposable Canisters

FIG. 13.5   C0$_2$ absorbtion, using small granule sofnolime (*Photo: Molecular Products Ltd*)

Freon-21 (CHCl$_2$F). They are inert but dangerous: because they collect in the lower levels of a small compartment, gradually displacing the oxygen; and some may be turned into poisonous phosgene (COC1$_2$), when passed through the CO and H2 burner.

The only way to deal with escaping freon is to find and stop the leak quickly, whilst the atmosphere onboard is still fresh. Once there is more than just a whiff of the stuff around, finding the actual source becomes nigh impossible. Therefore, it pays the engine room team to search hard for escaping gas in the first two days after shutting down. The alternative, of having to ventilate the submarine at regular intervals through a huge snort induction, is unlikely to endear the SEO (**Senior Engineer Officer**) to his commanding officer.

Methane and Trace Gases

Early boats discharged sewage as it was produced, having a separate hull opening and air blow by each head. Control could be exercised over this noisy operation, but only by temporarily forbidding its use. In modern submarines, heads can be used at any time, as all sewage is quietly collected into a sanitary tank, and discharged en masse when convenient to the command, a better system both operationally and domestically.

Trials have shown that tank capacity, in relation to numbers onboard, is such that sewage is always discharged before significant levels of methane accumulate. However, looking ahead, if tank size is increased in future boats, to allow sewage

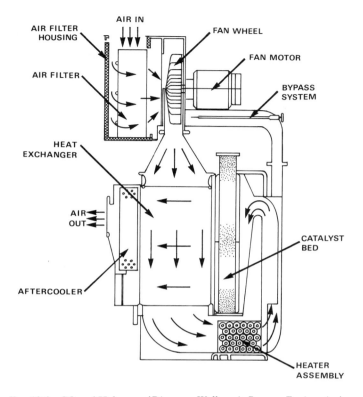

FIG. 13.6   CO and H₂ burner (*Diagram: Wellman's Process Engineering*)

to be held longer, or any action is taken which could accelerate decomposition, methane levels ought to be tested again. This policy of keeping them under review applies equally to all gases and aerosols, but most of those that could be harmful, including CTC, can be tackled by fitting carbon filters, or by refusing entry into the submarine to any product likely to produce them. Aerosol cans, gas operated lighters, Dabitoff, liquid shoe cleaners and glues are a few of the many substances excluded.

GAS MONITORING

The key to atmosphere control in a shut down environment is conscientious use of good monitoring equipment. The best systems use a mass spectrometer in a fixed cabinet, centrally located. They determine all gas levels in the boat continuously; and display resultant readings in the combat centre so clearly that the command cannot overlook their significance. A less good but still adequate system can be established, if operators go round regularly with portable analysers, log the results, and then present them to the command. (Figure 13.7)

CENTRAL ATMOSPHERE MONITORING SYSTEM WITH DOOR OPEN

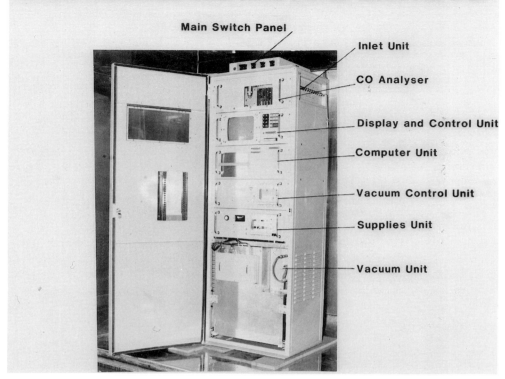

Main Switch Panel

Inlet Unit

CO Analyser

Display and Control Unit

Computer Unit

Vacuum Control Unit

Supplies Unit

Vacuum Unit

Fig. 13.7   Mass spectrometer gas monitoring equipment (*Photo: VG Gas Analysis Systems*)

CIRCULATION AND AIR CONDITIONING

SSs have supply and extraction ventilation systems and air conditioning units, for cooling and dehumidifying. Going to ultra quiet state, or just a need to save power, may force one into selectively switching off these systems, but there will be penalties. Some electronic equipment produces too much heat to run effectively for long without its ventilation and chilled water supplies; and operator efficiency falls off rapidly once ambient temperature goes above blood temperature, because the body cannot radiate heat.

However, some relief is obtained if ventilation can be kept on, after air conditioning has been turned off, as evaporation of sweat from the skin removes latent heat. To ensure that such ventilation is as effective as possible, supply fans in an SS normally draw from the forward end of the engine room, (near snort induction entry). Extracted foul air also goes back there, to be removed from the boat via diesels and snort exhaust.

Extraction and supply fans in SSNs and SSBNs are fitted in special fan spaces, one of which also contains the CO_2 treatment unit, coolers, carbon filters, and an electrostatic precipitator. This has a high voltage discharge electrode, which charges up particles, then collects them on plates of opposite polarity, removing 99 per cent of all dust and fibres. It also seems to do a good job of killing germs, as new coughs and colds are rare after a week shut down.

It would be convenient if all air treatment equipment could be located in one area; but CO and H_2 burners give off enough heat to need watching, and are unhelpful in a fan space, where one is trying to keep things cool. They are best put in a manned machinery room aft. Fan rooms are also noisy areas, which need to be well insulated and as far from the hull as possible; unlike the electrolyser, which has to be close to the hull for hydrogen discharge, and therefore normally has its own small space forward.

SSN air conditioning is thermostatically controlled to maintain an even temperature in different parts of the submarine, which have their own temperature sensors. The grouping of compartments for sensing, and cooling demands of individual areas, needs very careful thought. Moreover, once the air conditioning needs of an area have been settled, one should not import extra equipment into it, without also reviewing cooling requirements. For instance, when HMS *Warspite* was built, Combat Centre and Sonar Room were grouped together. Later, more sonar equipment was fitted, but the air conditioning not changed. This resulted in the system running flat out, yet barely keeping the sonar room bearable. Meanwhile, in the combat centre it was icy cold!

HEALTH PHYSICS

Submarine reactors are very strongly shielded to prevent escape of radiation. Indeed, in British and American nuclear boats, men receive less radiation than they would on dry land, from cosmic rays. Moreover, the outside world is properly protected too, because radioactive materials are contained by an exceptionally strong pressure vessel, inside a very strong reactor compartment shell, inside the strongest sort of ship hull in the world. These three 'containment boundaries' compare well with any civilian reactor ashore.

The submarine also carries a special health physics team, which in the first boat of a new class will be led by a medical officer. Their task is to supervise any activity which involves making a reactor compartment entry, and to set up strictly formal nuclear medicine procedures for monitoring the plant and keeping dosimeter records for watchkeepers in selected spaces.

Reactor Compartment Entry

The reactor compartment is unmanned when the reactor is critical but entry can be made to carry out a quick repair quite soon after reactor shut down. In the picture, USS *Michigan* (SSBN 727) is exercising the drill for dealing with a reactor compartment steam leak. The petty officer coming out of the reactor compartment is wearing a metallic heat reflecting suit, which is inflated with insulating air through an umbilical in the front. Ordinary anti-contamination clothing, is much lighter and easier to work in. It is worn to prevent anyone carrying contamination out of the compartment, on those very rare occasions when work involves the primary circuit. (Figure 13.8)

Fɪɢ.13.8   USS *Michigan* (SSBN 727)—Sailor wearing a heat reflecting metallic
suit, used when dealing with a major steam leak (*Photo: YOGI INC 1987*)

SS Needs

Diesel submarines do not have a specialist health physics team but they are given radiation monitoring equipment for two reasons. In war, they need to detect radioactive matter coming down the snort induction as the boat enters nuclear fallout. In peace, like any other warship, if they carry nuclear tipped weapons, they should be able to test them for radiation. Properly made, such weapons are completely safe until used, and anyway are often in non-reloadable external launch tubes, like those housing the Russian 650 millimetre 100 kilometre anti-convoy torpedoes. (See Note 1 to Table 9.4) Nevertheless, submarines carrying such weapons must have the ability to check them following a mechanical handling accident, however unlikely that may be. (Figure 13.9)[2]

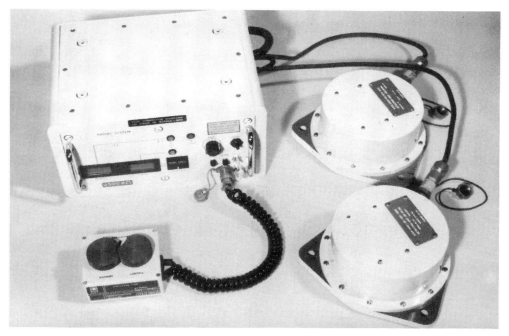

Fig. 13.9   Installed submarine RADIAC system 23 NRS—high and low detecting units—plus an indicating unit (*Photo: Siemens Plessey Controls Ltd*)

SUMMARY

The penalty for atmosphere control failure is exposure of a large, detectable snort induction to ventilate the boat. In an SSN/SSBN, this makes a nonsense of everything we tried to achieve in Chapter 6 and is worth a lot of effort to avoid.

Any nuclear submarine has ample power for O_2 supply, CO_2 absorption and CO & H_2 burning, on a continuous basis. The main job is monitoring all these gases and looking after some rather sensitive machinery. Other gases are controlled largely by administrative means.

In an SS, whenever temporarily embarrassed by not being able to snort, O_2 and CO_2 levels are maintained by equipment which makes only modest power demands, but uses up finite resources. Other gases do not accumulate enough to matter.

All submarines need efficient ventilation of their batteries to remove hydrogen, and effective means of keeping salt water out of them, to prevent the generation of chlorine.

In a nuclear powered boat, monitoring is also the most important task of the Health Physics team, who ensure that radioactive material remains within the very effective containment boundaries; and that activities such as a reactor compartment entry are carried out using strictly formal procedures. All this to minimise risk for those in the submarine *and those outside it*.

Diesel submarines have no equivalent organisation but they carry monitoring equipment, primarily to check the snort intake.

14
Conduct of Operations

SSBN patrols, and offensive operations, whether in support of sea control or sea denial strategies, are mostly conducted alone. They can be divided into fairly distinct phases: exit from base, passage, and on patrol. Roles dictate the importance to be attached to each phase. For example, the exit is one of the most important for SSBNs. Whereas, on a low level offensive sea control operation of a surveillance nature, often the only real business takes place close to an enemy shore, and there is little threat during other phases. However, the best and quickest way to get ready for the phase that matters is to put the boat on a war footing as soon as one sails.

When departing for offensive operations *after* shooting has begun, survival will be important throughout, both to achieve the patrol aim, and to ensure that enough boats return safely to base to continue operations. In either event, submarines, other than SSBNs, take the initiative, act positively, and accept risks to gain contact, when on patrol; but they behave more cautiously and avoid contact, especially with enemy ASW forces, when on passage. SSBNs avoid contact throughout.

Of course, the operations of SSNs cannot always be divided quite so neatly. When acting as escorts in the defensive sea control role, as we saw in Chapter 2, they may be actively seeking out the enemy, as soon as they leave a friendly port. And, on offensive sea control operations, instead of staying in a neat little box marked 'patrol area', they may be ranging over vast areas of ocean in pursuit of enemy groups, and coordinating their activities with friendly air and surface forces.

EXITS

An exit is the culmination of a preparation phase, but if it has to be made discreetly, it cannot also be hurried. So jobs like aligning sensors and trials of new equipment, which are important, but often take longer than expected, are done in the local areas well before sailing. During the exit itself, the submarine must be taken deep as soon as possible, to check water tightness, especially of masts with anything novel on them. This is also the time to get the trim right and monitor propeller noise, to make sure that no minor blade damage has occurred whilst running on the surface.

The two main dangers during exits are seabed devices sown in a channel being used, and a 'hostile' submarine waiting at the end of an exit route. For SSBNs, such threats always exist. In peacetime, recoverable devices may be planted at the seaward end of routes to collect data on their sonar signatures; and unfriendly SSNs may try to follow them out to their operating areas, which must be prevented. In quite low level conflicts, SSs and SSNs leaving a forward base may face ground mines in the channel, which could appear anywhere. And at a higher level of conflict, enemy submarines might attack as soon as we emerge through our own defensive minefields.

Exit routes, particularly those used by SSBNs, need regular vetting by MCM (*Mine Counter Measures*) vessels to establish an inventory of objects already on the seabed, making the appearance of something new more obvious. Computerising data greatly helps the process, but route checking is a time consuming business, and the channels which can be guaranteed clear of devices are likely to be narrow. Therefore, approaches to any submarine base must be well marked, to ensure that such channels can be accurately navigated. If there is any real danger of mines having been sown, submarines may need leading out by a mine hunter for at least part of the route.

In times of tension, the best defence against picking up an enemy submarine trailer on the way out is to site the base where there are many different possible exit routes. One can also send the submarine out either hidden under a noisy merchant vessel or accompanied by other boats, to draw off any potential shadower. In war, there is no substitute for leaving base at speeds slow enough to give minimal help to those listening outside. (Figure 14.1)

PASSAGES

A prime risk to submarines in transit to and from offensive operation areas is detection by enemy sonars, of all sorts. Danger rises as the routed speed is raised. In an SSN, a step change increase of risk occurs if a passage has to be conducted at more than maximum quiet speed, whatever that may be. In an SS, the risk rises steadily, not only because of increased radiated noise but also the greater amount of snorting which will be needed.

Conversely, risk can be reduced by keeping to slow speeds when passing through the three dangerous areas where an enemy might expect us to be. These are: close to his forces, at choke points on a route, and, depending on the level of conflict, possibly outside our own harbour. Particular care is needed, on offensive sea control operations, when nearing an enemy base whose approaches might be protected by bottom array sonars. (Figure 14.2)

Risk can be further reduced by using natural background noise to conceal submarine noise. For example, a Russian SSN based in Murmansk, wishing to make a discreet winter passage to conduct surveillance operations off the eastern seaboard of Canada, has a wide choice of routes. It can go under the Arctic ice and down the west coast of Greenland, or through any of the Greenland, Iceland, Faeroes, UK gaps. The noisiest route is likely to be that between Greenland and Iceland, because the SSN will be able to travel under an ice edge most of the way. Here, grinding of the pack-ice by the Atlantic swell will offer excellent cover. (Figure 14.3)

The Denmark Strait also happens to be the shortest route from North Cape to

FIG. 14.1   Multiple exit routes

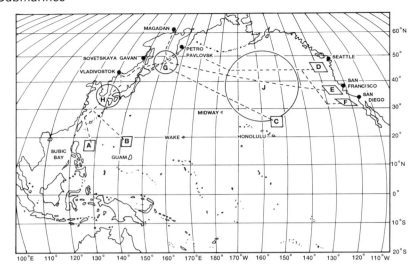

NOTES	
1	A, B, C, D, E & F: Increased risks in patrol areas due to proximity of US base.
2	G & H: Choke point risk areas. G (The Kurile Is.) are also a choke point for US SSNs trying to enter Sea of Okhotsk.
3	J: Deep ocean basin - ideal for SOSUS coverage.
4	Petropavlovsk is only base with direct access to Pacific and therefore is one most likely to have enemies ring fencing it.
5	Boats from Vladivostok, Sovetskaya Gavan and Magadan will all have to go through Kuriles or Tsu Shima straits.

FIG. 14.2   Danger points on passage for Pacific Fleet Russian SSGNs and SSNs

Nova Scotia, but choosing the noisiest or safest route often increases passage distance. Thus, risk reducing measures tend to cut time on patrol, and increase the number of boats needed to man one slot continuously at a given distance from base. For instance, during the Second World War, Fremantle based SSs trying to maintain offensive sea denial patrols in the South China Sea, over 3900 kilometres away, had to go very cautiously through either the Sunda or Lombok Straits, which were full of Japanese ASW forces. As a result, only short patrols were made, hardly justifying the risks taken. However, faster, safer routeing via straits further east would have lowered time on patrol to zero, because passage distance would have been so much greater. (Figure 14.4)

A balance has to be struck. It used to be considered that four SSs were needed to keep one on patrol up to 2700 kilometres from base. Of these, one would be on the way out, one on the way back, one on patrol, and the other rearming and restoring in harbour. For special occasions, one can always temporarily raise numbers at sea, and modern SSNs do generate slightly more availability; but it is a well-known fact that the British, who have four SLBM fitted SSBNs, generally keep one on patrol, one restoring in harbour, one in long refit and one in post refit

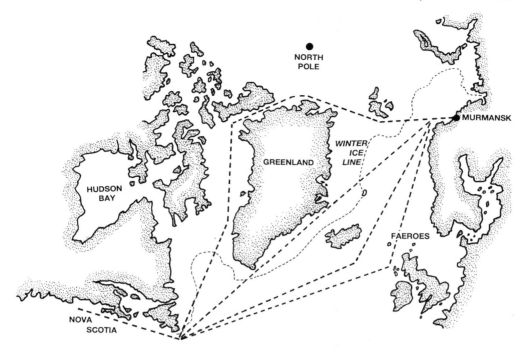

FIG. 14.3   Murmansk to Nova Scotia. Following the ice edge

workup. So, albeit for different reasons, four are still needed to guarantee one on patrol; though a RESOLUTION class boat, or an SSN, can patrol much further afield than an SS.

RUNNING INTO AN AREA

When moving into any new area, but particularly one close to an enemy base during offensive sea control operations, it pays to acclimatise gradually. Moreover, if one is to be there for some weeks, what is the point of racing in? Much better to go up to periscope depth quite often, or maybe stay there, during the last hours of the passage. Then, as potentially hostile ASW aircraft and ships become more numerous, one steadily builds up a good general picture, and a meaningful contact evaluation plot. If shallow during this first run in, one also gets the electronic warfare operator's library off to a good start, which is the best insurance against *data shock* problems.

FIXED AREA PATROLLING

The sort of operations carried out in a fixed patrol area vary, depending on the role that is being performed, and the type of submarine one is in. Such factors also dictate the pattern of life for everyone on board. Since they are used to implement both sea control and denial strategies, we will look first at barrier patrols, then review a couple of operations needed when patrolling offensively closer inshore, and finally consider the SSBN patrol.

Barrier Operations

The effectiveness of any barrier depends on whether one can put it in a choke point or not, because in the open ocean enemy units may find some way of rounding the end of it. Even a choke point barrier is not impenetrable. Much depends on giving submarines in it the right sized areas. This in turn is governed by their sensor, weapon and ship capabilities, and sonar conditions likely to prevail in the barrier area.

Whilst rules of engagement still forbid attacks, boats can only report units passing through the barrier, and any one with a good towed array sonar can cover a wide front from a fairly static position. However, once shooting is allowed, a barrier submarine has to be mobile enough to reach weapon firing range before an enemy can slip past. Hence, SSs with shorter range weapons may get smaller areas to patrol than SSNs, to avoid making them do long closing runs. Where SSs do have SSN sized areas, it is probably because they can call up maritime patrol aircraft support to prosecute their contacts; but this is only possible where friendly air predominates. (Figure 14.5)

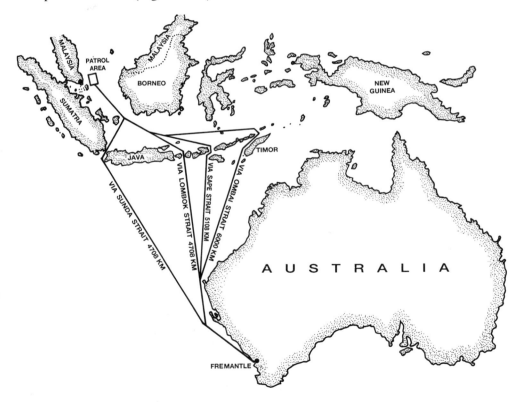

FIG. 14.4   The Fremantle problem

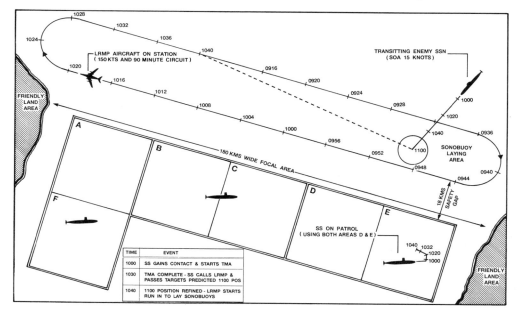

FIG. 14.5   Cooperating in the Barrier

A barrier submarine should always have some sonar advantage over all forces attempting to transit the area; since they must keep up a reasonable speed of advance, and we are lying doggo, a complete reversal of the situation when on passage. Moreover, enemy submarines do not necessarily know the exact barrier location, so may slow down too late, or speed up too soon, as they move into and out of the key area. However, an SS barrier defender becomes a less efficient listening platform every time it has to snort, and is then open to counter attack by the transitter. It must therefore arrive with a nearly full battery, and be very sparing with energy whilst on patrol, to reduce the snorting requirement.

It is not just electrical energy which has to be conserved. Use of Low Pressure Air to supply water for domestic purposes advances the time at which the compressors will have to be run again, which prolongs the snorting periods. Heavy use of hydroplanes at periscope depth in bad weather means more running of hydraulic pumps, therefore faster use of battery power. Crew activity leads to greater use of heating and lighting, further adding to the aptly named ***hotel load***. Life in a barrier SS, therefore, has to run at a very slow pace, with those not on watch doing routine maintenance and taking their meals, but otherwise mostly staying in their bunks—waiting for the enemy. (Figure 14.6)

Long range sonar capability often means hours spent sorting out very faint distant contacts. All the while, the boat must be trying to maximise sonar advantage. It is a tiring process and can be made more so if one keeps closing up the full combat team unnecessarily early. Hopefully, training of sonar operators, supervisors and all officers will be good enough to allow early stages of many interceptions to be handled by the third of the ship's company already on watch. But if CPO Diego

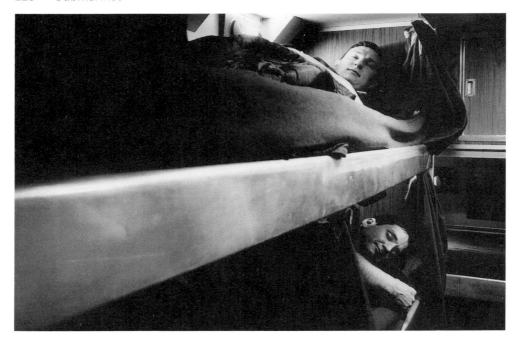

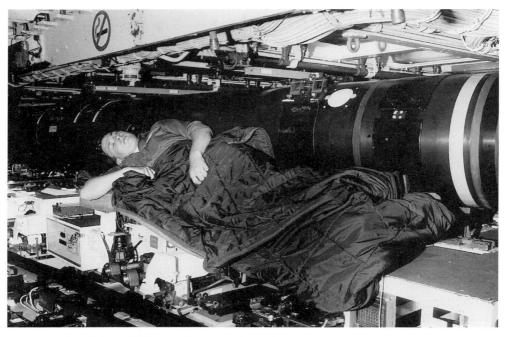

FIG. 14.6   a. Waiting for the enemy—in bunks in which there is only just room to turn over   b. When extra personnel are embarked, they often sleep on empty racks in the reload compartment (*Both Photos: HMS Neptune © British Crown Copyright 1993/MOD*)

Costa is the one person onboard your 209 class Chilean SS who can recognise the signature of a SANTA CRUZ class Argentinean SS, and that is what you are waiting for, he must be got to the sound room in plenty of time. Then, the best organisation may be a two watch system, which allows for a progressive closing up of other people as needed, but stands them down in turn when not required.

Above everything, the energy of the commanding officer needs to be husbanded. It is the most precious commodity onboard and all too easily squandered. With this in mind, modern submarines have a set of ship control instruments in the CO's cabin and the ability to listen to sensor operators making their reports, all of which helps delay the moment when one must take a more active part in proceedings.

Bombardment Operations

It is not known exactly where Tomahawk-carrying US SSGNs patrolled during operations against Iraq, but a good area would have been centred on position 23° 30′N 37° 30′E. The Red Sea is a confined space for such boats, but its widest deep water area lies on the Tropic. Here, they could have continued to provide defensive sea control for aircraft carriers patrolling in northern reaches of the Red Sea. Meanwhile, they would have been ready to conduct offensive bombardment operations, and close to Ras Abu-mad, a very conspicuous promontory. On this, missiles could lock terrain-following systems, before turning towards Baghdad,1400 kilometres to the north east. (Figure 14.7)

With such long ranges available, there is no need for Tomahawk firing areas always to be close to enemy bases, nor even a hostile shore. Often, they can be well offshore and the only real danger is that of being trailed into the area. This may not have been a great risk in 1991, but if the threat does exist, it is good practice to run missile-carrying boats past another SSN, to check for shadowers, before entering the sensitive area in which one is going to wait, a drill known as delousing. (Figure 14.8)

Inshore Operations

Patrolling close inshore, monitoring maritime activities of some nation that might turn hostile, may require a boat on offensive sea control operations to stay reasonably near to the main base of that country, if only to ensure that no important departure is missed. But much more will be learned, of a general nature, at times of less high tension, if the boat can be allowed to leave the immediate port approach, and trail ships and submarines out to their training and weapon trials areas. For this reason, it is usually best to give commanding officers a large area and a reasonably free hand over the conduct of inshore operations. However, if monitoring for a general deployment becomes the paramount consideration, a boat then needs warning to make a timely return to the focal area.

Freedom of action and a large area are even more necessary when operations involve putting special parties ashore, to carry out any of the lesser tasks mentioned in Chapter 2. A big area is more likely to provide a choice of landing places; important, because reconnaissance may show the enemy to be busier in

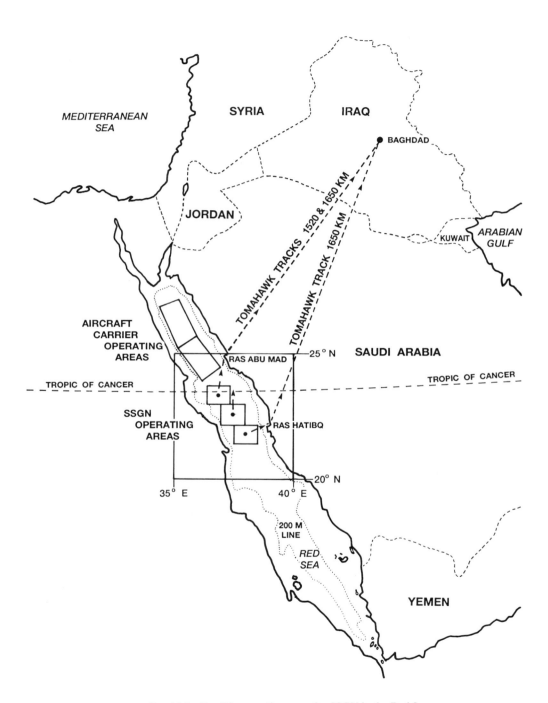

FIG. 14.7 Possible operating areas for SSGN in the Red Sea

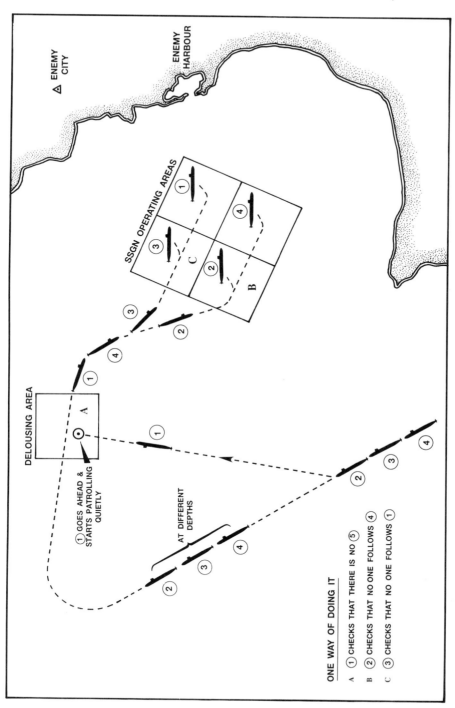

Fig. 14.8 Delousing

some areas than others. A perfect location has deep water close to shore, beaches suitable for lightly built craft, few enemy and no surf. The careful, inconspicuous navigation needed during the laying of ground mines, (see Chapter 9), is equally necessary during this first recce.

For the submarine, the most difficult and dangerous stages of a special operation are the launch and recovery of craft taking people ashore. Ideally, swimmers lock in and out of an escape tower, and use electrically propelled swimmer delivery vehicles, which have been stowed in a chamber fitted outside the pressure hull for this purpose. The launch can take place quite close inshore without the submarine ever surfacing. (Figure 14.9)

When rigid craft are stowed inside the pressure hull, one has to surface and then bring them up onto the casing for launch. However slick the drill, no one wants to do this close to land, but it may not be calm enough to open the torpedo embarkation hatch out at sea. Understandably, those landing do not wish to be launched too far out, especially if using hand paddled canoes. A fair weather compromise is to launch well offshore, then dive again and tow the craft some way, using an attack periscope to engage a line strung between them. In foul weather, one should postpone the landing; unless delay spells failure for some larger operation, when greater risk inshore may have to be accepted. (Figure 14.10)

Fig. 14.9   US Navy Special Party preparing to remove rubber swimmer delivery vehicle from casing space hangar, whilst USS *Cavalla* (SSN 684) remains dived.
(*Photo: YOGI INC*)

Fig. 14.10   Towing special parties to avoid surfacing close inshore

With an LLII equipped periscope, there may be enough light to reverse the process on the recovery day. If not, the rendezvous will have to be further off shore, where the submarine can surface and set up an infra red beacon. There must always be an alternative R/V anyway, as the local fishing fleet have been known to arrive in the area, whilst the special party has been ashore.

SSBN Operations

Three main objectives govern an SSBN patrol: uninterrupted reception of communications, quick reaction to receipt of drill firing messages, and remaining undetected. The first guarantees receiving an SLBM firing message *from* Government. The second establishes effectiveness of the deterrent service provided *for* Government. The third prevents blackmail *of* Government, and is particularly important for nations like France and the United Kingdom keeping only one or two boats on patrol and with no other strategic forces. Believable threats to kill their submarines pre-emptively could paralyse political action.

Most broadcast messages received during a deterrent patrol are advisory, full of information on friendly and potentially hostile forces approaching the patrol area. Both have to be avoided, or patrol locations will soon be compromised. Therefore, much time is spent finding evasive courses which keep long range sonars covering approaching threats, but put the boat on an opening track from them. Often, best evasive courses are poor for communications or take the boat away from places where accurate navigation is more easily performed, leading to difficult decisions.

Meanwhile, at any moment the submarine may receive a message ordering it to carry out a drill practice firing, which will be analysed in great depth afterwards, with particular emphasis on whether a ready to launch state was reached within the required short time interval. The boat must also always be prepared to fire a defensive torpedo salvo. This too requires frequent rehearsal.

FAST MOVING OPERATIONS

Although there are many submarine activities which require boats to use moving havens, two illustrate perhaps better than any other the problems which can arise during fast moving submarine operations. They are a Russian SSN trying to monitor major NATO exercises, and an SSN attempting to trail another.

Russian Surveillance Patrols

Russian SSNs, probably improved VICTOR class boats, are known to take part in NATO exercises, because surface ships sometimes stumble upon them as unexplained sonar echoes or, more positively, an ESM operator detects their Snoop Tray radar transmissions. We cannot know the details of these operations but can consider how they might be run. In particular, we can comment on the sort of instructions which the commanding officer would find it helpful to receive and why he might use active sensors.

The first thing that Captain Ivan Sergeivich in his VICTOR III is going to want is freedom to range very widely. Major NATO exercises sprawl over vast tracts of the North Atlantic ocean, and once in contact with a particular Task Group, Ivan wants to be able to follow it wherever it goes, without running into some artificial boundary just as the action is getting interesting. Bear in mind that he may be forbidden to communicate, and certainly would rather not do so whilst close to NATO units. This poses an immediate difficulty if he has to ask for an area extension. (Figure 14.11)

To ensure that he intercepts forces as soon as they enter his area, Ivan needs a steady stream of information on all known movements of NATO naval units. This should be no problem. NATO announces its intention to hold exercises well in advance. Pre-exercise assembly of surface forces is often readily detectable by satellite reconnaissance and slower moving Task Groups are usually tailed and reported by one of the many Russian AGIs. All these are excellent sources of *steerage*.

Once in contact, Ivan may be happy to have a much more restricted area, in the form of a moving haven, based on the movements of the NATO group which he is trailing. He will certainly not want other Russian forces to enter this area, even in a 'guns tight' situation, because they will make the NATO units go silent on electronic systems.

Since he is now tied to the NATO group, Ivan will want his boss to be completely unequivocal about areas not to be entered, with no use of double standards. No orders which say 'stay out', but expectations that he will go in. For example, if the group which he is monitoring enters the Irish Sea, is he allowed to

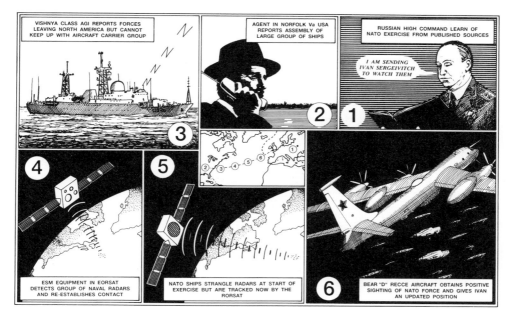

Fig. 14.11   Russian surveillance of NATO

follow them? If so, can he stay with them as they go out through the North Channel? What about The Minches? Normally, Russian units are kept on a tight rein and overtly observe international law, including limits of the Territorial Sea. Therefore, the VICTOR probably carries very specific orders. That is not to say that incursions into inshore waters are never authorised. There have been too many odd incidents off Sweden and Norway to doubt that Russian boats have been there, but it must have been with official permission. (Figure 14.12)

Clearly, intelligence collecting has a better chance of success if the forces being monitored remain unaware that they have an intruder with them. However, there are times when Ivan must find it helpful to be allowed to use sensors actively. For instance, if sonar conditions are poor and contact on a surface force has been lost, use of radar may help relocate them. A couple of sweeps on the radar may also attach ranges to a large number of sonar contacts, assisting data fusion. The response, if any of the NATO forces detect the use of a Russian Snoop Tray radar, could itself be instructive. Similarly, going through a NATO submarine versus submarine exercise area with long range sonar booming away actively, might increase the amount of movement in the area, and produce other reactions worth recording.

The main danger Ivan faces is that his VICTOR could get too closely involved in an exercise incident. NATO ASW units might then mistake his submarine for an exercise boat and pay more attention to it than he would wish. This almost guarantees interesting intelligence!—but there is also danger of collision with the NATO submarine, which will be harder to hear in a melée situation.

A more serious risk is that of having live ordnance dropped on him. This may seem a bit far fetched but if the VICTOR deliberately enters a declared weapons

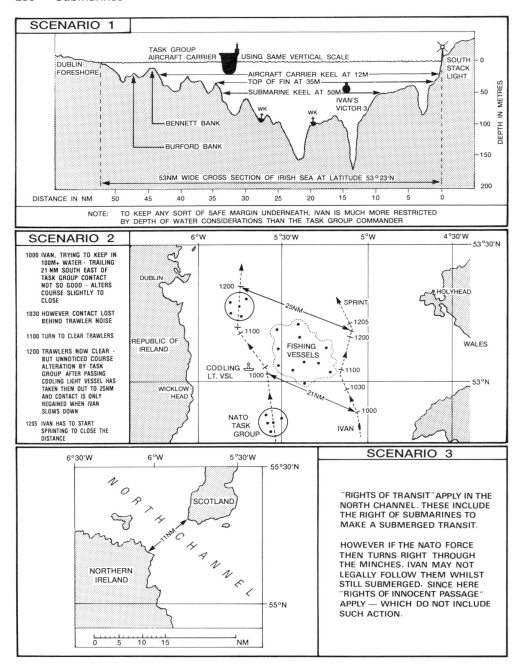

SCENARIO 1

TASK GROUP
AIRCRAFT CARRIER   USING SAME VERTICAL SCALE

DUBLIN
FORESHORE

SOUTH
STACK
LIGHT

AIRCRAFT CARRIER KEEL AT 12M
TOP OF FIN AT 35M
SUBMARINE KEEL AT 50M
IVAN'S
VICTOR 3

WK   WK

BENNETT BANK

BURFORD BANK

53NM WIDE CROSS SECTION OF IRISH SEA AT LATITUDE 53°23'N

DEPTH IN METRES

0

50

100

150

200

DISTANCE IN NM   50   45   40   35   30   25   20   15   10   5   0

NOTE: TO KEEP ANY SORT OF SAFE MARGIN UNDERNEATH, IVAN IS MUCH MORE RESTRICTED
BY DEPTH OF WATER CONSIDERATIONS THAN THE TASK GROUP COMMANDER

SCENARIO 2

1000 IVAN, TRYING TO KEEP IN
100M+ WATER - TRAILING
21 NM SOUTH EAST OF
TASK GROUP CONTACT
NOT SO GOOD - ALTERS
COURSE SLIGHTLY TO
CLOSE

1030 HOWEVER CONTACT LOST
BEHIND TRAWLER NOISE

1100 TURN TO CLEAR TRAWLERS

1200 TRAWLERS NOW CLEAR -
BUT UNNOTICED COURSE
ALTERATION BY TASK
GROUP AFTER PASSING
CODLING LIGHT VESSEL HAS
TAKEN THEM OUT TO 25NM
AND CONTACT IS ONLY
REGAINED WHEN IVAN
SLOWS DOWN

1205 IVAN HAS TO START
SPRINTING TO CLOSE THE
DISTANCE

6°W   5°30'W   5°W   4°30'W
53°30'N

DUBLIN

1200

25NM

SPRINT

1205

1200

1100

HOLYHEAD

WALES

REPUBLIC OF
IRELAND

WICKLOW
HEAD

CODLING
LT. VSL   1000

FISHING
VESSELS

1100

1030

1000

21NM

NATO
TASK
GROUP

IVAN

53°N

SCENARIO 3

6°30'W   6°W   5°30'W
55°30'N

NORTH CHANNEL

SCOTLAND

11NM

NORTHERN
IRELAND

55°N

0   5   10   15   NM

"RIGHTS OF TRANSIT" APPLY IN THE
NORTH CHANNEL. THESE INCLUDE
THE RIGHT OF SUBMARINES TO
MAKE A SUBMERGED TRANSIT.

HOWEVER IF THE NATO FORCE
THEN TURNS RIGHT THROUGH
THE MINCHES, IVAN MAY NOT
LEGALLY FOLLOW THEM WHILST
STILL SUBMERGED, SINCE HERE
"RIGHTS OF INNOCENT PASSAGE"
APPLY — WHICH DO NOT INCLUDE
SUCH ACTION.

FIG. 14.12   Problems in the Irish Sea

trial zone it is not impossible. Entering an exclusion zone during a period of polit-ical tension, it becomes quite likely. And entering Swedish territorial waters, where they drop depth charges on unexplained contacts, it is certain. Ivan will want clear orders to say if, when and what he may fire back in any such situation, and what else he is to do.

Trailing Submarines

The main difficulty for any SSN trailing another boat is to find a comfortable range at which to do it. Unlike surface ships, which generally keep moving, sub-marines may suddenly slow right down. However, a slow down is only one reason for losing contact. The boat ahead may have reversed course, putting the trailer into a much quieter part of its polar diagram of radiated noise. In this event, it cer-tainly does not pay to be too close. Or it may have changed depth and now be in a different sound velocity layer to its trailer. Or, it may always have been going faster than the trailer, and now have run out of range.

If the trailer slows down, to improve sonar listening conditions, and does not regain contact at once, the target has probably changed depth, speed or course. However, the chances of regaining contact are quite good. But, in the meantime, one must approach the last known target position with great caution. If, on slow-ing down, contact is immediately regained, the target was probably running out of range; and one is faced with the unpalatable need to do a sprint to a closer trail-ing position, during which one will be deaf. All of which emphasises the need to have a quieter boat and better sonar than the enemy—and one which works well at relatively high speeds.

DOMESTIC ROUTINE

On patrol, purely internal activities, such as relieving the watchkeepers, cook-ing and eating meals, baking bread, machine maintenance, writing up records, practice drills, film shows, perhaps even planned sleeping time for the command-ing officer, can all be arranged in an unvarying daily routine.[1] It gets distorted a bit when enemy units appear but provides a good basis for regular, efficient and harmonious running of the boat. (Figure 14.13)

Activities which disturb the environment and may be detectable by the enemy: particularly snorting, but also discharging sanitary tanks, streaming communica-tion buoys, and raising extra masts for any routine activity such as satellite navi-gation, need handling rather differently. Now, the emphasis is on avoiding regularity, which may produce recurrent patterns for enemy sensor operators, assisting and hastening classification. For instance, a random 15 minute burst of broad band snorting machinery noise, if it lacks individual frequency peaks, may not be correctly identified fast enough for anyone to complete an attack. However, if the enemy have set up their barrier in the same area as ours, and one of their boats gets an unexplained pattern on its CEP from 1000 to 1015 several days running, they should not need discrete frequency peaks on sonar to guess what it means. (see Figure 8.3) Next day, they may be in position to start an attack at 1002, as soon as the pattern begins to reappear. (Figure 14.14)

Fig.14.13   A generous steak being served to the author during a spell of duty in
USS *San Francisco* (SSN 711) in 1981 (*Photo: Author*)

Fig.14.14   JULIETT Class Russian SSG caught snorting—with too many masts
up—and too shallow (From forward to aft: Search periscope, Snort Mast,
VHF/UHF, STOPLIGHT C ESM, Attack Periscope and HF Communications)
(© *British Crown Copyright 1993/MOD*)

Even with irregular snorting and a tough energy-saving régime, quite a smooth domestic routine can be enjoyed in an SS, either in the barrier or inshore, because periods at close quarters with enemy units are rare. Life in an SSBN is smooth to the point of blandness because one is never at close quarters at all. The one really difficult situation in which to run a smooth domestic routine is provided by the SSN, not at war but near potentially hostile forces. Whether the boat is on surveillance operations like Ivan in his VICTOR, or marking some group just prior to hostilities, long hours, maybe days, can be spent at close quarters, making it very difficult for the combat team, particularly the commanding officer, to get any respite. Of these two activities, surveillance is marginally less demanding, because Ivan can always drop back into a trailing position for an occasional break, whereas the marker, by definition, must remain within weapon firing range with a solution set on fire control instruments. (Figure 14.15)

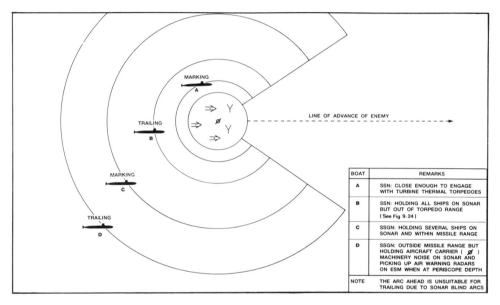

FIG. 14.15   Marking and Trailing

SUMMARY

All submarine operations may be divided into similar separate phases, but the nature of the patrol or operation itself, when the boat is most able to be offensive, varies widely.

Paramount considerations also vary with both submarine and operation. In the barrier SS, it is saving energy of all sorts. In the SSBN, it is keeping in communication, ready, and undiscovered.

SSNs too can be lying in wait: in barriers like SSs—but without their limitations; or primed ready to fire cruise missiles, when their objectives closely resemble those of the SSBN. However, the really demanding SSN role is maintaining contact with fast moving potential enemy forces for very long periods, without letting them know you are there and without exhausting yourself or your combat team.

None of these operations can be successful unless one reaches the operating area unheralded and unaccompanied in peace—and safely in war. Therefore, effort has to be put into keeping exit routes open and baffling those lying in wait for our boats, wherever they choose to set their trap. Success can also be threatened by equipment failure, prevention of which is discussed in the next chapter.

15

Support

Major submarine material failure has serious consequences in war and losing a boat gets high political visibility in peace. These facts usually combine to ensure that one receives wholehearted support. In Western navies, it takes four forms: on board support, base support, dockyard support, and direct assistance from defence contractors. All are important and need tight coordination, not only to avoid mutual interference when working in small enclosed spaces but also because there is some flexibility over who does what, within the overall support programme.

CARRIED ON BOARD

SSNs take to sea with them about 115 men and SSBNs about 150. Both are well endowed with senior enlisted personnel, because their manoeuvring rooms must always be manned by highly trained men, even in harbour. Such experienced people are well able to produce the engineering skills needed to carry out preventative maintenance and can complete some astonishingly difficult underway repairs. For example, in HMS *Warspite* they once fixed a bad, metal drawing, steam leak on a turbine in under 24 hours.

An SS like HMS *Oberon* needed about 65 people to run it. A modern SS, say HMS *Upholder* carries only 45, but nearly a third are senior ratings. Moreover, the support task has been made easier in recent years by introduction of good self-diagnosis in machinery fault-finding systems, and widespread use of printed circuit boards, which make all electronic equipment more reliable and far easier to repair, by simply fitting a spare board. (Figure 15.1)

COB (*Carried On Board*) spares are the other form of at sea support. There are thousands of items and in an SS they may have to be stowed all over the boat, wherever space can be found. This calls for very precise inventory keeping. In nuclears, there are proper store spaces, but there are far more items and the larger ones are still widely distributed. (Figure 15.2)

One measure of effectiveness for front line support is the percentage of allowed COB spares actually onboard on the day of sailing. It is popular with supply departments who like to claim that SSBNs always sail with 99.97 per cent of their stores. Yet, when 30,000 spares are allowed, you are still in bad shape if the electrolyser has been playing up recently and all 9 absent items are electrolyser spares. Remembering that most submarines are less fortunate than the SSBN, it pays to find out what is actually missing and if it is significant, to make a fuss.

Fig. 15.1   HMS *Upholder*. Ship control team—Trimming Officer, Systems Console
Operator and OMC operator (*Photo: VSEL. All instrumentation : Ferranti*)

BASE SUPPORT

Any nation setting up a submarine force from scratch has to consider: minimal
needs at each base; the number of bases; their siting; and the degree to which
existing facilities can be used. They also must decide: how to ensure an even load
on their base support staff; how to provide training and conduct trials; how much
protection to give the bases; and whether to invest in mobile, depot ship type support as well as fixed bases. Answers given to these questions determine support
effectiveness, invulnerability, flexibility and cost.

Minimal Needs

A small Division of diesel submarines can be run from any naval dockyard,
once normal surface ship facilities are augmented to meet a few special needs.
These include: a periscope and mast workshop, a battery workshop, a weapons
store and workshop, and a safe warhead stowage facility. The mast workshop must
be air conditioned to stop moisture getting into optics, and the battery shed should
have a complete set of 112 spare cells, if the cell manufacturers are located a long
way from the base. (Figure 15.3)

FIG. 15.2   Recovering COB spares from an awkward stowage space. (*Photo: HMS Neptune. © British Crown Copyright 1993/MOD*)

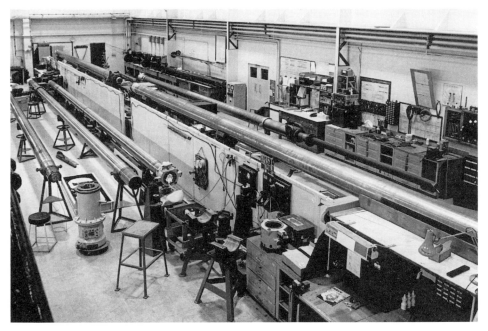

FIG. 15.3   A periscope and mast workshop (© *British Crown Copyright 1993/MOD*)

All submarines need to have their underwater fittings examined regularly, and before going to war. Any dry-dock or floating dock long enough can be adapted to take them. In the past, they have even been drawn out of the water up an inclined slope on a cradle; but the neatest and fastest method of getting them high and dry, used by both Canada and South Africa, is to bring them up on a synchrolift, ship-lift facility. This also offers the opportunity to trundle the boat ashore into a transfer bay and put it under cover for maintenance during bad weather. (Figure 15.4 a and b)

A small division needs a set of offices for about six staff officers and accommodation for three groups: the crews when in harbour; some spare crew personnel; and the base support staff, whose task is to run the workshops and, depending on their numbers, help submarine crews with second line maintenance.

Unit Size

The largest manageable unit is a Squadron of about seven SSNs or ten SSs. The ideal size to support is six SSNs or eight SSs. The minimal economical unit for a nation starting up is a Division of four diesels. With fewer boats, the same number of support staff are needed but some of them will be underemployed. Thus, in the 1990s, if Britain intends to maintain twelve SSNs and four SSs, these boats will still need three base support teams. However, some boats are always away in long refit, and a three squadron organisation would be most economical when supporting a total force of about 14 SSNs and 10 SSs, from which twelve and eight would be kept operating.

One can have a mixed squadron of SSNs and SSs, but it complicates many aspects of support, especially spares supply. So when the UPHOLDER class boats had to be sent somewhere other than their original base at Gosport, it made more sense to keep all four together, than to split them between existing SSN squadrons. However, neither squadron could sensibly take on running all four SSs in addition to a full complement of SSNs. Therefore, the SSs had to bring their base support with them.

Number and Siting of Bases

One does not have to have as many bases as one has squadrons. For instance, France operate units of both SSNs and SSs from their base at Toulon; and Britain has SSNs and SSBNs in Gare Loch. The main advantages of such collocation are savings achieved by sharing workshops and having access to the higher skilled, more senior support staff which a bigger base attracts. However, concentration of assets makes any air attack potentially more damaging, and considerably simplifies the planning of the enemy's mining campaign.

Even in peacetime, a base needs to be near 200 metre deep water, to let modern boats dive and safely use high speed as soon as possible after leaving harbour. (see Figure 4.5) In war, such deep water close to the base also provides earlier, and greater, protection from detection and attack to submarines deploying. Some nations seek economies, by locating the base providing *second line support*, in the Dockyard port selected for submarine refits—which are the *third line* of support.

FIG. 15.4   a. Submarine base at Halifax Nova Scotia—showing Synchrolift and covered repair building (*centre*) b. Raising an OJIBWA Class SS on the Synchrolift (*Both photos: Canadian Forces*)

But long distance from deep water may be the deciding factor. For example, in Britain, Devonport is regarded as suitable for both purposes. Whereas Rosyth, being 720 kilometres from good deep water, is only suitable for refitting. Hence the need for an SSBN base at Faslane.

Steady Base Loading

All submarines like to be in harbour for national holidays but peaks and troughs in base loading can only be avoided by operating boats on a strict cycle, which brings back to base at any one time just a small proportion of the force. Cyclic running achieves high utilisation but is hard work and may keep submarines away from their base port for 65 per cent or more of the year.[1] Thus, although submarine crews can, and often do, carry out their own second line maintenance, during SMPs (*Self Maintenance Periods*) away from base; boats on cyclic running mostly come back to base for an AMP (*Assisted Maintenance Period*), which allows them to send some of their own people on leave.

The need to maintain the cycle is greatest in SSBNs, a proportion of whom must always be on patrol. Therefore, they are given two complete crews. On return from sea, the boat is turned round very quickly because both crews, and the base staff, are working on the boat. Indeed, the crew just returned do not go on leave until their reliefs have taken the boat to sea for its pre-sailing shake down.

Training and Trials

Training has to be conducted at many different levels. For everyone, basic training starts at a submarine school ashore, where emphasis is on learning first principles, getting acquainted with the more important equipment which anyone might have to operate, and doing everything safely. It includes escaping from a simulated submarine disaster, to make a 30 metre free ascent through a water tower. (Figure 15.5)

Simultaneously, operators, maintainers, nuclear watch keepers and combat teams have to learn their specialist skills. Theory is taught in the classroom, and practical instruction given in large and expensive simulators; which allow one to practice anything from the after planes jamming at full dive whilst travelling at 25 knots in an SSN, to carrying out a full scale attack on an enemy surface group, using all the sensors one would normally have available; or recovering from a reactor scram whilst on watch in the manoeuvring room of a nuclear submarine— all without any risk of doing damage in the real world. (Figures 15.6, 15.7 and 15.8)

Then, everyone goes to sea, where they are under probation, learning a lot more. Eventually, they have to satisfy a board, composed of their senior shipmates, that they have learned enough to merit wearing the prized dolphins that are only awarded to those fully qualified for a sea-going billet. Board members take their responsibilities very seriously, not least because their lives will be in the hands of the newcomers, once qualified.

Basic training facilities are normally located at a base which is also supporting submarines but are too expensive to be replicated everywhere. However, all bases

FIG. 15.5   Rear Admiral RT Frere—Flag Officer Submarines—arriving at the top of the 30 metre tank during escape training—1992. (© *British Crown Copyright 1993/MOD*)

F<small>IG</small>. 15.6   VANGUARD Class Submarine Control Simulator in motion (*Photo: Link-Miles Ltd*)

should provide continuation training facilities, at least for sonar and EW operators, and if possible for nuclear watchkeepers and combat teams, to allow them to maintain skills without having to travel to some other location during their precious harbour time.

Prospective submarine commanding officers also have to be trained, in a course lasting several months, during which the student may complete as many as 90 practice attacks and take a submarine through advanced exercises, making all the decisions. Affectionately known as 'The Perisher' in UK, it is a very tough course. No one even starts it unless already recommended for command. Yet the average failure rate is about 30 per cent and it has been known for every single student of a course of five to fail, clear proof that there is no compromising on standards to avoid political embarrassment.

The officer running the course is looking for some exceptional qualities. Not only must the CO be able to handle the submarine safely, he must also be comfortable operating totally unsupported deep into enemy waters. Thus he needs a strongly aggressive personality, but must also be capable of cool, calculated thinking, and agile at mental arithmetic. Unlike a surface ship commanding officer, who receives data in a steady stream, the submarine CO may have to envisage a whole tactical situation after only occasional snatches of data, such

Fɪɢ. 15.7   UPHOLDER Class Machinery Control Trainer viewed from the
instructor's station (*Photo: Link-Miles Ltd*)

as that obtained during a single ten second all round periscope look.

Finally, every boat leaving a building or refitting yard needs an extensive work up period: to ensure that it can handle any situation it might face in war or peace, and is an efficient enough fighting vehicle to justify sending it to an operational squadron. In the US Atlantic command, the final stage of work up is a supervised tactical exercise conducted on a huge, three dimensionally instrumented open sea range off the Bahamas, which is able to follow the boat and its opponents, and track all weapons fired throughout their travel above or below water.[2] (Figures 15.9 and 15.10)

Such a range can double as a superb weapons trials facility but most navies have to settle for something more modest. Nevertheless, base support does also include arranging access to facilities such as: noise ranges, deperming berths, torpedo recovery vessels for practice firings and the means to check sensor bearing accuracies, either on a special range or against another vessel. The nearer all these facilities are to the base port, the more useful the base. (Figure 15.11)

Protection and Mobility

Cyclic running alone gives partial protection against bolt from the blue type attacks, since some boats ought always to be away from home, with a good

Fig. 15.8   TACTICIAN—the Combat Team Trainer—in use at Faslane (*Photo: Ferranti International*)

proportion of their war outfit weapons embarked. Protecting a static base is much harder, since it can only be turned into an impregnable fortress by tunnelling into the side of a large mountain and putting massive doors on the resultant caves. Sweden and Norway have used this method and work seen at Russian Northern Fleet bases suggests that they may be providing strong shelters for some boats.

Depot ships too can provide protection, by dispersing assets, but their main task is to bring support closer to a desired area of operations. This may seem less necessary in the age of the SSN and the 12,000 kilometre missile. However, both the United States and Russia operate such ships. They have huge workshops and are designed to tend nuclear submarines. Of course, being a finite size, their support carrying capacity is not limitless; but the cost conscious might see this as a positive advantage, since unlike shore bases, ships cannot grow by Parkinson's Law! (Figure 15.12)

DOCKYARD SUPPORT

The Royal Navy has much strengthened its base facilities over the last twenty five years, in a deliberate attempt to become less dependent on dockyards, but a

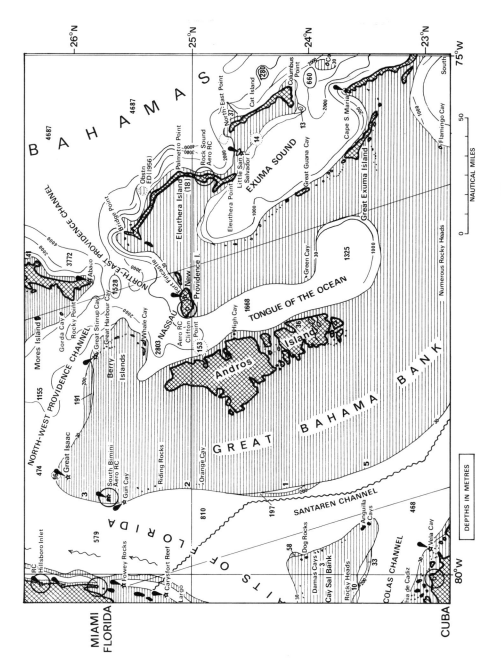

Fig. 15. 9 Tongue of the Ocean—Bahamas. The AUTEC Range—Where it is.
(© *British Crown Copyright 1993/MOD*)

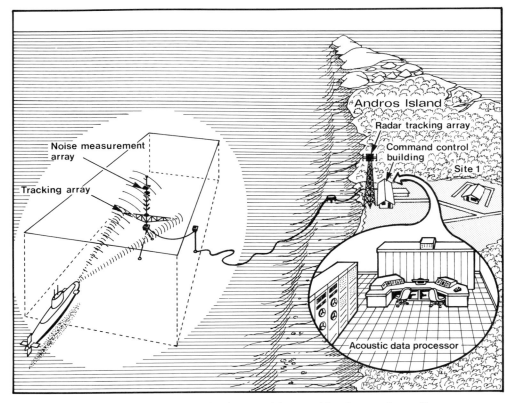

FIG. 15.10   AUTEC Range—showing one of three tracking sites—and one of hundreds of underwater arrays. (*From Urick, Principles of Underwater Sound
(McGraw- Hill 1983)*)

submarine still has to have their support for tasks that a base could not handle, or
which would take so much longer than the normal AMP, as to disrupt operating
cycles and draw off support owed to other submarines. The largest items in this
category are refuelling a reactor core and the major work which becomes due on
diesel engines after about 4000 hours of running. These tasks have a big influence
on the frequency of yard overhauls and usually govern their length, unless fitting
of new equipment involves major construction work. (Figure 15.13)

Refit Cycles

Some nations give submarines a 'safe to dive date', x months after completing
building or dockyard refit, beyond which they should not be dived again until the
hull has been examined for metal erosion. In peace, if an SS is being run very gently, this date can come up before diesels need their big overhaul, just as a car may
be taken in for servicing on time rather than miles. In war, SSs go into refit whenever it is operationally convenient, usually after completing a particular number
of patrols.

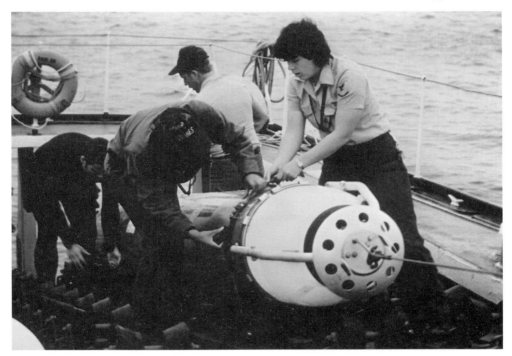

FIG. 15.11   Bringing a Mk48 weapon aboard a Torpedo Recovery Vessel after an exercise firing. Women carry out many such duties in the Submarine Support Services of both the UK and US Navies (*Photo: YOGI INC 1987*)

Whereas, an SS can always be run on if the engines are still working well, a nuclear powered boat must refit once the reactor core is exhausted. Therefore, time to next SSN major refit depends on the amount of power loaded in, and the rate of usage. Reactor physics tests carried out every six months give an approximate figure for the amount of FSH remaining. (See Chapter 5) They are rather inaccurate at first but get better as fuel is used. The operations staff also know from experience roughly how many FSH are used per day carrying out various activities: zero when at the static noise range, five or six when patrolling quietly, maybe fifteen during fleet exercises etc. Armed with such figures, they audit the proposed programme, then adjust it to ensure that fuel is not exhausted before the next refit is due to start.

The overall submarine command plan needs a lot of juggling to keep each refitting slot filled and all the submarines ending their commissions just as a new slot becomes vacant. Dockyard failure to complete refits on time and the sudden appearance of demanding new operational commitments—such as the need to make repeated 30,000 kilometre round trips from the United Kingdom to the Falklands area—can wreck any plan. Therefore, some boats are kept on high and some on low usage rates, allowing both increase and decrease of activity.

When nuclears have very long core lives, perhaps half the life expectancy of the boat, they too must be brought in on a time basis, as much of the auxiliary

FIG. 15.12   US Navy SSN tender USS *McKee* (S41) in San Diego (*Photo: US Navy*)

FIG. 15.13 Submarine Base and Nuclear Refitting complex Devonport (*Photo: Rolls Royce & Associates*)

machinery will deteriorate unacceptably if not given third line maintenance until the core is renewed. There may also be need for dockyard support with activities such as docking for hull cleansing, if the base does not have its own dock. Always, the battle is to prevent these occasions turning into mini-refits.

CONTRACTOR INVOLVEMENT

The prime cause of work package growth during intermediate visits to dock-yards is the wish to fit new equipment. Often, news about potential enemy capabilities makes it seem unacceptable to delay providing a compensating advantage until the boat is due for mid-life refit. No doubt with this in mind, MOD(UK) now deliberately encourage defence contractors to plan on carrying out quite major equipment modifications and new installations during an AMP, using only their own and limited base staff resources.

Many contractors have been very responsive to this initiative, especially those who already have their own well worked up afloat support teams. A good example was the fitting of new EW equipment into OBERON class boats, which have a congested internal layout. After visits to several boats, MEL development engineers constructed a model which showed both possible locations, all obstacles to be got round in reaching them, and existing equipment which was not to be disturbed. Using the model, they *then* planned their cabinet sizes and shapes. Actual fitting of the new equipment took 28 days, which included putting in a replacement mast and all the office cabinets, setting to work and a harbour acceptance trial. (Figure 15.14)

SUPPORT IN PERSPECTIVE

One day in January 1991, the British submarine manpower computer coughed out the following numbers: **Teeth** 3875, **Support** 2400, **Tail** 1648, an overall force of 7923. This last number includes all those at sea and ashore still under training. There were also about 200 contracted civilians. 'Teeth' means trained and in a boat.

Bearing in mind that the largest contributor to through life costs is people, this might seem generous support. However, from those human resources Britain was producing twelve capital ships each carrying a huge punch, four other impressive major war vessels operating on a high rate of utilisation, and their strategic deterrent.

A nation with more limited resources can have a small submarine arm of three or four diesel powered boats with a much less impressive outlay, but support still has to be provided on board, at base and in the yard; and there are minimal additions to infrastructure which must be made, even when grafting onto a good existing surface ship navy organisation. However, small navies can reduce submarine support costs in several ways. They can send people and maybe submarines for all sorts of training with other navies. This is very common. And they can reduce base support numbers by running submarines at lower intensity. This allows extra time in harbour, during which more of the second line maintenance can be performed by the crew themselves.

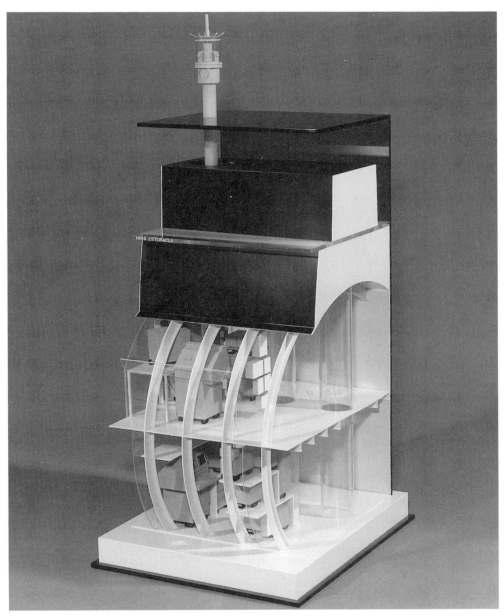

FIG. 15.14   MEL 'O" boat ship fitting model [based on visits to HM Submarines *Otter* and *Oracle*]. (*Photo: Thorn EMI*)

Unfortunately, as always when one cuts costs, there are penalties. Abandoning cyclic running produces larger numbers of submarines in harbour simultaneously, raising vulnerability to pre-emptive attack; and low intensity of operations tends to produce less efficient war machines. Nations, which are just getting by on minimal support, to provide boats as opposition for their surface forces in peace, cannot expect these same boats to produce the deadly effectiveness in war of submarines given intensive work up on all the latest tactical doctrine, and then employed largely on surveillance operations against a potential enemy.

16

Future Trends

Announcements about submarine building programmes, can give the impression that future boats and weapon systems are going to be totally different from present ones. In reality, change is mostly evolutionary rather than revolutionary, with novel equipment ideas being tested in current submarines and then, if successful, more widely fitted as new boats are built. Thus, although US SSNs of the SEA WOLF class may be a new shape, much of their equipment will have been proved in the later LOS ANGELES class boats. This is wise, since submarines in which everything is newly designed are often bedevilled with problems, very late into service and astronomically expensive—all sure ways of losing political good will.

However, having said those cautionary words, we will now do a bit of crystal gazing: first considering future material possibilities, then likely changes in operational needs, and finally the future of submarines themselves.

CONSTRUCTION

High tensile steel is likely to remain the most common submarine hull material until well into the next century, but cold rolling and welding plate may not be the only construction method used. A possible alternative, is to create a toroid of thick hollow pipe rings. This is about five times stronger than a plated hull using a similar weight of HY 80 steel and needs little internal framing. Abutting pipe rings form natural 'V' shaped spaces, making welding easy; and the required hull profile can be created by gradually altering the diameter of successive pipe rings. Maritalia of Italy have already built a prototype 29 ton midget submarine, 3 GST 9, using these techniques. It has other interesting features, including double carvel-laid noise reduction strakes, on the outer skin, which stay in position much better than tiles. (Figure 16.1)

The trend in internal construction is towards raft mounted equipment modules. Some of these modules could still be bolted into position, after being slid into their hull sections during assembly; but many more are likely to be on hydraulic jacks for sound isolation. Either way, wide use of large modules might lead to future boats being built with a natural break point in them, about a metre wide. During major refits, the hull would be cut in half here, allowing all equipment from two whole sections to be taken out on their rafts to workshops ashore. This would speed up work on major items and make it easier to achieve a high quality reinstallation standard.

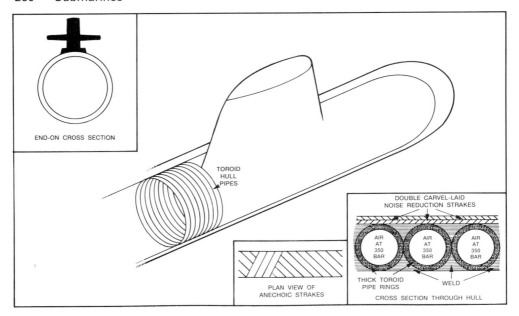

FIG. 16.1   Toroid hull construction

PROPULSION AND POWER GENERATION

Several non-nuclear power generation methods are currently being evaluated, or are well into development. Some hope to produce electricity direct from fuel cells. Others rely on external combustion engines, fed with oxygen and diesel fuel. In systems where space is limited, oxygen is stowed liquid in a tank, but in GST (*Gaseous Storage in Toroid*) it is held as a compressed gas in the hollow hull pipes, at a pressure of about 350 bar.

Generally, these systems are not meant to provide high speed, for which a battery is still needed. However, they are worth pursuing, because they enable an SS to run at slow speeds without snorting for as long as the stored gas lasts—two weeks now, maybe much more in the future.

Fuel Cells

A fuel cell can be regarded as an electrolyser working in reverse. Instead of passing a current through water and electrolyte, to get off oxygen and hydrogen, one passes hydrogen or carbon monoxide, through an electrolyte, where it combines with oxygen and generates current.

Electrolytes do not hold much hydrogen or oxygen in solution, so electrode design has to promote a very efficient reaction, which must take place virtually at the electrode/electrolyte interface. This means use of materials that also act as a catalyst, usually noble metals such as silver, platinum, or nickel; and porous construction, to provide the thinnest possible layer of electrolyte over the largest possible surface area of electrode.

To prevent bubbling through the electrolyte, which can produce an H_2/O_2 explosion, hydrogen must be introduced very gently. This consideration often limited fuel input pressures and the energy output of early cells. However, cells now on test at CJB Developments, with solid polymer electrolyte, platinum electrodes and a hydrogen and air input, can safely produce 10 kilowatts. Moreover, a hybrid fuel cell/battery propulsion system, designed by Howaldtswerke, has been undergoing prototype sea trials since 1987, and is expected to feature in the new German *Type 212* class diesel submarines, due to appear in 1995. They should be very quiet boats.

External Combustion Engines

Sweden was first into the field with ECE (***External Combustion Engines***). In 1987–88, they put a six metre extension into the hull of the first of the NÄCKEN class boats at Kockums shipyard, which contains two V4-275R multi cylinder FPSEs (***Free Piston Stirling Engines***), a liquid oxygen tank and some control equipment. (Figure 16.2)

The Stirling operates by applying external heat to a sealed chamber, which encloses a 'working gas'. A piston is used to change the volume occupied by this gas, whilst a second piston, called a displacer, moves it from the hot to the cold part of the engine. External combustion is continuous, as is the movement of both pistons. Therefore, by contrast with an internal combustion engine, changes in cylinder pressure are very gradual and a four cylinder Stirling provides almost constant torque. The quiet, smooth performance which this produces is well suited to the submarine environment. (Figure 16.3 and 16.4)

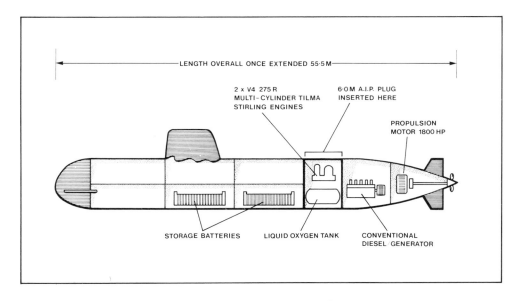

FIG. 16.2   Schematic layout of Swedish NÄCKEN Class

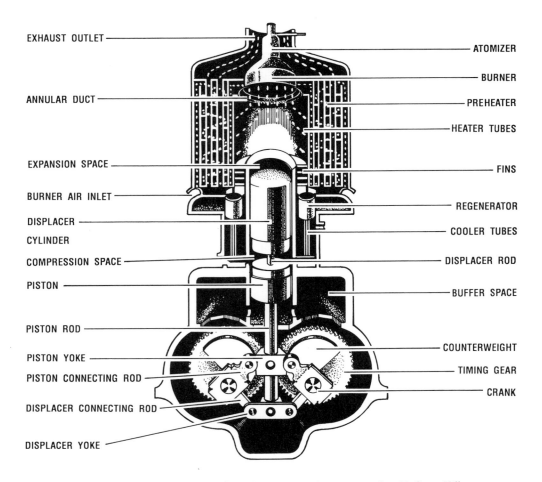

EXHAUST OUTLET

ANNULAR DUCT

EXPANSION SPACE

BURNER AIR INLET

DISPLACER
CYLINDER

COMPRESSION SPACE

PISTON

PISTON ROD

PISTON YOKE

PISTON CONNECTING ROD

DISPLACER CONNECTING ROD

DISPLACER YOKE

ATOMIZER

BURNER

PREHEATER

HEATER TUBES

FINS

REGENERATOR

COOLER TUBES

DISPLACER ROD

BUFFER SPACE

COUNTERWEIGHT

TIMING GEAR

CRANK

FIG. 16.3 Stirling Cylinder [*based upon a schematic in the McGraw-Hill Encyclopedia of Science and Technology*]

Stirling engines also incorporate means for recycling much of the heat energy given to the working gas and are about as efficient as one can make a diesel engine, so ensuring that maximum value is obtained from the stored oxygen. The main weakness in the system is that the CO_2 exhaust has to be discharged. This can be done down at 300 metres but not without creating noise and potentially a heat signature

GST System

In a GST (*Gaseous Storage in Toroid*) system, oxygen is tapped from the hull pipes onto a common rail and used to burn diesel fuel in the engines. Whilst still in home waters, the exhaust is discharged to sea, but when low signatures are needed, these gases are compressed and held onboard in empty toroid pipes. First,

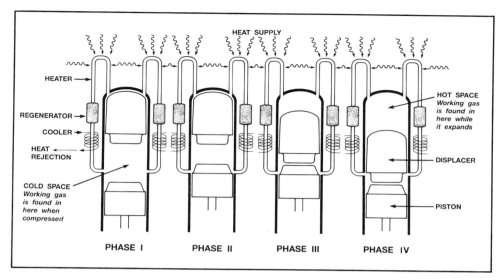

HEAT SUPPLY

HEATER →

REGENERATOR →

COOLER →

HEAT ←
REJECTION

COLD SPACE
*Working gas
is found in
here when
compressed*

HOT SPACE
*Working gas
is found in
here while
it expands*

DISPLACER

PISTON

PHASE I   PHASE II   PHASE III   PHASE IV

FIG. 16.4   The Stirling engine cycle [*source as for Fig 16.3*]

they have to be scrubbed and tested in a special treatment tank, mainly to ensure that corrosive sulphuric compounds have been removed.

GST certainly seems the most promising of these future AIP (**Air Independent Propulsion**) designs, mainly because large stowage space for the gas makes it more than just a get out of trouble system. For example, a 1000 ton GST boat might manage as much as 54,000 kilometres at 5 knots, or even 2,700 kilometres at 20 knots, with no resort to snorting. It will not be as quiet as a fuel cell, but should have quite a low signature, and inherently be the safest system, since it uses neither liquid oxygen nor free hydrogen.

MASTS

The most innovative move with above water sensors might be the invention of a workable pop-up optronics mast, that is one which can be floated to the surface from deep. The need is certainly recognised and existing fibre optic techniques could easily handle the transfer of information from the sensors to the submarine, probably down a single wire. However, there are formidable mechanical problems to be overcome if the mast is to be raised whilst running at even quite modest speeds. (Figure 16.5)

SENSORS

It is not possible to forecast whether noise reduction in submarines of other nations will be effective enough to force our boats to use active sonars. It is unlikely that all low frequency noise can ever be totally eliminated. However, if passive submarine sonars are still the primary anti-submarine sensor in twenty

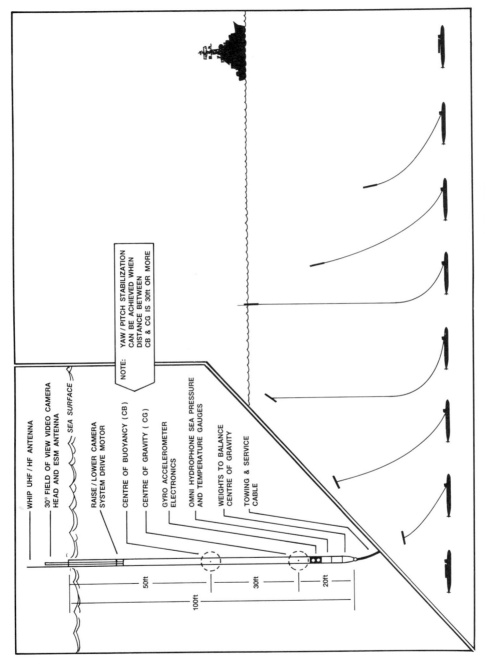

NOTE: YAW / PITCH STABILIZATION CAN BE ACHIEVED WHEN DISTANCE BETWEEN CB & CG IS 30ft OR MORE

WHIP UHF / HF ANTENNA
30° FIELD OF VIEW VIDEO CAMERA HEAD AND ESM ANTENNA
SEA SURFACE
RAISE / LOWER CAMERA SYSTEM DRIVE MOTOR
CENTRE OF BUOYANCY (CB)
CENTRE OF GRAVITY (CG)
GYRO ACCELEROMETER ELECTRONICS
OMNI HYDROPHONE SEA PRESSURE AND TEMPERATURE GAUGES
WEIGHTS TO BALANCE CENTRE OF GRAVITY
TOWING & SERVICE CABLE

50ft
30ft
20ft
100ft

FIG. 16.5   Deployable tactical mast [*based upon material supplied by Pilkington Optronics and Barr & Stroud*]

years time, it will be because they can routinely classify noises that today would be regarded as only marginally detectable.

The trend with all sensors is towards higher data handling speeds, and more comprehensive data fusion. To take full advantage of this trend, better displays will have to be provided in submarine combat centres. Beyond anything that the fire control team are given for carrying out an attack, commanding officers independently need a large flat plate display, on which information held in data banks can be presented, using alphanumeric or graphic form, as best suited to current tactical situations.

To be really useful, this command aid must be able to correlate all historical information and have a preview capability, showing the situation which will exist in various increments of future time, should all contacts maintain present course and speed, and one's own submarine take various different courses of action. Ideally, it will also help select the best moment to fire homing torpedoes, by allowing one to examine the effect on the torpedo running range of likely enemy manoeuvres after weapon launch, and of allowing for a re-attack, a command problem which was discussed in Chapter 9.

WEAPONS

Most likely submarine weapon trend, not already covered in earlier chapters, is development of anti-helicopter self-defence systems. All large navies now have ASW helicopters, and a well worked up pair of them, fitted with medium range dunking sonars and good modern torpedoes, can prove tough opposition for the best of SSNs. Mobile decoys may be enough to frustrate the first attack, but not to lose such opponents altogether, bearing in mind that one cannot outrun them. However, knocking down even one helo with a SAM would greatly increase the chance of escaping from the other. Many boats already have elevated launch tubes. It can only be a matter of time before some nation starts carrying medium range SAMs in two of them. (Figure 16.6)

Agreement on strategic arms limitations by the major powers is likely to be followed by a run down of the number of ballistic missile carrying submarines, and a large increase in the number of submarines of all sorts carrying cruise missiles. The flexibility of cruise, which can be used against land or sea targets and carry HE or nuclear warheads, made this move likely long before Iraq was attacked in 1991. The precision and devastating success of the HE headed weapons during that short war makes the trend inevitable.

COMMUNICATIONS

At sea, the requirement is for better buoys and wires, that can be streamed for broadcast reception from deeper, whilst going faster. This seems likely to be achieved, but only gradually. Ashore, although Britain ought to have ELF, both expense and practical considerations may well restrict its use to the USA and Russia. However, the UK should soon have at least one unitised VLF station. Other nations intent on operating SSNs and modern SSs are likely to invest in similar stations, of which there are still surprisingly few. Beyond this, the main

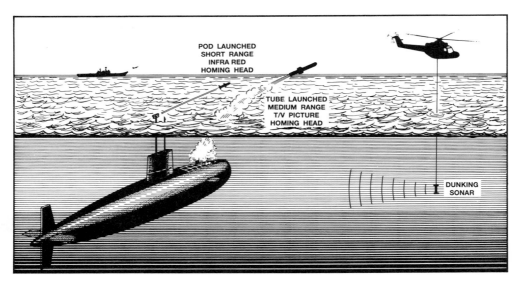

FIG. 16.6   Anti-helicopter SAM options

trend will be for ever more two-way satellite working. It is essential for the maintenance of tight control over free ranging SSNs, and not so vulnerable in a post Cold War age, since small nations do not have the means to shoot down satellites.

There may also be research into the use of lasers. These operate at light frequencies, $(5 \times 10^{14}$ Hertz). Here, band widths are so large that a single beam could carry as much information as all the radio channels in the world put together. The spatially coherent, monochromatic light which they emit can be concentrated to near parallel rays, and the wavelength adjusted, (to decide colour), by small changes of lasing material chemical composition. Intensity of emission also is alterable, in trillionths of a second, to encode very complex digital signals. Already, these properties are being used by the gallium arsenide, semi-conductor laser chip. This can send huge amounts of data down glass fibre tubes thinner than a human hair, at near infra red wavelengths, (1300–1550 nanometres), to meet the sensor information fusion needs identified in Chapters 7 and 8, a vital internal communication function.

Lasers, working from a stationary satellite also offer another means of broadcasting communications and, since the blue/green wavelengths (450–570 nanometres) have some ability to penetrate sea water, might be read without raising a mast. The high data carrying capacity makes it an attractive idea. However, there are problems. The satellite can only cover its whole footprint with such a narrow beam by transmitting the same material many times over. Thus, although the laser sends its message quickly enough, it only covers any one area very infrequently. It might be possible to localise the submarine position for the satellite, but staying too much on one part of the footprint risks focussing enemy attention on that area. As lasers also have problems penetrating bad weather, at best they seem restricted to being back up systems.

NAVIGATION

Inertial Navigation Systems will be much more dependable when RLG (*Ring Laser Gyro*) technology is applied to submarine equipment, since MTBF (*Mean Time Between Failures*) of RLGs are five or six years, not a matter of weeks.

An RLG is a glass block, square or triangular, with an internal laser path. Beams are sent around the block in opposite directions. Then, if the RLG rotates about its axis, an optical frequency shift occurs, and one beam takes more time, one less, to complete the distance. This sets up an interference pattern where the two beams are combined. An optical sensor counts the fringes produced and gives a digital readout proportional to rate. (Figures 16.7 and 16.8)

The name is misleading because an RLG is not ring shaped and has no gyro. This also means that it cannot be used in a conventional SINS, in which the submarine rotates about an inertial weight, held rigid in space by three spinning-mass gyros. (see Chapter 11) Instead, it is used in a 'strap down' system, one in which the inertial platform rotates with the boat. Thus, RLG rates are first processed to

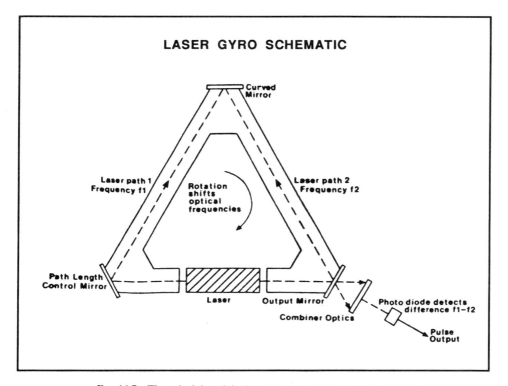

Fig. 16.7   The principles of the laser gyro (*Diagram British Aerospace*)

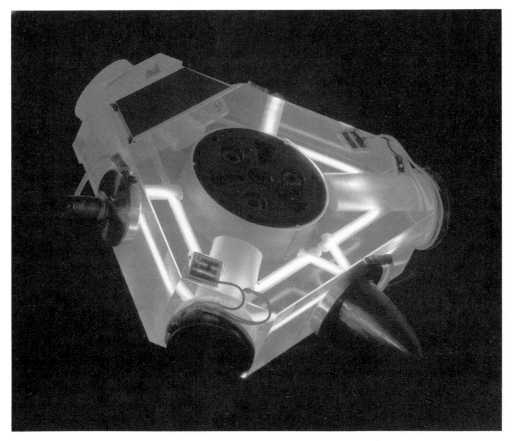

Fɪɢ. 16.8   Triangular Ring Laser Gyro—30 cm path length. (*Photo: British Aerospace*)

establish submarine attitude, then body axis accelerations are integrated into navigational displacements.

An RLG also would provide a very reliable SSN compass. Insensitive to gravitational accelerations (g), it remains accurate throughout high rate turns, does not suffer from precessing problems in high latitudes, and is available minutes after switch on.

SIGNATURE REDUCTION

Once machinery discrete frequency peaks have been removed, future noise reduction efforts have to be directed at the very items, mentioned above, for which future sonars will be searching. Top of the list is likely to be flow noise from pipes, being produced almost continuously somewhere in the boat by hydraulics; but also intermittently by the salt water main line and many other auxiliary systems. It may be that nuclear-powered submarines, with their large electric generating capacities, should operate more equipment by quiet electrics and much

FIG. 16.9   Twin unit low pressure electrolyser [compare, for complexity, with Fig. 13.2] (*Photo: CJB Developments*)

less by noisy hydraulics. But this might increase the induced component of the magnetic signature, a quite unacceptable penalty.

One thing is certain: the trend will be for much more comprehensive self monitoring, second by second, of the various signatures, with corrective action being taken by closed curcuit systems—including perhaps anti-noise to canel noise—wherever such methods can be used without loss of operational capability.

ATMOSPHERE CONTROL

Once SSs do long periods without snorting, they require better atmosphere control arrangements. This need is anticipated in UK Upholder class boats, who have a CO_2 removal system worthy of an SSN. It is neatly arranged so that MEA absorbs noxious gas continuously, but the power hungry heat recycling process is delayed until the next snort period. On the O_2 side, although chlorate candles will still be carried by all submarines, any SS with an AIP system, is likely to have ample liquid oxygen, or oxygen stored under pressure in the toroid hull, to bleed some for the crew. Their needs are minute compared to those of the engines.

SSNs and SSBNs too will soon benefit from important new developments. The first is a better electrolyser, which no longer needs caustic electrolyte to make its water conduct current. Instead, like a modern fuel cell, it has a solid polymer

Fig. 16.10   A Temperature Swing Molecular Adsorber Unit. (Removes water vapour, C02, CO, H2 and Freon) (*Photo: CJB Developments*)

electrolyte and the only operating fluid is the demineralised water. This produces a cell able to accept high current densities, which can generate a lot more oxygen from smaller, lighter units, operated at low pressure. It is much safer and simpler, and available immediately after switch on. (Figure 16.9)

Another major advance, now appearing in some nuclear boats is the TSMA (***Temperature Swing Molecular Adsorber***), multi-purpose unit for removing CO_2, hydrogen, carbon monoxide and Freon R12. In a TSMA, air at low temperature

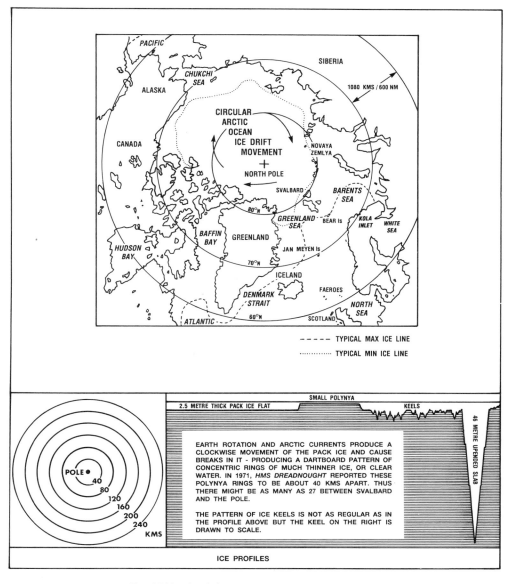

FIG. 16.11   Arctic ice coverage and polynya formation

is forced through a bed of molecular sieves of different pore diameter, which trap water vapour, then adsorb CO_2 and Freon. When the bed is saturated, electrical heaters switch on to release the trapped molecules, which are sucked out by a vacuum pump. The CO_2/Freon mixture is then compressed and discharged overboard. The air is also passed through beds of platinised alumina and hopcalite, which catalytically oxidise CO and H2. (Figure 16.10)

OPERATIONAL TRENDS

Whilst Russia is still seen as a possible threat, which it must be until it reduces its huge Northern Fleet, the most likely of future operational trends is that Arctic patrols will still be necessary. Russian SSBNs are based in 70 degrees North, at worst only a 24 hour run from the ice edge. They are well suited to Arctic operations and putting them under ice for extra defensive cover would be a wise move. Equally, the Arctic is a good holding area for US and UK SSGNs with cruise missile targets lying in northern parts of Russia. These SSBNs and SSGNs will be sought out by opposing SSNs. In short, if Superpower relations go sour again, the Arctic Ocean will be a busy and crucially important submarine battle arena. (Figure 16.11)

Russian boats probably use this area quite regularly, albeit covertly. French SSNs have certainly been there. And both US and UK SSNs have conducted annual operations in the Arctic, often together, for some years. In the West, one aim of such patrols has been to make clear to Russia that the Arctic is not their lake, hence the press pictures of UK/US SSNs at the North Pole. However, a much

FIG. 16.12   British SSNs at the North Pole (© *British Crown Copyright 1993/MOD*)

more important objective is to build up experience of submarine versus submarine operations in the unfamiliar Arctic environment. (Figure 16.12)

There is certainly plenty to learn. Just getting there can be quite awkward, especially if entering from the Pacific, through the Bering Strait and Chukchi Sea, where there is very little room between ice keels overhead and the sea bed underneath. Throughout the Arctic, these keels, caused by slabs of pack ice breaking and getting upended, may extend down to nearly 50 m.[1] This means adjusting the safe operating envelope. Keels also produce a large number of echoes on active sonars, making it hard for homing torpedoes to engage targets which are tucked up close under the pack ice.

Submarines must be practised in surfacing through the ice without causing themselves damage, since missile firers have to do so to launch their weapons. And SSNs might need to do so to raise a mast for SATNAV or SATCOM purposes. Also, a surfacing could be necessary if there was a fire onboard. Some submarines, like the giant TYPHOON class, may be able to use their large hulls and big reserve buoyancy to break up through the pack ice. But most boats have to find a polynya of thinner ice and come up through it very carefully.

Post Cold War

As likelihood of confrontation with Russia diminishes, the possibility of conducting future operations in much warmer climates will increase. Several potential world trouble spots seem to lie in tropical or semi-tropical waters. And many important raw materials come from nations in these geographic regions. If future wars are not to be about ideologies, they will probably be about interference with such vital resources. Therefore, the UK policy of regularly sending a well balanced task group around the world, accompanied by SSNs, to work with Commonwealth and other friendly nations, ought to be continued.

Warm water operations are not as difficult as Arctic operations, but they produce different sonar conditions and are often more demanding on electronic equipment. It helps to have exercised under these conditions before having to fight under them. Moreover, SSNs must get plenty of experience of making long deployments in support of surface groups, the most likely pattern of operations in lower level confrontation situations. In particular, command, control and communications techniques will need practising as new equipment is developed.

Once Cold War certainties are gone, there is worrying uncertainty over who the next opponent will be. With over 40 nations owning submarines, there is a very wide range of different boats against which submarine versus submarine operations might be necessary, one day. Surveillance may have to be conducted on a much wider basis, therefore, to build up data on some of these countries, and on their submarine noise signatures in particular. Not least of the problems Britain faced in April 1982, was the very poor data bank maintained on Argentina in the years before it became necessary to fight her.

Finally, with operations likely to be conducted much further afield, it may be necessary for SSNs to become more proficient in the closer in shore, lesser submarine roles, hitherto left mainly to SSs.

FUTURE OF SUBMARINES

All these material and operational trends do, naturally, beg the larger question of whether submarines have a secure future as fighting vessels. And if so, whether the types likely to be needed in the next century can be foreseen. Doing such thinking, it is well to remember that, as early as the 1930s, a submarine carrying a single 305 mm gun was built, and another which had four 132 mm guns. A third carried an aircraft, launched after surfacing. Only the last of these ideas caught on, much later and in a different form, with the invention of missiles. Many other ideas have died before reaching the building stage, because the type of submarine proposed was not seen as militarily useful in the years immediately ahead. For example, troop carrying and large liquid-cargo carrying submarines are both perfectly feasible, if they should ever be needed.

The Secure Future

There are several clearly discernible trends in maritime warfare at the start of the 1990s, which will probably continue into the next century. One, is growing elusiveness of submarines. Another is the widespread sale of missiles around the world. The third is the mounting difficulty and rocketing cost, of providing surface ships with adequate ASMD (***Anti-Ship-Missile Defence***) against such missiles. Thus, on one hand, AIP for SSs, rising quiet speeds and reducing signatures in SSNs, augur well for boats being able to continue performing all the roles discussed in Chapter 2. On the other, there are growing worries about survivability of surface warships in future tactical scenarios, when they lack the protection of a US Aircraft Carrier Task Force—but have to operate a long way from base. Even inside such cover, defensive problems are difficult enough, when fending off major air launched missile attacks.

These trends prompt three thoughts. First, submarines will feature in as many navies in the next century as they do in this, because their weapon range is increasing and detectability diminishing. Nations want such capable war vessels, whether one likes it or not. Hence, the rumour that Argentina is seeking to augment its navy with an SSN capability. Second, the relative safety of the SSN in its defensive sea control, escort role, might be used as a platform for providing greater protection to the surface ships being escorted. Third, imaginative constructors ought to be pondering now, how to make even better use of submersible principles, to frustrate missile attacks on surface ships, once they cannot be withstood, since these ships must still go about their business, if sea control is to be maintained.

Submarine Implications

Once SSs have AIP, they could be deployed close to enemy bases again. And if they had fuel cell propulsion, might be quite a bit smaller than the UPHOLDER class, without becoming noisy. This would allow more to be built and avoid the current UK dilemma, of only getting two SSs for the cost of a far more capable SSN—a questionable investment decision, even if the boats are impressive SSs. However, nations who want to operate SSs a long way from base, will need reassuring that the AIP system adopted is going to give them the range they need; or that boats are going to have depot ship support, to shorten passages.

SSs required to man a perimeter, and provide defensive sea denial against another nation with a more capable surface fleet, increasingly will be fitted with improved versions of Sub Harpoon type missiles. These provide good deterrence against adventurism by the other nation, and compensate for the problems SSs can have in closing a fast moving group. They also make it easier to blockade a port from further offshore.

SSNs will remain a key component of any navy which has them, well into the next century, and are likely to escort all important surface groups, deploying to deal with emergencies around the world. They already provide a good way of tackling threatening surface ships. And whether active sonar has to be used again or not, they will be a very important means of detecting enemy submarines closing the force. They could also play a greater part in ASMD, if their weaponry was augmented to include sub surface to air missiles.

Short range self defence missiles are going to be needed anyway. It is not a great extension of this idea to fit longer range missiles, which could be launched vertically, in response to commands from the surface force—and subsequently controlled by it. The advantage would be that the missiles would be launched from much further up threat, that is from a position already some way out towards the incoming enemy, considerably extending the MEZ (*Missile Engagement Zone*). Good communications would be needed, to call submarines up to launch depth, and pass firing orders, but these are likely to be provided for other reasons anyway. SSBNs that have SLBMs removed, could also be adapted for this purpose.

In short, submarines cannot replace surface escorts; not least, because surface forces like to be able to see some of their defenders. But SSNs could do more to help them. For this, and their other roles, they need to carry plenty of weapons. They also need large hulls to contain quiet, thermal circulation reactor systems. It is not likely, therefore, that UK and US SSNs will get smaller than the TRAFALGAR class.

The paramount design consideration for all future SSNs is to be as quiet as possible, whilst matching any running speed of surface ships, and being able to operate sonar at full efficiency at this speed. This too is likely to rule out a small hull. These requirements are needed both to trail enemy surface forces and to escort our own. They are more important than being able to go very deep or very fast. The first is not necessary, so long as one carries weapons that can go as deep as an enemy submarine. And ultra high speeds of 40 knots and over are not too helpful if one is noisy and deaf.

However, SSNs do also need to have an advantage over their likely submarine opponents, in the sonar equation, sufficient to be able to trail them at comfortable ranges, when they are deploying at sensibly cautious speeds. This could become harder to achieve against nations investing heavily in submarine noise reduction.

Surface Ship Implications

Advent of zero time of flight weapon systems, say damage lasers, might give surface ship ASMD a new lease of life, but the safety margins will still be very small.

FIG. 16.13 Possible design start point for a submersible surface ship.
SSP *Kaimalino* (*Photo: US Navy*)

Looking well into the next century, therefore, it does seem likely that a radical new approach to defence against airborne attack is going to be needed. The idea that this might take the form of making some of the key ships submersible is not put forward in any spirit of facetiousness. When faced with high speed air attack, going underwater is the best stealth tactic in the world. It could be a lifesaver for Pickets and Towed Array ships.

The vessel would not of course look like a present day Frigate. It would probably have to be built with two separated cylindrical lower hulls, containing hull mounted sonars, fuel, propulsors and canards, which could be independently moved to control pitch and roll on the surface, and depth when dived. These lower hulls would support a single, pancake shaped upper hull, containing accommodation, power generation equipment and weapons, all fired from flush decked vertical launch tubes. Above water sensors would be put on retractable telescopic masts, or be fixed, phased arrays. All three hulls would have to be strong enough to withstand the water pressures experienced down to about 40 or 50 metres. The whole structure would be built with a ballast range wide enough to give it safe neutral buoyancy under water, but also able to bring its upper hull high enough above water, when ballast tanks were empty, to be an efficient, high speed surface ship. (Figure 16.13)

SUMMARY

Great efforts will be made to ensure that diesel boats remain viable. This should be no surprise. Some roles are still best performed by them, and they are the only type of submarine that most people can afford. However, even an SS represents a hefty outlay, and a nation buying it wants to know that it can survive to do its job. AIP may offer such reassurance, especially if the boat can be given an atmosphere control system, whose shut down endurance matches that of the chosen propulsion system.

It is important to make the point that none of the possible face-lifts for the SS reduce the desirability of owning SSNs, nor offer an alternative way of carrying SLBMs.[2] Moreover, only nuclear propulsion confers the ability to send a large submarine, with lots of weapons, at high speed, to an area on the far side of the world, to conduct a very active patrol there, unsupported, for a long time. Thus, SSNs are not just indispensable for under ice operations, like those described above, which must feature in any resumption of East/West confrontation. They are also tailor made for rapid reaction operations, and provide capability well beyond anything that an SS could offer, no matter how much improved.[3]

The SSN already is a fine fighting vehicle, superbly adapted to its environment. If it gets a pop up tactical optronics mast, a well thought out Command Combat Aid, and communication reception arrangements that can be used with less operational constraint, it will be that much more effective. Fitted with anti-helicopter SAM and made as quiet as present UK/US boats, even Russian SSNs will become difficult opponents to defeat. No wonder they continue building them at an impressive rate, despite the easing of international tension and their economic difficulties.[4]

We in the West would do well to remember that it is capabilities, not intentions, which count when estimating threats. There is political talk of having 18 months warning of a major attack. Maybe so. But it takes a good deal more than that to rebuild our own submarine force, if it has been run down. Far from doing that, we should be seeking new ways to use SSNs to beef up our surface groups—and maybe trying to give some surface ships the great protection which comes from being able to go just a few metres under water, when one needs to.

Chapter Notes

1. INTRODUCTION

1. The ebb and flow of German submarine fortunes is well described in John Terraine's interesting book *Business in Great Waters* (Leo Cooper, **1989),** from which these statistics are taken, as is the quotation in Note 2.

2. On 20 June 1917, just after two months of appallingly bad sinkings and before convoying could start to have an effect, the First Sea Lord, Admiral Sir John Jellicoe, told the British War Policy Committee that ' . . . he felt it improbable that we could go on with the war next year for lack of shipping.'

3. Lord Alanbrooke, CIGS from 1941 to 1946, constantly refers in his diaries to lack of ships for all purposes, and Sir Winston Churchill wrote: 'The Battle of the Atlantic was the dominating factor all through the war. Never for one moment could we forget that everything happening elsewhere, on land, at sea, or in the air, depended ultimately on its outcome, and amid all other cares we viewed its changing fortunes day by day with hope or apprehension.'

4. Statistics taken from *United States Submarine Operations in World War II* by Theodore Roscoe.

2. ROLES

1. Admiral Sir John Woodward GBE KCB.

3. CONSTRUCTION

1. Dr. PJ Gates and NM Lynn, *Ships, Submarines and the Sea*, (Brassey's (UK) 1990).

2. The French *Daphne* class SSs have a safety factor of 1.9.

3. Russian submarines have about 50 per cent of their MBT fitted with quick acting hull valves. After surfacing and blowing out the tanks, they shut the valves and open and shut the main vents to reduce pressure in the MBTs to normal atmospheric pressure. This enables them to dive very quickly and quietly, as there is no 10 psi pressure locked in the MBT to inhibit the start of flooding.

5 PROPULSION AND POWER GENERATION

1. Responsiveness of some naval reactors, especially Soviet, French and Chinese, may be limited by their fuel element design but even these can step up power by 15–20 per cent per minute. And those using DC electric drive can temporarily draw on the battery, whilst waiting for the steam system to catch up.

2. *Rickover: Controversy and Genius*, Norman Polmar & Thomas B Allen, (Simon & Schuster 1982) Page 114.

3. *The Nuclear Engineer* Volume 25 No. 1 Jan/Feb 1984 (The Institution of Nuclear Engineers) Page 4.

4. Admiral Rickover's decision to abandon liquid metal coolants completely, without seeking an alternative to sodium, had many critics in the US Navy, not least amongst those who served in USS *Sea Wolf* herself.

5. For comparison, the 753 ton Type VII Second World War German U-boats had a surface range of 15,660 kilometres at 10 knots and routinely made unrefuelled 8 weeks patrols.

6. Also, given that both are fully submerged, and have similar power available, the single screw boat can be nearly 10 per cent faster.

7 ELECTRONIC SUPPORT MEASURES

1. Performance figures quoted in this chapter do not refer to any particular national ESM but are typical of specifications used in MEL's MANTA system.

2. For a more detailed discussion of ESM processing, see Chapter 3 of *Naval Electronic Warfare* by Dr. D G Kiely (Brassey's (UK) 1988)

8. SONAR

1. Other commentators have suggested that this nacelle contains an advanced low speed secondary propulsion system.

2. The Russian VICTOR class torpedo tubes are above the conformal sonar array.

10. COMMUNICATIONS

1. In theory, buoys could also give two way communications, (on VHF/UHF), if towed at the surface, but would then be detectable and need their own ESM facility.

2. It takes roughly 45 digital bits to make up an average length word. Therefore, 200 baud (bits per second) working means about 265 words per minute. This may sound fast but can seem painfully slow when a long intelligence summary and several other messages have to be read on the same broadcast routine, and one is desperate to get back up to speed again.

3. Military SATCOMS are usually concentrated in the 7–8 GHz part of the SHF band.

4. Morse skills are still maintained by British radio operators, for use in emergencies. It is a sensible precaution but commanders find it difficult to justify the increased training time needed.

12. SIGNATURE REDUCTION

1. Loss of USS *Thresher* in 1963 probably began with a silver braze joint blowing out on a large circulating water pipe, carrying full diving pressure, whilst the boat was at more than 300 m.

2. In magnetostrictive hydrophones, received acoustic signals cause compression of magnetic material, which distorts the magnetic field in which it is placed, producing an EMF in the associated electrical wiring. In piezoelectric hydrophones, crystals are used, which change dimension when hit by acoustic waves, creating an electrical field.

3. The currents which flow through cathodic protection systems were well explained by Gates and Lynn (op. cit)

13. ATMOSPHERE CONTROL AND HEALTH PHYSICS

1. Battery ventilation systems have extraction fans, which suck clean air in at the far end of the tank or compartment and draw it and the battery gas out at the near end. Battery explosions can occur if siting of inlets and outlets leaves pockets of cells with poor airflow over them. Operators can cause the problem if they fail to check that extraction fans are pulling a suction at the inlets, as it has been known for fans to be replaced about face after repair.

2. The words *properly made* are important. Swedish teams boarding the Russian WHISKEY class boat stranded off Karlskrona in 1981 were astonished to find significant levels of radiation in the torpedo reload compartment, which was also used as a living area.

14. CONDUCT OF OPERATIONS

1. When commanding an SSN, the author used to plan two spells of 2 hours sleep per 24: one from 0030 to 0230, when his second in command was on watch; the other during the forenoon, when there was normal white lighting in the combat centre and plenty of people up and about to handle emergencies. Any extra was bonus and failure to get sleep during planned periods a reminder not to overtax oneself.

15. SUPPORT

1. A figure of 65 per cent represents severe stretch for those operating it. The UK now aims to achieve 50 per cent base port time, which husbands men and material better—and is in keeping with an era of reducing tension between major nations.

2. By UK/US/Bahamas agreement, AUTEC range in the Tongue of the Ocean, east of Andros Island, is shared. Britain uses it mainly for weapon trials.

16. FUTURE TRENDS

1. Average thickness of the pack ice slabs was about 2.5m in 1971 when HMS *Dreadnought* went to the North Pole. But the deepest keel recorded during the same voyage was 46m.

2. Early Russian SS-N-4 ballistic missiles were carried in ZULU and GOLF class diesel powered SSBs but the missile was short range and the submarine vulnerable.

3. The most capable of the AIP systems discussed in this chapter still only produces about 75 full speed hours.

4. As the editor of Jane's Fighting Ships pointed out in his foreword to the 1992–93 edition, Russia must be having problems with component suppliers, who now lie in the other independent republics of the old Soviet Union. But in Spring 1992, the AKULA and SIERRA SSNs, and the OSCAR SSGN were all still in series production—and YANKEE SSBNs were still being converted to a variety of other roles. In 1991, the last year for which figures are quoted, they launched three new SSNs and three KILO class SSs .

Index